BREAKTHROUGH

A TREASURY OF CONTEMPORARY
AMERICAN-JEWISH LITERATURE

BREAKTHROUGH

❦❦❦

A TREASURY OF CONTEMPORARY AMERICAN-JEWISH LITERATURE

Edited by Irving Malin and Irwin Stark

PHILADELPHIA

The Jewish Publication Society of America

1963–5724

BREAKTHROUGH:
A Treasury of Contemporary American-Jewish Literature.

THE
JACOB R. SCHIFF
★ LIBRARY ★
OF JEWISH
CONTRIBUTIONS TO
AMERICAN DEMOCRACY

"Eli, the Fanatic" by Philip Roth. Reprinted from *Goodbye Columbus* by Philip Roth, by permission of Houghton Mifflin Company. Copyright © 1959, by Philip Roth.

"The Einhorns" by Saul Bellow. Reprinted from *The Adventures of Augie March* by Saul Bellow, by permission of The Viking Press, Inc. Copyright 1949, 1951, 1952, 1953 by Saul Bellow.

"Take Pity" by Bernard Malamud. Reprinted from *The Magic Barrel* by Bernard Malamud, by permission of Farrar, Straus and Cudahy, Inc. Copyright © 1958 by Bernard Malamud.

"Aristotle and the Hired Thugs" by Herbert Gold. Reprinted from *Love and Like* by Herbert Gold, by permission of Dial Press, Inc. Copyright © 1960, 1957 by Herbert Gold.

"Joey Goldstein: The Cove of Brooklyn" by Norman Mailer. Reprinted from *The Naked and the Dead* by Norman Mailer, by permission of the author.

"King Solomon," by Isaac Rosenfeld. Copyright © 1956, by *Harper's Magazine*. Reprinted by permission of Vasiliki Rosenfeld.

"A Prayer for Dew" by Paul Goodman. Reprinted by permission of the author.

"The Loudest Voice" by Grace Paley. Reprinted from *The Little Disturbances of Man* by Grace Paley, by permission of Doubleday & Company, Inc. Copyright © 1959 by Grace Paley.

"Taub East" by Ivan Gold. Reprinted from *Nickel Miseries: A Collection* by Ivan Gold, by permission of The Viking Press, Inc. Copyright © 1963 by Ivan Gold.

"The Country of the Crazy Horse" by Wallace Markfield. Reprinted by permission of Russell & Volkening, Inc. Copyright © 1958 by the American Jewish Committee. The story first appeared in the March 1958 issue of *Commentary*.

"The Synagogue" by Karl Shapiro. Reprinted from *Poems 1940-1953* by Karl Shapiro, by permission of Random House, Inc. Copyright 1943 by Karl Shapiro.

"Second Elegy: Age of Magicians" by Muriel Rukeyser. Reprinted from *Selected Poems of Muriel Rukeyser* by permission of New Directions, Publishers. Copyright 1935, 1951 by Muriel Rukeyser.

"Letter to the Front" by Muriel Rukeyser. Reprinted from *Beast in View*, 1944, by permission of Monica McCall, Inc. Copyright 1944 by Muriel Rukeyser.

"The Way Out" by Muriel Rukeyser. Reprinted from *Waterlily Fire*, 1963, by permission of Monica McCall, Inc. Copyright 1962 by Muriel Rukeyser.

"Lot's Wife" by Howard Nemerov. Reprinted from *The Image and the Law*, 1947, by permission of the Margot Johnson Agency.

"Pharaoh's Meditation on the Exodus" by Howard Nemerov. Reprinted from *Mirrors and Windows*, 1958, by permission of the Margot Johnson Agency.

"Abraham" by Delmore Schwartz. Reprinted from *Summer Knowledge* by Delmore Schwartz, by permission of Doubleday & Company, Inc. Copyright © 1959 by Delmore Schwartz.

"Jacob" by Delmore Schwartz. Reprinted from *Summer Knowledge* by Delmore Schwartz, by permission of Doubleday & Company, Inc. Copyright © 1958 by Delmore Schwartz.

"The Sands of Paran" by Allen Grossman. Reprinted from *A Harlot's Hire* by Allen Grossman, by permission of the author.

"The Law" by Allen Grossman. Reprinted from *A Harlot's Hire* by Allen Grossman, by permission of the author.

CONTENTS

NONFICTION

INTRODUCTION

*After the final no there comes a yes
And on that yes the future world depends.*
Wallace Stevens: "The Well Dressed Man with
the Beard"

IN A 1944 "COMMENTARY" SYMPOSIUM LIONEL TRILL-
ing declared that "as the Jewish community now exists, it can give no
sustenance to the American artist or intellectual who is born a Jew."
Today, just two decades later, circumstances have radically changed.
For the first time in history a large and impressively gifted group of
serious American-Jewish writers has broken through the psychic barriers of the past to become an important, possibly a major reformative
influence in American life and letters.

Of the many variables which may be said to account for this situation
perhaps the most forceful is the modern Jew's search for identity and
authenticity, a search already documented with remarkable accuracy
in the literature of Europe. Whether as Swann, Bloom or Shem, Mann's
Joseph or Kafka's Joseph K., the Jew has long been recognized as the
great contemporary archetype. He is, as Delmore Schwartz says of
Bloom, "at once alienated and indestructible, he is an exile from his own
country, exiled from himself, yet he survives the annihilating fury of
history." He belongs to a century in which religious symbols are considered vestigial, and ritual and tradition too feeble to transmute the
raw materials of daily existence into a system of communally accepted
beliefs. He inhabits a world where value is groundless except as man
creates it out of suffering and nothingness, where the absurd is the
condition of his being.

But this crisis of existence is no longer peculiar to Europe, however

1

much we try to challenge or ignore its pertinence in this country. As a writer in *Commonweal* put it recently: "In America there is a myth which denies that life is broken and incomplete, denies the distortions in man's life, the difficulty of being faithful to oneself, the irrationality of events and motivations." Yet studies like *White Collar, The Organization Man, The Lonely Crowd, The Vanishing Adolescent, The Power Elite,* and *Growing Up Absurd* have told us plainly enough that the crisis is here and now—for all of us.

Nor is the Jew an exception. As an American he is subject to all the forces making for isolation, fragmentation, alienation, anxiety and the loss of individual identity. He pays tribute to happiness, security, popularity, wealth, power, success, and social status. As a Jew he clings precariously to a tradition which continues to recede into the gray anonymity of modern life. Attempting to be what Arthur A. Cohen has called the "natural Jew," the man who accepts the label but has lost the sense of Jewish vocation, he cannot forget the "supernatural Jew," the man whose life expresses his sense of the historical Jewish mission. The double jeopardy marks the role he plays in American life.

It is not so much that the Jew has caught up with America. America has at long last caught up with the Jew. His search for identity is its search. Its quest for spiritual meaning is his quest.

While the American-Jewish writer has generally rejected the God of Jewish theology (he refuses to pronounce the Name not because of fear but because of disbelief), he has devoted a large portion of his creative energy to a definition of self. He has sought a substitute for God in the absence of God, he has sought to rediscover the ways by which God is manifest in the world—and he has done so within the context of a Jewish tradition only partially literary.

In the process, especially in his fiction, he has conducted a sometimes angry polemic against the values which he finds not only in American society but in the community which he knows best. As the "pinochle-player of the Lord" in Paul Goodman's "Prayer for Dew" pushes up the bidding for the honor of opening the Ark, a clap of thunder extinguishes the light over the reading table, and the rain turns the as-yet-unspoken *Tefilas Tal* into an empty formality. Asa Leventhal of Saul Bellow's *The Victim* learns that he must share the guilt of his persecutor, Tommy Wilhelm of *Seize the Day* is a pathetic if not tragic portrait, and the apparent amorality of Augie March is hardly calculated to endear him to the orthodox. Mailer's disgust with conventional society, with its corruption, emptiness, vanity, apathy, and confusion erupts in such novels as *Deer Park* and *Barbary Shore* like the fulminations of some Old Testament prophet come down from the hills to excoriate the transgressors in the cities of the plains. In "Goodbye, Columbus" and "Eli, the Fanatic" Philip Roth bitterly assails the euphoria of the middle-class Patimkins and the Jews of suburban Woodenton. No wonder that exacerbated Jewish sensitivities have responded so violently in self-defense!

But a sober appraisal discloses that in almost every instance the destructive element implies the reconstructive intent. Goodman's "no in thunder" is the measure of his faithfulness to values opposed to those of the marketplace. Truth, love, peace, bounty, usefulness and harmony are the virtues Augie advocates for the regeneration of man. Mailer's revolt against the "amoral standards of the concentration camp" is balanced by a messianic dream of a libertarian social order. And, as Theodore Solotaroff has perceived: "Roth is so obviously attached to Jewish life that the charge of his being anti-semitic or a 'self-hater' is the more absurd. The directness of his attack against arrogance, smugness, finagling and acquisitiveness should not obscure the perfectly obvious fact that he does so flying a traditional Jewish banner of sentiment and humaneness and personal responsibility. . . ."

This quest for values and meaning within a living Jewish ethos and under the auspices of ideals derived largely from the Hebraic tradition goes far toward explaining why there is an American-Jewish context, a "community of feeling" which transcends individual styles and genres. It is this community and the fundamental questions it raises which are the starting point of the present selections. What is true human fulfillment? Can it be achieved without God? Consciously or unconsciously, these are the questions that plague the most talented American-Jewish writers and their sympathetic readers.

The quest is multifaceted and "eccentric." If we describe it in an admittedly schematic way, a construct that can only approximate the reality, we choose the approach in the hope of illuminating the quest and indicating the basis for answers to the questions posed in the literature itself. Although we assume that each of the selections is an independent and satisfying work, our interest is not primarily evaluative. It is thematic and argumentative.

I. THE OLD COUNTRY

Philip Rahv has edited an anthology entitled *Discovery of Europe*, offering selections by Washington Irving, Cooper, Emerson, Hawthorne,

Howells, Mark Twain, Henry James, and Henry Adams. For most of these writers, Rahv tells us: "Europe has always been one of the poles of American culture, the other pole being that of the most indigenous of indigenous places—the frontier." The very fact that the Old Country has fascinated, almost obsessed, previous generations of Americans should be remembered when we speculate about why gentile readers in Fort Wayne read a Herman Wouk or, on a more sophisticated level, a Bernard Malamud. Americans are curious about the European sensibility, especially the Jewish one. "Europe," says Delmore Schwartz, "is the greatest thing in North America."

Rahv's introduction to his *Discovery of Europe* is more important than an interesting guidepost to our "passionate pilgrims." It is meaningful in itself as a typical piece of literary criticism by an American-Jewish writer. Neither aloof nor scientific, it is a glowing celebration of both Europe and America, a completely committed, personal testament in which Rahv confronts America in much the same way James confronted Europe. Both confrontations present the "ambiguity of [the] attempt to reattach [oneself] to the old soil—an ambiguity the source of which is nothing less than doubt of . . . true national identity." True national identity is still a problem for many American Jews. Can they completely embrace America which is, after all, different from Russia or Israel? Can they have *two* fatherlands? Can they renounce their ties with European civilization? The introduction ultimately avoids answering these questions. "Our share in that civilization," Rahv concludes, "now fully equals that of the Europeans, and to make good its promise we must be ready to assume the responsibilities that go with an equal partnership." This plea for partnership, noble as it is, assumes that the dualities of Old Country and New can be reconciled. But the differences remain and they often inherit the earth.

The differences between Old Country and New are stated in another way by Isaac Rosenfeld. For him Cahan's *The Rise of David Levinsky is* the Old Country. Although he tells us he had avoided reading it because it seemed another "badly-written account of immigrants and sweatshops. . . ," when he finally did read it, he discovered that the novel not only captured the spiritual beauty of the Old Country (and the New)—it compelled him to see that at crucial points the Jewish and American character meet. He does not suggest that "Jewish and American character are identical." But he realizes that cultural themes—the emptiness of materialism, for example—somehow succeed in crossing national boundaries; in this crossing lies the hope for reconciliation of cultural differences, for what Rahv calls "partnership."

The problem of national identity arises surprisingly in Lionel Trilling's essay on Isaac Babel. We usually think of Trilling as a critic committed to the world of E. M. Forster and Matthew Arnold—to a poised, somewhat "cool" England. But the present selection (as well as "Wordsworth and the Rabbis") demonstrates that, like Rahv and Rosenfeld, Trilling cannot escape the Old Country even if he wants to. He records his startling discovery in 1929 of Babel's bitter tales. The shock of recognition—neither poised nor cool—was so great that he returned to these tales in 1955 (after the books on Forster and Arnold), finding Babel an archetypal Jew "torn between violence and peace." The essay is passionate and obscurely personal. Confronting the Old Country, Trilling understands "spiritual facts of consummate value" not gleaned from *Howard's End*.

In fiction the attempt to reattach oneself to the old soil is presented more dramatically. Roth's "Eli, the Fanatic" takes us to a suburban American community which has been invaded by a band of refugees led by a Mr. Tzuref who is bent on establishing a local Yeshiva. At first Eli believes that there should be a strict demarcation between the Old Country and the New. "Purity" is essential. But he gradually learns that he (and all Jews) are homeless. They reside in *galut* even when they least suspect it.

Saul Bellow's Einhorns seems to be better adjusted to life in America than is Tzuref (or Eli). They are the "most important real-estate brokers in the district and owned and controlled much property, including the enormous forty-flat building where they lived." They love their miraculous, powerful reign. But in spite of this they are not fully at home: they think and talk constantly of old-fashioned, European ways; they remain a clan; they indulge in parochial pleasures; and they need to adopt Augie to make themselves feel loved.

For Grace Paley the exile of Jews takes a comic turn. The schoolgirl heroine of "The Loudest Voice" is chosen to participate in the annual Christmas play. Her home and her school represent "two countries of the mind." Yet she does not feel trapped in either one; being able to move nimbly and "loudly" from one to the other, she finally—and ironically—experiences a sense of pity for all the poor "lonely" Christians.

Contrast this point of view with that of a poet like Karl Shapiro, who illustrates the plight of homelessness more sharply than any other poet represented in the collection. He has moved from his early Auden-

Eliot influenced poems through the mild *sturm und drang* of *Trial of a Poet* to the spiritual definitions of *Poems of a Jew*, trying desperately to adjust himself to some compatible tradition. Even in his earliest poems he could not resist the pull of his Jewishness. But if it burst through the discipline of "Travelogue for Exiles" and "University," there was no substantial evidence that Shapiro would ever be satisfied with an old-world formulation. In *Poems of a Jew*, he returns to his heritage, informing us in his introduction, however, that he is not concerned with the Jewish question, Judaism, Israel or religion: "Being a Jew is the consciousness of being a Jew, and the Jewish identity, with or without religion, with or without history is the significant fact." But what are the contents of this curious consciousness when it has been drained of religion, history, and Israel?

Muriel Rukeyser has also learned to confront the Old Country. Her pilgrimage, which began with the radical political and sociological poems of her early volumes, turned full circle during World War II. Then for the first time she realized that "To be a Jew in the twentieth century/ Is to be offered a gift. If you refuse,/Wishing to be invisible, you choose/ Death of the spirit, the stone insanity." In "Second Elegy. Age of Magicians" against "the march-step, the staircase at night, the long cannon" she counterposed the Prophets who "separated/ unity from blindness/ living from burning/tribute from tribute." She effected, too, a reconciliation with the personal past and in her "Sixth Elegy" acknowledged her wish "To keep the knowledge that holds my race alive,/Spiritual grace in the material world." At last she could accept "Akiba" and the story of her descent from the man who escaped to life from the holocaust of Jerusalem. The way out for Muriel Rukeyser has been "The song of the way in."

It is easy to multiply examples. Irving Howe on Yiddish stories, Shlomo Katz on the pogroms in Russia, Norman Podhoretz evaluating the Howe and Greenburg collection—these reveal involvement in one aspect of spiritual quest: the need for national roots. In an oblique manner all these essays, stories, and poems reflect such classic American books as *English Traits, Our Old Home, Clarel* and *The Europeans*. They assert that one must go home again. But one must first know where home is. (The poignancy of Ivan Gold's "Taub East" derives in part from the fact that the Jews of the story carry their exile with them.) What remains uncertain is whether American-Jewish writers have as yet established the location.

II. FATHERS AND SONS

One way of symbolizing the Old Country and the New—of personifying the confrontation—is by viewing one as parent and one as child.

When we consider great American fiction, we see many "symbolic families"—*The House of the Seven Gables, Billy Budd,* and *The Ambassadors* employ fathers and sons as counterparts of national identity. *Billy Budd* contains the struggle between Captain Vere and Billy, who constantly remind us of England (Europe) and America respectively. Vere is civilized, "authoritarian," perplexed by moral problems; Billy is natural, primitive, and innocent. Certainly Melville is not saying that Billy *is* America—this would be allegory—but he is saying that America can be symbolized as a good-natured, reckless orphan.

This kind of symbolic correspondence may seem far-fetched. However, certain sociologists have made much of the belief that America is a rebellious son, obsessed with the fatherland it once hurt. Geoffrey Gorer writes in *The Americans:*

In some significant ways the birth of the American Republic can be compared with the mythological scene which Freud imagined for the origin of civilization and the institution of totemic observations. In Freud's "Just So" story the downtrodden sons combine together to kill the tyrannical father; then, overwhelmed by their crime, and fearful that one of their number will attempt to take the murdered father's place, they make a compact which establishes the legal equality of the brothers, based on the common renunciation of the father's authority and privileges. England, the England of George the Third and Lord North, takes the place of the despotic and tyrannical father, the American colonists that of the conspiring sons and the Declaration of Independence and the American Constitution that of the compact by which all Americans are guaranteed freedom and equality on the basis of the common renunciation of all authority over people, which had been the father's most hated and envied privilege.

If we use Gorer's somewhat fanciful notion (which is Freud's also) of the father's privileged authority as a point of departure for discussing old Jewish literature—especially the Bible, which intrigued the New England patrician class of a Hawthorne or James—we can see that Abraham, Isaac, or Jacob holds complete authority over his sons. Rebellion against such order is sinful because the patriarch symbolizes the Father of the Chosen People. When rebellion occurs, as in the case of an Absalom, it is immediately and sadly punished.

In the present selections the symbolic family—the father as authority, the son as guilt-ridden rebel—recurs, showing us again that Jewish and American character meet. Shlomo Katz, Herbert Gold, Saul Bellow, and Norman Mailer may not be especially aware of archetypal family ties, but the unconscious, highly personal blood feelings do assert themselves, exemplifying a tradition, a unity of American-Jewish writing, we often neglect.

The *tone* of the father-son relationships varies greatly though the tensions are similar. Shlomo Katz' memoir demonstrates that the conflict of generations arises "naturally." The narrator is not an Absalom; he simply cannot live his father's life. But this very separation makes him so guilty that he asks: "Who isn't guilty before his father?" The whole point of the essay is that he can understand his father's Old World values, if only at rare moments, and love them. Heroism is defined as admiration for the father triumphing over guilt and fear.

Herbert Gold has admitted that "The American-Jewish community is most important to me as a writer because it is a mirror in which the rest of America can be seen. Like all mirrors, it invites distortions." In his fiction he has remorselessly examined the reflection—the effects of contemporary mores on "lovers." Burr Fuller of *The Optimist* is a typical Gold character, a man for whom sex has been converted into a ritual to fill the emptiness of life. Love for Fuller and his wife "had become a consumer product in which simultaneous delight was part of the purchase together with the green stamps. . . . The anxious consumers consume themselves. Poor children, poor lonely Americans, poor us, Burr thought. This is exactly a religion of love, but with only a hell to prove it." And Dan Shaper of *Salt* thinks "we put too heavy a burden on love" though one suspects that, like Fuller and so many of Gold's other characters, he is talking not about love but about lust —their desperate answer to the spiritual questions which crowd their subconscious.

Love in its truly redemptive sense, however, remains Gold's most treasured value. He rediscovers it in his best stories which he draws from the memory of his father. In this almost mythic figure a number of recurrent themes coalesce into a single symbol that comments on the moral vacuum, the anomie, of Gold's adult world. The father in his *Therefore Be Bold* enjoys the saving grace of knowing how "to build on the credit of love." In "The Heart of the Artichoke" surface values are separated from interior values: we glimpse the father "giving himself to a snack of artichoke with Kraft's dressing, the heart his end but the money-colored leaves loved for what they were." And it is the father's heart which instructs him to make the nice moral discrimination, the key to "Aristotle and the Hired Thugs."

The grandfather as "authoritarian" appears in *The Naked and the Dead*. His message nags at Goldstein (and Mailer?) like a dream he has been trying to remember or forget: "I think a Jew is a Jew because he suffers. *Olla Juden* suffer." The message is unheeded at first. "God," says Goldstein, "is a luxury I don't give myself." But it is Goldstein —not the self-pitying Roth—who comes through. He bears the wounded body of Wilson, the Jew-baiter, and protects him against his frantic craving for water. Delirious, Goldstein finally seizes upon his grandfather's words, " 'Yehuda Halevy wrote that Israel is the heart of all nations,' " and as he fights exhaustion the metaphor is repeated like an incantation until he is bearing not Wilson on the stretcher but life —life which cannot be permitted to perish. Only after Wilson's death does Goldstein allow himself to think that all the suffering of the Jews came to nothing and was lost. But the extremism of the thought mocks itself—and Goldstein does endure.

In the very first chapter of *The Adventures of Augie March*, we are introduced to the "dead" father: "My own parents were not much to me, though I cared for my mother." Augie's father has disappeared— the sons never mention him except when Grandma Lausch becomes passionate about money. Then the entire family wonders just what he was—a sailor, soldier or truck driver? If Augie is right in claiming that a "man's character is his fate" [quoting Heraclitus], we would assume that the loss of his real father should force him to act in definite ways. He remains a son lacking the "family sense." His relationships with men—in Chicago, Mexico and France—are never satisfactory because he hates and loves them. He talks more about the *love* he has for an Einhorn or Mintouchian, but this is his means of escaping from confusion. Consider Einhorn as spiritual father. Although Augie thinks of him as the "first superior man I knew," he hints at the inferior qualities of the man—his crippled legs, his "sneaky" deals. Does Augie really enjoy carrying him to the cat house? Does he truly admire his selfish statesmanship? Obviously not. We do not intend to imply that he goes to the other extreme, but the ambivalence is evident as in the following passage: "Nevertheless I was down on him occasionally, and I said to myself he was nothing—nothing. Selfish, jealous, autocratic, carp-mouthed and hypocritical. However, in the end, I every time had high regard for him."

The father-son relationship occurs so often in American-Jewish literature—the father figures and patriarchs in the poetry of Schwartz, Rukeyser, Nemerov, Grossman and Ignatow, the real and surrogate fathers of "Seize the Day," "Eli, the Fanatic," and *The Assistant*—that we assume the relationship to be an archetypal one especially for Jews, one which is full of fear, love, and spiritual authority.

III. THE SENSE OF THE PAST

Although it is impossible to say that there is something distinctively American or Jewish about recollection, it is striking that "historic memory" recurs so frequently in the work of American-Jewish writers. If we examine the two separations—Old Country and New, fathers and sons—in terms of an author or a character's attitude toward his Jewish heritage or family past we can understand why such recollection recurs so frequently in American-Jewish literature.

Like Billy Budd and Isabel Archer, Americans regard themselves as "young." They lack a deep sense of the past, going back when the patriotic occasion demands only to the founding fathers or the Constitution. American literature is obsessed by the search for a "usable past," for a more profound sense of time. In his preface to *The House of Seven Gables,* for example, Hawthorne explains that the book is "an attempt to connect a bygone time with the very present that is flitting away from us. It is a legend prolonging itself, from an epoch now gray in the distance, down into our own broad daylight." In the "Jolly Corner" Henry James presents Brydon as a man possessed by his search for the ghost of what he might have been. From the contemporary scene of *All the King's Men* Robert Penn Warren turns to the historical romance of *World Enough and Time.* And such recent works of literary criticism as *The American Adam* by R. W. B. Lewis, *An End to Innocence* by Leslie Fiedler, and *The Complex Fate* by Marius Bewley regard the time dimension as a crucial element in American literature.

Unlike these Americans who hunt the past (attracted to and repelled by the "beast"), the Jew is aware of historic depth: "By the rivers of Babylon, there we sat down,/ Yea, we wept, when we remembered Zion." And the Psalm continues: "If I forget thee, O Jerusalem,/ Let my right hand forget her cunning." The Jew is haunted by the separation between past and present; aware that he has fared better or worse once upon a time, he contemplates the eternal return. As Morse Peckham writes in *Beyond the Tragic Vision:* "The striking, the almost unique element in the Hebraic vision of a world of perfect order and value is its historical character. As far as the Western world is concerned, it was the Hebrews who introduced History into history."

Recollection is the guiding principle of many of the present selections. Shlomo Katz' "earliest recollections" of his father go back almost forty years; he views his condition now as a challenging commentary on time's cruel ways. But the father also recollects how things were in Russia—the pogroms in the small village, his acts of heroism. The memoir insists that Jews perpetually carry the knowledge of their ancient burdens and glories—in St. Paul, Minnesota, or in Russia itself. Significantly, after shifting back and forth in time, the memoir ends in the distant past: the "regular sentry call" is for him, for all Jews now and forever. (As Theodore Solotaroff suggests, many American-Jewish stories involve a confrontation with the past. The anti-nostalgia of Wallace Markfield's "The Country of the Crazy Horse" is based upon this confrontation. And Roth's Eli travels to the "edge of night," donning the garb of the "greenie," just as Mr. Katz *becomes* for a moment the listener of the sentry call, seeing himself as a member of the Auschwitz community, not of Scarsdale. Mysteriously, past and present fuse—time stops.)

In the essay by Leslie Fiedler time is again burden and glory. Reviewing James Baldwin's *Notes of a Native Son*, he recognizes the "Negro" and "Jew" in their historic roles—the Negro as "native son," the Jew as "sojourner." Fiedler returns to Melville, Whitman, and Emma Lazarus to give substance to these images, but even this groping is insufficient: he must return to Montaigne, Spinoza, and Dante. A single book by a contemporary writer carries Fiedler back to the childhood of Europe—the past is never dead. And Fiedler hears other voices from his own childhood: "I was born there." He must listen to them to understand his personality and his role as critic for the two are inextricably bound. Consequently, an autobiographical piece like "Roman Holiday" echoes "Negro and Jew: Encounter in America." There are no holidays, only holy days filled with reclamations of history. Fiedler "explicates" Rome as he does Baldwin's book, noting in it dim shadows of eternal return. Fiedler resembles Harold Rosenberg's Joseph who had "read his own history in the Bible. Thus he feels himself to be less the author of his history, in the sense that we today make our lives, than its stage manager."

One of the fascinating things about American-Jewish poetry is its use of Biblical figures—"eternal" representatives of the spirit. By recollecting (or re-creating) an Abraham, the poet acknowledges the depths of memory, time and creative divinity, and his division from—or involvement with—these depths.

Howard Nemerov has always accepted the fact of his Jewishness as an integral part of his poetic tradition. "The purpose of poetry," he has said, "is to persuade, fool or compel God into speaking." But Nemerov began his quest for spiritual meaning only on the borders of that tradition. "Europe" stands at the forefront of his initial volume, *The Image and the Law*, though it stands there as an American image, a Jamesian gargoyle symbolizing the Old World's blurring of good and evil. Similarly, the alternative to the surrealist "Frozen City" is "The Place of Value" where we must face the "neurosis" of constant decision. But this is still a "private fight." Only "Lot's Wife," a reminder that there can be no escape by merely looking back, belongs tentatively in the Jewish tradition. Starting with *Guide to the Ruins,* however, Nemerov's emphasis became more pronounced. "A Song of Degrees," for example, is his first completely Jewish poem, a poem in which he can "fiercely exult/In Zion everywhere." And "Nicodemus" is a salute to the universal modern Jew who "Bears the old law with the new,/And must suffer Israel/As stranger nations suffer hell." The "Moses" of *Mirrors and Windows* and the numerous other Biblical poems of *The Next Room of the Dream* contuine to portray the quest for timeless meaning within the Jewish tradition.

Delmore Schwartz employs the patriarchal "Abraham" to tell us about his own predicament: "Estranged among strangers, dismayed by the infinite sky,/An alien to myself . . ." But Schwartz differs from Nemerov because he has not yet come to terms with the ambivalence which tortures so much of his poetry and probably accounts for the relentless experimentation. He is still, as Heinz Politzer described him several years ago, "a writer trying as hard as he can to discover his own identity." One of the sources of this inner conflict—Schwartz has himself called it "the wound of consciousness"—is the incongruity of past and present. It is the father of "Father and Son" who advises the son to return to his history; it is the son who insists on being responsible to himself. But Schwartz is haunted by God and the "inevitable" past even while through Kant, Marx, and Freud he is involved in the violent iconoclasm of his age. Another source of conflict is the world of experience as it infringes on the abstractions of mind—the incompatibility of the banal ugliness of everyday life and the pure beauty of the intellect. In "Jacob" he therefore confesses "The solitude of eminence, the exiled intelligence,/Which separated me even as it created me." So in the verse drama "Shenandoah" the circumcised son with the grotesque name, half-American, half-European, is forced to be outsider, exile, solitary. The recompense for all this personal turmoil is a poetry nearly always interesting and surprising—a poetry born out of the tension of time.

The poetry of Allen Grossman resounds with the *Psalms*, the *Song of Songs* and the prophetic books. Like Nemerov, he is an intensely religious poet. In "The Sands of Paran" he looks back longingly to Moses and the direct dialogue with God. And he welcomes the Sabbath bride who confirms his vision that "The Law" is "young and beautiful." But he is also a thoroughly contemporary Jew. Although he believes God to be faceless like himself, he is resolved to "rehearse/All rites of purity that ever served/ To clean the murderer, or to solicit/ The prophetic dream." He accepts past and present without illusion. "We live in the silence after speech,/And the silence before speech begins," he writes in "A Poem for Statesmen." But he has the courage to add that "Under the wreck of incorruptible things/ Seed conspires with desert to thrust life/ Into the deathless night." Grossman's poetry stems from a tradition that is simultaneously past and present. Fixed in history, it can face the reality of modern life with brutal honesty. "Our beauty," he comments in his poem on postwar Berlin, "is become the strange greatness of the maimed,/And God himself is known at last by a scar." Still, the final word is "exult." It is not a cheap exultation because Grossman knows that only the man willing to live his own exile can speak of God and freedom and suffering with any depth of conviction.

IV. DUALITIES

These various dualities—Old Country and New, fathers and sons, past and present—imply that American-Jewish literature begins with incomplete images, antitheses and fragmentations. Only when we understand such specific dualities can we gauge the true depths of alienation and marginality.

Many analysts of American culture believe it is a "culture of contradictions." In discussing the differences between the "stable" English novel and the American novel, Richard Chase, for example, offers this insight into social values:

The American novel tends to rest in contradictions and among extreme ranges of experience. When it attempts to resolve contradictions, it does so in oblique, morally equivocal ways. . . . By contrast, the English novel has followed a middle way. It is notable for its great practical sanity, its powerful, engrossing composition of wide ranges of experience into a moral centrality and equability of judgment.

Chase advances various reasons for the contradictions in the American novel (and culture), citing such other commentators as De Tocqueville, who claimed that a democracy creates a void in which each citizen contemplates himself, not any shared, inherited body of beliefs; D. H. Lawrence, who saw duality arising from the separation of morality and body energy; and Van Wyck Brooks, who in *America's Coming-of-Age* saw a split of culture into "highbrow" and "lowbrow." No matter which set of dualities we accept, the general result is the same: our culture is, to use Chase's phrase, a "broken-circuit."

Among our foremost social critics are those American-Jews who by being "different" are aware of the nature of dualities. In effect, they respond to American dualities even more sensitively than do most other Americans. Traditionally, Jews have had the vision which Bellow describes in a review of Sholom Aleichem: "The Jews of the ghetto found themselves involved in an immense joke. They were divinely designated to be great and yet they were like mice." Chosen by God, rejected by the gentiles—no wonder they shrug ironically and make proverbs which stress these dualities: "A Jew's joy is not without fright." . . . "If God were living on earth, people would break His windows." . . . "So many Hamans and but one Purim." As Clement Greenberg writes: "Invoked to correct a disequilibrium caused by religious preoccupations and by the need to preserve self-esteem, [the Jewish sense of humor] learned to argue with God and dispute with Him, ironically, those final questions around which generations of sages had spun their reverent dialectic."

When we read these various essays in criticism and autobiography, we sense this underlying dialectical note. Thus Philip Rahv in his introduction to *Discovery of Europe* discusses the ambiguity felt by Henry James who as an American in England had a doubt "at once creative and inhibitive." This doubt "if it lifts the individual out of his national mold, thus weakening his capacity for simple adaptations, it on the other hand intensifies and refines his powers of memory and appreciation, his consciousness of origins, of the intermixture of past and present, and of the values gained as well as lost in the process of constructing a new civilization." Rahv implies that simple adaptation, if such a thing exists, is less valuable, less *human,* than refined dialectic. Isaac Rosenfeld's implication is the same; he says of David Levinsky:

"all things in [his] life are divided, alienated from themselves, and simplicity is impossible." Levinsky as *Jew* knows constant hunger for the resolution of opposites. We are not really concerned with the reasonableness of Rosenfeld's interpretation. That he regards this dialectic as profoundly Jewish (and American) *is* significant. *Galut*, for him, is an archetypal symbol of constant longing for "better food," though he knows that such food is inferior to hunger itself.

Other essayists follow Rahv and Rosenfeld. Harold Rosenberg's piece on Mann's *Joseph and His Brothers* is a dialectical exercise on *divine dialectic.* "Like the shaping of the individual," Rosenberg writes, characteristically, "the telling of the story also involves a doubling of God and man and commands a double language, in order that the odd, accidental doings of human beings shall reveal their steadfast core of divine plot-direction." Accidental doings, divine plot-direction—Rosenberg suggests that any new Joseph, even a literary character, must know the Biblical Joseph as the latter knew his own story. Mann gives us a divine comedy of mirrors, masquerades, absurdities, controlled by classical calm. Trilling's Isaac Babel—unlike Rosenberg's Mann—is a violent mixture of opposites uncontrolled by such calm. Trilling says of Babel: "[his work] was all too heavily charged with the intensity, irony and ambiguousness from which I wished to escape." This cruel ambiguity resulted from Babel's Cossack-Jew contradictions. The stories of *Red Cavalry*, we are told, "have as their principle of coherence what I have called the anomaly, or the joke, of a Jew who is a member of a Cossack regiment. . . . Traditionally the Cossack was the feared and hated enemy of the Jew. But he was more than that. The principle of his existence stood in antithesis to the principle of the Jew's existence." And Theodore Solotaroff in his discussion of "Philip Roth and the Jewish Moralists" regards them as ambivalent creators, aware of the tensions between Jews and their American setting, and their own tensions. One of the strong energies of Roth, Solotaroff claims, arises from the fact that he doesn't fall into traps set for him—"judgment dictated to by his world" or simple rebellion against the Jews: "In either case, Jewish material can be as intractable morally as it is imaginatively: one result is that until fairly recently American-Jewish fiction has been mainly a vehicle for either reverence or outrage but seldom for both. . . ."

Norman Podhoretz' search for great Jewish literature to equal Western literature is regarded with hostility at the seminary because, as he realizes, Jewish literature's prime purpose is to serve the Lord: "I think my teachers rightly resented the arrogant assumption that Jewish culture had to be justified in the eyes of the *Kenyon Review* or be set at naught." Still, Podhoretz is aware of his self-division. Raised in a "good" Jewish home" and well-read in Western literature—as eager as Matthew Arnold to study "the best that has been thought and known in the world"—he is not at ease in the Seminary.

Contrast Podhoretz to Arthur A. Cohen, who chooses to be a Jew as a result of having known Christian truth through reading St. Augustine, St. Anselm, and the sermons of Meister Eckhart. Only by *opposing* Jewish truth to Christian truth can he attain spiritual completion:

It was extremely important to me to return to Judaism through the medium of Christianity—to choose after having first received the impress of Western education and Christian thought. Since it would have been possible to become a Christian—to accept Christian history as my history, to accept the Christian version of Judaism on the grounds of my own repudiation of Judaism, to believe that a Messiah had redeemed *me*—I could only conclude that Judaism was not an unavoidable fate, but a destiny to be chosen freely.

American-Jewish fiction is engaged with numerous dualities which are frequently expressed in extreme, melodramatic modes. Alienation and acceptance, power and humility, disbelief and faith, suffering and joy are dealt with in styles which are themselves charged with tensions. Form and theme become dialectical.

Philip Roth's nervous irresolution about his Jewishness tends to produce the wild visions of such stories as "The Conversion of the Jews" (with 13-year-old Ozzie Freedman threatening to leap from the synagogue roof to compel the onlookers to admit that God can do anything) and "Eli, the Fanatic" (with Eli Peck striding through Woodenton in the old-world costume which he has made his own). Eli argues with Tzuref in much the same way Ozzie argues with his Rabbi, law and reason opposing the "higher" law of the heart in a dialectic which falls short of synthesis. The drug administered to Eli at the hospital "calmed his soul but did not touch it down where the blackness had reached." The onlookers are "converted" but under duress. And Sergeant Marx of "Defender of the Faith" chooses to mete out justice instead of mercy but, after the victim accepts his fate, Marx concludes, "And then, resisting with all my will an impulse to turn and seek pardon for my vindictiveness, I accepted my own." There is no final synthesis and style is congruous with events—a fast-placed colloquialism that is at once dynamic and controlled.

A comparable lack of resolution can be detected in the work of Saul

Bellow. Joseph, the hero of *Dangling Man,* is "separate, alien, distrust-ful," dangling between what he is and what he could be. "All the striv-ing," Bellow writes, "is for the one end. I do not entirely understand this impulse. But it seems to me that its final end is the desire for pure freedom." And Augie is torn as much by the forces within himself as by the Machiavellians who surround him. He insists on being himself, Protean and free. He is a *luftmensch,* a man of the air, his image that of Caligula, the eagle, who refuses to be trained to subservience. But while Augie knows what freedom is *for*—he *tells* us about the "axial-lines of life, with respect to which you must be straight or else your existence is merely clownery, hiding tragedy"—it is his freedom *from* which is *dramatized* in *The Adventures of Augie March.* The style is again a comment on substance—an electrically charged idiom, a com-bination of irony, elegance and slang, free-wheeling slapstick, Ameri-can argot, Yiddish dialect and Talmudic sententiousness, which captures the complexity of our lives and suggests that we can never achieve purity or stasis.

Mailer's argument with himself as a Jew is split in *The Naked and the Dead* into the contrasting characters of Roth and Goldstein. The self-pitying Roth perishes; the quietly heroic Goldstein endures—though he (like Mailer) appears to reject his racial memory: "All the suffering of the Jews came to nothing. No sacrifices were paid, no lessons learned. It was all thrown away, all statistics in the cruel wastes of history. All the ghettos, all the soul cripplings, all the massacres and pogroms, the gas chambers, the lime kilns—all of it touched no one, all of it was lost." Yet the argument continues. One may well ask, for example, whether "The White Negro" with its appeal "to accept the terms of death, to live with death as immediate danger, to divorce oneself from society, to exist without roots, to set out on that uncharted journey into the rebellious imperatives of self" could have been written, or written at its curious depth of passion and conviction, by any white man other than a Jew. When Mailer writes: "So it is no accident that the source of Hip is the Negro for he has been living on the margin between totalitarianism and democracy for two centuries," can we doubt that he is writing from a memory of a Jewish experience which has been marginal for more than two millennia? His recent commentaries on Buber's *Tales of the Hasidim* would appear to offer further evidence of the direction in which he is moving.

Even in the relatively unfamiliar fiction of Isaac Rosenfeld, Paul Goodman, Ivan Gold, and Grace Paley style would seem to embody awareness of dualities. These four writers refuse to give themselves to a classical, pure style; they express themselves erratically and idiosyncratically. Rosenfeld was, in Theodore Solotaroff's words, a "specialist in alienation," irresistibly drawn to Kafka's parables through his own need to comprehend and redeem the disorder of his world. His "King Solomon" reveals the thrust of an imagination operating in the hallucinatory sphere of East European Jewry but oriented toward the New World in which the ghetto sensibility was striving to accommodate itself. Its style is folksy and rhetorical, dull and playful, fictional and philosophical. Like Rosenfeld, Goodman is committed to a sanity that seems utopian only in the asylum of modern life. He is idealist and realist, an uneasy combination held in suspension by a style which vacillates frenetically, uncertain whether to rest in imaginative fiction or argumentative essay. In the short stories of Ivan Gold a nervous energy powers the prose in consonance with the exiles, Negro and Jew, who people the army camps of *Nickel Miseries*. The peculiar rhythmic subtlety and the antic humor of Grace Paley's collection *The Little Disturbances of Man* persuade us that she, too, refuses to come to rest in a disordered world. She celebrates its dualities, finding them disturbing and exhilarating at the same time.

V. THE HEART

In the solemn, ironic, or joyful consciousness of dualities the individual faces great suffering—suffering which can be blessing or curse. It can so stunt him that he retreats into his own problematic self and neglects the terrifying world, or it can help him recognize everyone as "all-too-human"—like himself.

Many of these critical essays emphasize the value of suffering. In this, they are noticeably different in temper from the pure, scientific, rather aloof criticism of the "New Critics" who avoid committing themselves to any real understanding or sympathy for passion and torment. The refreshing quality of American-Jewish criticism, lies precisely in this involvement with passionate spiritual questions, which is certainly a more humanistic involvement than close scientific explication. This is not to say that American-Jewish critics are merely impressionistic—they think as well as feel.

Introducing Yiddish stories to the critical reader, Irving Howe spends a page or so on the problem of "sentimentality" because the New Critics —Ransom, Brooks and Warren—regard it (according to their definition) as a vice. For Howe it is a social value, not a textbook term: "The desperate reliance upon blandness and composure, the cult of under-statement, the assumption that it is good to feel but bad to show one's feelings—these attitudes, familiar enough to us, are quite alien to the Yiddish ethos. Perhaps this means that the Yiddish is more primitive. Perhaps it means that the Yiddish is healthier."

The emphasis on suffering—and on feeling in general—is evident in the other critical essays. For Issac Rosenfeld "character" in fiction is crucial—his whole approach to *The Rise of David Levinsky* is one of sympathetic identification. From the very first lines, we note the per-sonal voice. Levinsky as a Jew is Rosenfeld's "brother": *"our whole history"*—to italicize the phrase—is centered in a single person. The entire essay is loaded with such words as "yearning," "desire," "satisfac-tion." The same tone recurs in Alfred Kazin's appreciation of Sholom Aleichem, whose stories are not treated as specimen texts to be cold-bloodedly dissected; they are "holy" because they embody the "eternal struggle and the inestimable privilege of being a Jew." Images are less important for Kazin than an almost ritualistic *participation* in the suf-fering, ironic vision of Aleichem, who himself identifies with his char-acters.

In this approach, younger American-Jewish writers tread in the steps of Rosenfeld, Howe, and Kazin. Theodore Solotaroff is typical. The very fact that he chooses to write on Roth, Malamud, and Bellow rather than on "classical" American or British novelists demonstrates a choice of values. He goes right to the heart of their fiction—the intrinsic feel-ings of *Seize the Day,* "The Heart of the Artichoke," *et al.* Again, ex-plication is less necessary than cultural insight. Here is a representative passage from Solotaroff: "Thus in both works, there is the similar con-version into the essential Jew, achieved by acts of striving, sacrificing, and suffering for the sake of some fundamental goodness and truth in one's self that has been lost and buried." Regard such words as "sacri-ficing," "suffering," "conversion," and "fundamental goodness." His en-tire sentence could be inserted into a sermon. Not that Solotaroff dis-avows the primary task of literary criticism—he uses heart as well as head to convey the *experience* of reading contemporary fiction.

Along with these critics, Tzuref (of "Eli, the Fanatic") says: "The heart is law." The aphorism is a subtle one: we usually oppose the two principles, elevating one above the other. But the aphoristic union of these dualities is superior to casual separation. Nevertheless, it does in-troduce moral ambiguities. How can we know whether the heart is right? Can the heart deceive? Is suffering always good? Unfortunately, these questions are left unanswered by many of the autobiographers who simply assert the rightness of the heart without troubling to chart its deceptions.

Feeling—as suffering—informs Allen Ginsberg's "Howl," a barbaric yawp against a system which has destroyed "the best minds of my generation." "Kaddish" compounds the bitterness. The short, breathless phrases of its catalog of horror and its ironic closing hymn lash out furiously against a God who could allow Naomi Ginsberg to go mad. But even in this denial Ginsberg is unable to detach himself from what he is. The agony of feeling which throbs through these poems is the pain of six million Jews, a pain which for most of us is too vast and distant to be apprehended as emotion. We may not agree with or enjoy the crudities of judgment or expression but we cannot dispute the fact that Ginsberg has brought back to the language the raw wound of feeling too long lost in the modish intellectualism of so much modern verse. This is no mean achievement even if, unlike Hyam Plutzik, he has not yet learned the historic role of his people whose "only triumph can be a bitter knowledge/ Out of the suffering they make our worth."

The theme of suffering, which runs through American-Jewish fiction, has been exploited most effectively by Bernard Malamud. As a theme it must appear oddly dissonant to those in our affluent society who have joined the conspiracy against discomfort, pain, and death, and who prefer diversion and titilation. Malamud would have it otherwise. He has kicked over the stage props to expose the tragic reality behind the fabrication of life conceived as Hollywood romance and Broadway musical. And he is peculiarly equipped for the task because suffering infuses his tradition from the days of bondage in Egypt to the extermination camps of the Third Reich. He knows, besides, that suffering is not an abstraction but an inexorable fact which must be experienced communally and individually. Indeed, Malamud's special distinction as a writer in America is to have magnified the theme to almost Talmudic grandeur: "They shall see the majesty of God who meet with humiliation and do not humiliate, who bear insult but do not inflict it upon others, who endure a life of suffering for the pure love of God."

We encounter a preliminary exploration of the theme in *The Natural*, Malamud's first novel. "Experience makes good people better," Iris says to Roy Hobbs, the baseball *wunderkind*. "How does it do that?" he asks. "Through their suffering," she replies. "Suffering is what brings us toward happiness." But Malamud did not fully exploit the subject until he wrote *The Assistant.* In his *Tales of the Hasidim* Buber tells the story of a sick man who complained to Rabbi Israel that his suffering interfered with his learning and praying. The Rabbi said: "How do you know, friend, what is more pleasing to God, your studying or your suffering?" The best of Malamud is a commentary on this teaching. Jews suffer because they are Jews, the groceryman Morris Bober explains to Frankie Alpine, his Italian assistant: "But I think if a Jew don't suffer for the Law, he will suffer for nothing." Frankie asks: "What do you suffer for, Morris?" Bober replies: "I suffer for you." Frankie is puzzled. "What do you mean?" "I mean you suffer for me," Bober says. And so Frankie is eventually converted through his own suffering into the essential Jew. He chooses to keep up the grocery, to obey the law of righteousness, to confirm in act (by means of circumcision and conversion) what he already knows through suffering, that "All men are Jews."

Most of the stories of *The Magic Barrel,* Malamud's finest achievement thus far, play variations on the meaning of Jewishness—as suffering, as compassion, as moral choice, as belief in the goodness and joy of life, as responsibility for others. A shoemaker pounds leather seven years for his love; a landlord joins his tenant in the act of mourning; a calamity-ridden tailor forces himself to believe in a Negro angel and is saved; a young man preparing a study of Giotto falls victim to an all-resourceful refugee and is grateful to him in the end; a baker beholds the bread of affliction turn into "charred corpses" as a result of his wife's lack of compassion; a rabbinical student falls in love with a marriage-broker's prostitute daughter in whom he foresees his own salvation; an ex-coffee-salesman recounts his futile efforts to dispense charity. But the stories defy synopsis. They constitute an *Agada* of suffering—suffering which can either kill feeling through a failure of compassion or exalt it through an acceptance of life into a strange and luminous joy.*

VI. TRANSCENDENCE

Given the previous moments of spiritual quest, we should expect American-Jewish writers to seek "health," unity or communion—some transcendent state which reconciles, if only briefly, the split-conscious-

---

* "Fathers and teachers, I ponder 'What is hell?' I maintain that it is the suffering of being unable to love." So muses the hero of J. D. Salinger's "For Esme—with Love and Squalor." But Salinger—the Jew as Jesus and Zen master—deserves a chapter to himself. Unhappily, he will no longer permit any of his stories to be anthologized.

ness of the self. In earlier ages God was the Transcendent Being. But for American-Jewish writers, less interested in theology than in human relatedness, He is symbolized by acts of reconciliation or wholeness. Their work reiterates E. M. Forster's "Only connect." It would therefore be a serious misconstruction of their roles to dismiss them as "irreligious," especially when we know that one of the central concerns of traditional Jewish law and custom has been ethical action—God on this earth. As Isaac Rosenfeld writes in "Adam and Eve on Delancey Street": "It is for such reasons . . . that the Jewish religion enjoys the reputation of being one of the most worldly and immanent, one of the most closely connected with daily life."

In discussing the qualities of Yiddish literature, Irving Howe posits an "inner dialectic" and notes that Yiddish and Hebrew balance each other: "Yiddish literature releases a profound yearning for a return not to the supremacy of Hebrew but to those conditions of life that would make possible the supremacy of Hebrew—that is, a yearning for the end of the dispersion and a reintegration of Jewish literature." Hebrew in "the background enables Yiddish literature to avoid the painful fate of those literatures of small countries which either become stalled in provinciality or fall into a slavish imitation of the latest vogue from Paris." Moreover, Howe sees Yiddish literature as *unifying* the community, "both consecrating and transcending the shtetl." Yiddish becomes "the only avaliable unifying principle." These images of unity—of Hebrew and Yiddish, of literature binding its readers into a transcendent community—are supplemented by a third one. Howe tells us that Yiddish literature is less concerned with individual character than with what Emerson called "representative men": "the student tortured by a conflict between belief and secular desire"; the Jewish child; the saintly fool. These figures have "the endurance of archetypes." Whenever a fool appears, we see, in effect, that he mirrors previous ones. The archetype contains *individualized present and eternal present.*

(Of course, archetypal figures recur in much of the poetry and in "Eli, the Fanatic," "The Einhorns," "King Solomon" and "Take Pity" —to name only a few of the stories. Perhaps Malamud's fiction, so reminiscent of the archetypal narratives of Isaac Bashevis Singer, best illustrates the quality of timelessness which adheres to legendary figures. But this quality is evident throughout the selections.)

While Howe does no more than defend Yiddish archetypes, other American-Jewish critics employ them relentlessly to elucidate their subjects. In his discussion of Negro and Jew, for example, Leslie Fiedler assumes that any modern Jew is the shadow, the incarnation, of ancient "brothers." There seems to be a transcendent, eternal Jew who lurks in the consciousness of all peoples: "The Jew is the father of Europe (irksome as that relationship may sometimes seem on both sides); the Negro only an adopted child. If Christendom denies us, it diminishes itself; but if we reject the West, we reject not our legend, only a historical interpretation of it. We are what we always were—ourselves." For Fiedler there is a true, complete, untarnished image—no matter the historical distortion. Archetypes are above individual consciousness and identity. They transcend what he has elsewhere called personal "signature." As a "myth critic" Fiedler is representative of the Jew who has accepted an "expansive variation" of his religion; the myth supplants theology. But his devotion to myth rather than to pure explication means that he is committed to his heritage, much more committed than those who divorce explication from personal gesture.

Although Kazin cannot be classed as a myth critic, he shares Howe's belief in the ineluctable *social* origins of art. His references are therefore to capitalism and the social structure rather than to Osiris or Moses. But in his essay on Sholom Aleichem (and in much of his later criticism) he is reaching toward a ceremonial approach. Art is regarded as a kind of ritual, capturing—and "purifying"—the struggles we all engage in. Malamud has said, "All men are Jews." Kazin implies that all Jews who read Aleichem share in a "community" transcending their own: "We enjoy things only when we can commit some of our daily life to tradition, when we can act ceremonially, ritualistically, artistically, instead of having to decide in each case which act to perform and how to go about it and what we are likely to get out of it. What we enjoy is, in fact, nothing less than the unconscious wealth of humanity, which is its memory."

Harold Rosenberg likewise insists that Mann's Joseph overcomes "mental duality" through being "enclosed in a known history." Joseph lives a life that "has the character of a celebration and wherein action is inseparable from the pleasure of the mind in contemplating with mingled awe, credulousness and skepticism a legend that has become part of itself." But is not Joseph an ideal Jew who knows that he is a walking legend, surviving—and even moving beyond—the flawed civilizations which seem to enclose him? Rosenberg's tone is prophetic. He sees his own heritage in Mann's epic hero.

Arthur A. Cohen asserts that American-Jews can choose more freely than others to be or not to be Jews. Fear of the "irresistible forces of history" no longer counts. Cohen chooses to be a Jew for religious reasons. His belief in the theology of Judaism—the God of the patriarchs, the law of Moses as the word of God, the redemption of history, Israel as the "holy instrument of divine fulfillment"—comprehends the *community* (a cultural phenomenon) of Kazin, the mystical *humanism* of Shapiro, and the fictional *archetypes* of Malamud and the myth critics. Theology for Cohen transcends these as God transcends man.

In the quest for meaning—through the revitalization of language as a vehicle for a fresh sensibility, the resurgence of humor and wit in the service of philosophical irony, and the uses of fantasy and obliquity in mastering a reality that is itself fantastic and sometimes grotesque—the American-Jewish writer has enriched the central current of American literature in the present decade. To repeat, his concerns are predominantly ethical and social rather than metaphysical and theological. Bellow's "dangling man" can admit that the source of grace is a universal God. But he stubbornly refuses "to catch at any contrivance in panic." The overriding problem, then, is not God but self-identification, the problem of locating the self within the community of other men. Paradoxically, the American-Jewish writer has approached the divine by seeking to make his way to what is most human whether he searches for it in Old Country or New, in the image of the father or in the discoverable if unrecoverable past, whether he violently assaults the corrupt values of his society, endeavors to mediate between the dualities which divide him from himself, recognizes suffering as the necessary condition of compassion, insists on the sanctity of life or—in the face of man's alienation from man as well as from God—reasserts the prophecy of the heart, the centrality of love, in the reconstruction of the social order.

The Editors

STORIES

PHILIP ROTH

✡✡✡

ELI, THE FANATIC

LEO TZUREF STEPPED OUT FROM BACK OF A WHITE
column to welcome Eli Peck. Eli jumped back, surprised; then they
shook hands and Tzuref gestured him into the sagging old mansion. At
the door Eli turned, and down the slope of lawn, past the jungle of
hedges, beyond the dark, untrampled horse path, he saw the street
lights blink on in Woodenton. The stores along Coach House Road
tossed up a burst of yellow—it came to Eli as a secret signal from his
townsmen: "Tell this Tzuref where we stand, Eli. This is a modern
community, Eli, we have our families, we pay taxes . . ." Eli, burdened
by the message, gave Tzuref a dumb, weary stare.

"You must work a full day," Tzuref said, steering the attorney and
his briefcase into the chilly hall.

Eli's heels made a racket on the cracked marble floor, and he spoke
above it. "It's the commuting that's killing," he said, and entered the
dim room Tzuref waved open for him. "Three hours a day . . . I came
right from the train." He dwindled down into a harp-backed chair.
He expected it would be deeper than it was and consequently jarred
himself on the sharp bones of his seat. It woke him, this shiver of the
behind, to his business. Tzuref, a bald shaggy-browed man who looked
as if he'd once been very fat, sat back of an empty desk, halfway
hidden, as though he were settled on the floor. Everything around
him was empty. There were no books in the bookshelves, no rugs
on the floor, no draperies in the big casement windows. As Eli began
to speak Tzuref got up and swung a window back on one noisy hinge.
"May and it's like August," he said, and with his back to Eli, he

27

revealed the black circle on the back of his head. The crown of his head was missing! He returned through the dimness—the lamps had no bulbs—and Eli realized all he'd seen was a skullcap. Tzuref struck a match and lit a candle, just as the half-dying shouts of children at play rolled in through the open window. It was as though Tzuref had opened it so Eli could hear them.

"Aah, now," he said. "I received your letter."

Eli poised, waiting for Tzuref to swish open a drawer and remove the letter from his file. Instead the old man leaned forward onto his stomach, worked his hand into his pants pocket, and withdrew what appeared to be a week-old handkerchief. He uncrumpled it; he unfolded it; he ironed it on the desk with the side of his hand. "So," he said.

Eli pointed to the grimy sheet which he'd gone over word-by-word with his partners, Lewis and McDonnell. "I expected an answer," Eli said. "It's a week."

"It was so important, Mr. Peck, I knew you would come."

Some children ran under the open window and their mysterious babble—not mysterious to Tzuref, who smiled—entered the room like a third person. Their noise caught up against Eli's flesh and he was unable to restrain a shudder. He wished he had gone home, showered and eaten dinner, before calling on Tzuref. He was not feeling as professional as usual—the place was too dim, it was too late. But down in Woodenton they would be waiting, his clients and neighbors. He spoke for the Jews of Woodenton, not just himself and his wife.

"You understood?" Eli said.

"It's not hard."

"It's a matter of zoning . . ." and when Tzuref did not answer, but only drummed his fingers on his lips, Eli said, "We didn't make the laws . . ."

"You respect them."

"They protect us . . . the community."

"The law is the law," Tzuref said.

"Exactly!" Eli had the urge to rise and walk about the room.

"And then of course"—Tzuref made a pair of scales in the air with his hands—"The law is not the law. When is the law that is the law not the law?" He jiggled the scales. "And vice versa."

"Simply," Eli said sharply. "You can't have a boarding school in a residential area." He would not allow Tzuref to cloud the issue with issues. "We thought it better to tell you before any action is undertaken."

"But a house in a residential area?"

"Yes. That's what residential means." The DP's English was perhaps not as good as it seemed at first. Tzuref spoke slowly, but till then Eli had mistaken it for craft—or even wisdom. "Residence means home." he added.

"So this is my residence."

"But the children?"

"It is their residence."

"*Seventeen* children?"

"Eighteen," Tzuref said.

"But you *teach* them here."

"The Talmud. That's illegal?"

"That makes it school."

Tzuref hung the scales again, tipping slowly the balance.

"Look, Mr. Tzuref, in America we call such a place a boarding school."

"Where they teach the Talmud?"

"Where they teach period. You are the headmaster, they are the students."

Tzuref placed his scales on the desk. "Mr. Peck," he said, "I don't believe it . . ." but he did not seem to be referring to anything Eli had said.

"Mr. Tzuref, that is the law. I came to ask what you intend to do."

"What I *must* do?"

"I hope they are the same."

"They are." Tzuref brought his stomach into the desk. "We stay." He smiled. "We are tired. The headmaster is tired. The students are tired."

Eli rose and lifted his briefcase. It felt so heavy packed with the grievances, vengeances, and schemes of his clients. There were days when he carried it like a feather—in Tzuref's office it weighed a ton.

"Goodbye, Mr. Tzuref."

"Sholom," Tzuref said.

Eli opened the door to the office and walked carefully down the dark tomb of a corridor to the door. He stepped out on the porch and, leaning against a pillar, looked down across the lawn to the children at play. Their voices whooped and rose and dropped as they chased each other round the old house. The dusk made the children's game look like a tribal dance. Eli straightened up, started off the porch, and suddenly the dance was ended. A long piercing scream trailed after. It was the first time in his life anyone had run at the sight of him. Keeping his eyes on the lights of Woodenton, he headed down the path.

And then, seated on a bench beneath a tree, Eli saw him. At first it seemed only a deep hollow of blackness—then the figure emerged. Eli recognized him from the descripton. There he was, wearing the hat, that hat which was the very cause of Eli's mission, the source of Woodenton's upset. The town's lights flashed their message once again: "Get the one with the hat. What a nerve, what a nerve . . ."

Eli started towards the man. Perhaps he was less stubborn than Tzuref, more reasonable. After all, it was the law. But when he was close enough to call out, he didn't. He was stopped by the sight of the black coat that fell down below the man's knees, and the hands which held each other in his lap. By the round-topped, wide-brimmed Talmudic hat, pushed onto the back of his head. And by the beard, which hid his neck and was so soft and thin it fluttered away and back again with each heavy breath he took. He was asleep, his sidelocks curled loose on his cheeks. His face was no older than Eli's.

Eli hurried towards the lights.

The note on the kitchen table unsettled him. Scribblings on bits of paper had made history this past week. This one, however, was unsigned. "Sweetie," it said, "I went to sleep. I had a sort of Oedipal experience with the baby today. Call Ted Heller."

She had left him a cold soggy dinner in the refrigerator. He hated cold soggy dinners, but would take one gladly in place of Miriam's presence. He was ruffled, and she never helped that, not with her infernal analytic powers. He loved her when life was proceeding smoothly—and that was when she loved him. But sometimes Eli found being a lawyer surrounded him like quicksand—he couldn't get his breath. Too often he wished he were pleading for the other side; though if he were on the other side, then he'd wish he were on the side he was. The trouble was that sometimes the law didn't seem to be the answer, *law* didn't seem to have anything to do with what was aggravating everybody. And that, of course, made him feel foolish and unnecessary . . . Though that was not the situation here—the townsmen had a case. But not *exactly,* and if Miriam were awake to see Eli's upset, she would set about explaining his distress to him, understanding him, forgiving him, so as to get things back to Normal, for Normal was where they loved one another. The difficulty with Miriam's efforts was they only upset him more; not only did they explain little to him about himself or his predicament, but they convinced him of *her* weakness. Neither Eli nor Miriam, it turned out, was terribly strong. Twice before he'd faced this fact, and on both occasions had found solace in what his neighbors forgivingly referred to as "a nervous breakdown."

Eli ate his dinner with his briefcase beside him. Halfway through, he gave in to himself, removed Tzuref's notes, and put them on the table, beside Miriam's. From time to time he flipped through the notes, which had been carried into town by the one in the black hat. The first note, the incendiary:

To whom it may concern:

Please give this gentleman the following: Boys shoes with rubber heels and soles.

> 5 prs size 6c
> 3 prs size 5c
> 3 prs size 5b
> 2 prs size 4a
> 3 prs size 4c
> 1 pr size 7b
> 1 pr size 7c

Total 18 prs. boys shoes. This gentleman has a check already signed. Please fill in correct amount.

> L. Tzuref
> Director, Yeshivah of
> Woodenton, N.Y.
> (5/8/48)

"Eli, a regular greenhorn," Ted Heller had said. "He didn't say a word. Just handed me the note and stood there, like in the Bronx the old guys who used to come around selling Hebrew trinkets."

"A Yeshivah!" Artie Berg had said. "Eli, in Woodenton, a Yeshivah! If I want to live in Brownsville, Eli, I'll live in Brownsville."

"Eli," Harry Shaw speaking now, "the old Puddington place. Old man Puddington'll roll over in his grave. Eli, when I left the city, Eli, I didn't plan the city should come to me."

Note number two:

Dear Grocer:

Please give this gentleman ten pounds of sugar. Charge it to our account, Yeshivah of Woodenton, NY—which we will now open with you and expect a bill each month. The gentleman will be in to see you once or twice a week.

L. TZUREF, Director
(5/10/48)

P.S. Do you carry kosher meat?

"He walked right by my window, the greenie," Ted had said, "and he nodded, Eli. He's my *friend* now."

"Eli," Artie Berg had said, "he handed the damn thing to a *clerk* at Stop N' Shop—and in that hat yet!"

"Eli," Harry Shaw again, "it's not funny. Someday, Eli, its' going to be a hundred little kids with little *yamalkahs* chanting their Hebrew lessons on Coach House Road, and then it's not going to strike you funny."

"Eli, what goes on up there—my kids hear strange sounds."

"Eli, this is a modern community."

"Eli, we pay taxes."

"Eli."

"Eli!"

"*Eli!*"

At first it was only another townsman crying in his ear; but when he turned he saw Miriam, standing in the doorway, behind her belly.

"Eli, sweetheart, how was it?"

"He said no."

"Did you see the other one?" she asked.

"Sleeping, under a tree."

"Did you let him know how people feel?"

"He was sleeping."

"Why didn't you wake him up? Eli, this isn't an everyday thing."

"He was tired!"

"Don't shout, please," Miriam said.

"'Don't shout. I'm pregnant. The baby is heavy.'" Eli found he was getting angry at nothing she'd said yet; it was what she was going to say.

"He's a very heavy baby the doctor says," Miriam told him.

"Then sit *down* and make my dinner." Now he found himself angry about her not being present at the dinner which he'd just been relieved that she wasn't present at. It was as though he had a raw nerve for a tail, that he kept stepping on. At last Miriam herself stepped on it.

"Eli, you're upset. I understand."

"You *don't* understand."

She left the room. From the stairs she called, "I do, sweetheart."

It was a trap! He would grow angry knowing she would be "understanding." She would in turn grow more understanding seeing his anger. He would in turn grow angrier . . . The phone rang.

"Hello," Eli said.

"Eli, Ted. So?"

"So nothing."

"Who is Tzuref? He's an American guy?"

"No. A DP. German."

"And the kids?"

"DP's too. He teaches them."

"What? What subjects?" Ted asked.

"I don't know."

"And the guy with the hat, you saw the guy with the hat?"

"Yes. He was sleeping."

"Eli he sleeps with the *hat?*"

"He sleeps with the hat."

"Goddam fanatics," Ted said. "This is the twentieth century, Eli. Now it's the guy with the hat. Pretty soon all the little Yeshivah boys'll be spilling down into town."

"Next thing they'll be after our daughters."

"Michele and Debbie wouldn't look at them."

"Then," Eli mumbled, "you've got nothing to worry about, Teddie," and he hung up.

In a moment the phone rang. "Eli? We got cut off. We've got nothing to worry about? You worked it out?"

"I have to see him again tomorrow. We can work something out."

"That's fine, Eli. I'll call Artie and Harry."

Eli hung up.

"I thought you said *nothing* worked out." It was Miriam.

"I did."

"Then why did you tell Ted *something* worked out?"

"It did."

"Eli, maybe you should get a little more therapy."

"That's enough of that, Miriam."

"You can't function as a lawyer by being neurotic. That's no answer."

"You're ingenious, Miriam."

She turned, frowning, and took her heavy baby to bed.

The phone rang.

"Eli, Artie. Ted called. You worked it out? No trouble?"

"Yes."

"When are they going?"

"Leave it to me, will you, Artie? I'm tired. I'm going to sleep."

In bed Eli kissed his wife's belly and laid his head upon it to think. He laid it lightly, for she was that day entering the second week of her ninth month. Still, when she slept, it was a good place to rest, to rise and fall with her breathing and figure things out. "If that guy would take off that crazy hat. I know it, what eats them. If he'd take off that crazy hat everything would be all right."

"What?" Miriam said.

"I'm talking to the baby."

Miriam pushed herself up in bed. "Eli, please, baby, shouldn't you maybe stop in to see Dr. Eckman, just for a little conversation?"

"I'm fine."

"Oh, sweetie!" she said, and put her head back on the pillow.

"You know what your mother brought to this marriage—a sling chair and a goddam New School enthusiasm for Sigmund Freud."

Miriam feigned sleep, he could tell by the breathing.

"I'm telling the kid the truth, aren't I, Miriam? A sling chair, three months to go on a *New Yorker* subscription, and *An Introduction to Psychoanalysis*. Isn't that right?"

"Eli, must you be aggressive?"

"That's all you worry about, is your insides. You stand in front of the mirror all day and look at yourself being pregnant."

"Pregnant mothers have a relationship with the fetus that fathers can't understand."

"Relationship my ass. What is my liver doing now? What is my small intestine doing now? Is my island of Langerhans on the blink?"

"Don't be jealous of a little fetus, Eli."

"I'm jealous of your island of Langerhans!"

"Eli, I can't argue with you when I know it's not me you're really angry with. Don't you see, sweetie, you're angry with yourself."

"You and Eckman."

"Maybe he could help, Eli."

"Maybe he could help you. You're practically lovers as it is."

"You're being hostile again," Miriam said.

"What do you care—it's only *me* I'm being hostile towards."

"Eli, we're going to have a beautiful baby, and I'm going to have a perfectly simple delivery, and you're going to make a fine father, and there's absolutely no reason to be obsessed with whatever is on your mind. All we have to worry about—" she smiled at him "—is a name."

Eli got out of bed and slid into his slippers. "We'll name the kid Eckman if it's a boy and Eckman if it's a girl."

"Eckman Peck sounds terrible."

"He'll have to live with it," Eli said, and he went down to his study where the latch on his briefcase glinted in the moonlight that came through the window.

He removed the Tzuref notes and read through them all again. It unnerved him to think of all the flashy reasons his wife could come up with for his reading and rereading the notes. "Eli, why are you so *preoccupied* with Tzuref?" "Eli, stop getting *involved*. Why do you think you're getting *involved*, Eli?" Sooner or later, everybody's wife finds their weak spot. His goddam luck he had to be neurotic! Why couldn't he have been born with a short leg.

He removed the cover from his typewriter, hating Miriam for the edge she had. All the time he wrote the letter, he could hear what she would be saying about his not being *able* to let the matter drop. Well, her trouble was that she wasn't *able* to face the matter. But he could hear her answer already: clearly, he was guilty of "a reaction formation." Still, all the fancy phrases didn't fool Eli: all she wanted really was for Eli to send Tzuref and family on their way, so that the community's temper would quiet, and the calm circumstances of their domestic happiness return. All she wanted were order and love in her private world. Was she so wrong? Let the world bat its brains out—in Woodenton there should be peace. He wrote the letter anyway:

Dear Mr. Tzuref:

Our meeting this evening seems to me inconclusive. I don't think there's any reason for us not to be able to come up with some sort of compromise that will satisfy the Jewish community of Woodenton and the Yeshivah and yourself. It seems to me that what most disturbs my neighbors are the visits to town by the gentleman in the black hat, suit, etc. Woodenton is a progressive suburban community whose members, both Jewish and Gentile, are anxious that their families live in comfort and beauty and serenity. This is, after all, the twentieth century, and we do not think it too much to ask that the members of our community dress in a manner appropriate to the time and place.

Woodenton, as you may not know, has long been the home of well-to-do Protestants. It is only since the war that Jews have been able to buy property here, and for Jews and Gentiles to live beside each other in amity. For this adjustment to be made, both Jews and Gentiles alike have had to give up some of their more extreme practices in order not to threaten or offend the other. Certainly such amity is to be desired. Perhaps if such conditions had existed in prewar Europe, the persecution of the Jewish people, of which you and those 18 children have been victims, could not have been carried out with such success—in fact, might not have been carried out at all.

Therefore, Mr. Tzuref, will you accept the following conditions? If you can, we will see fit not to carry out legal action against the Yeshivah for failure to comply with township Zoning ordinances No. 18 and No. 23. The conditions are simply:

1. The religious, educational, and social activities of the Yeshivah of Woodenton will be confined to the Yeshivah grounds.

2. Yeshivah personnel are welcomed in the streets and stores of Woodenton provided they are attired in clothing usually associated with American life in the 20th century.

If these conditions are met, we see no reason why the Yeshivah of Woodenton cannot live peacefully and satisfactorily with the Jews of Woodenton—as the Jews of Woodenton have come to live with the Gentiles of Woodenton. I would appreciate an immediate reply.

Sincerely,

ELI PECK, Attorney

Two days later Eli received his immediate reply:

Mr. Peck:

The suit the gentleman wears is all he's got.

Sincerely,

LEO TZUREF, Headmaster

Once again, as Eli swung around the dark trees and onto the lawn, the children fled. He reached out with his briefcase as if to stop them, but they were gone so fast all he saw moving was a flock of skullcaps.

"Come, come . . ." a voice called from the porch. Tzuref appeared from behind a pillar. Did he *live* behind those pillars? Was he just watching the children at play? Either way, when Eli appeared, Tzuref was ready, with no forewarning.

"Hello," Eli said.

"Sholom."

"I didn't mean to frighten them."

"They're scared, so they run."

"I didn't do anything."

Tzuref shrugged. The little movement seemed to Eli strong as an accusation. What he didn't get at home, he got here.

Inside the house they took their seats. Though it was lighter than a few evenings before, a bulb or two would have helped. Eli had to hold his briefcase towards the window for the last gleamings. He removed Tzuref's letter from a manila folder. Tzuref removed Eli's letter from his pants pocket. Eli removed the carbon of his own letter from another manila folder. Tzuref removed Eli's first letter from his back pocket. Eli removed the carbon from his briefcase. Tzuref raised his palms. ". . . It's all I've got . . ."

Those upraised palms, the mocking tone—another accusation. It was a crime to keep carbons! Everybody had an edge on him—Eli could do no right.

"I offered a compromise, Mr. Tzuref. You refused."

"Refused, Mr. Peck? What is, is."

"The man could get a new suit."

"That's all he's got."

"So you told me," Eli said.

"So I told you, so you know."

"It's not an insurmountable obstacle, Mr. Tzuref. We have stores."

"For that too?"

"On Route 12, a Robert Hall—"

"To take away the one thing a man's got?"

"Not take away, *replace.*"

"But I tell you he has nothing. *Nothing.* You have that word in English? *Nicht? Gornisht?*"

"Yes, Mr. Tzuref, we have the word."

"A mother and a father?" Tzuref said. "No. A wife? No. A baby? A little ten-month-old baby? No! A village full of friends? A synagogue where you knew the feel of every seat under your pants? Where with your eyes closed you could smell the cloth of the Torah?" Tzuref pushed out of his chair, stirring a breeze that swept Eli's letter to the floor. At the window he leaned out, and looked, beyond Woodenton. When he turned he was shaking a finger at Eli. "And a medical experiment they performed on him yet! That leaves nothing, Mr. Peck. Absolutely nothing!"

"I misunderstood."

"No news reached Woodenton?"

"About the suit, Mr. Tzuref. I thought he couldn't afford another."

"He can't."

They were right where they'd begun. "Mr. Tzuref!" Eli demanded. *"Here?"* He smacked his hand to his billfold.

"Exactly!" Tzuref said, smacking his own breast.

"Then we'll buy him one!" Eli crossed to the window and taking Tzuref by the shoulders, pronounced each word slowly. "We-will-pay-for-it. All right?"

"Pay? What, diamonds!"

Eli raised a hand to his inside pocket, then let it drop. Oh stupid! Tzuref, father to eighteen, had smacked not what lay under his coat, but deeper, under the ribs.

"Oh . . ." Eli said. He moved away along the wall. "The suit is all he's got then."

"You got my letter," Tzuref said.

Eli stayed back in the shadow, and Tzuref turned to his chair. He swished Eli's letter from the floor, and held it up. "You say too much . . . all this reasoning . . . all these conditions . . ."

"What can I do?"

"You have the word 'suffer' in English?"

"We have the word suffer. We have the word law too."

"Stop with the law! You have the word suffer. Then try it. It's a little thing."

"They won't," Eli said.

"But you, Mr. Peck, how about you?"

"I am them, they are me, Mr. Tzuref."

"Aach! You are us, we are you!"

Eli shook and shook his head. In the dark he suddenly felt that Tzuref might put him under a spell. "Mr. Tzuref, a little light?"

Tzuref lit what tallow was left in the holders. Eli was afraid to ask if they couldn't afford electricity. Maybe candles were all they had left.

"Mr. Peck, who made the law, may I ask you that?"

"The people."

"No."

"Yes."

"Before the people."

"No one. Before the people there was no law." Eli didn't care for the conversation, but with only candlelight, he was being lulled into it.

"Wrong," Tzuref said.

"We make the law, Mr. Tzuref. It is our community. These are my neighbors. I am their attorney. They pay me. Without law there is chaos."

"What you call law, I call shame. The heart, Mr. Peck, the heart is law! God!" he announced.

"Look, Mr. Tzuref, I didn't come here to talk metaphysics. People use the law, it's a flexible thing. They protect what they value, their property, their well-being, their happiness—"

"Happiness? They hide their shame. And you, Mr. Peck, you are shameless?"

"We do it," Eli said, wearily, "for our children. This is the twentieth century . . ."

"For the goyim maybe. For me the fifty-eighth." He pointed at Eli. "That is too old for shame."

Eli felt squashed. Everybody in the world had evil reasons for his actions. Everybody! With reasons so cheap, who buys bulbs. "Enough wisdom, Mr. Tzuref. Please. I'm exhausted."

"Who isn't?" Tzuref said.

He picked Eli's papers from his desk and reached up with them. "What do you intend for us to do?"

"What you must," Eli said. "I made the offer."

"So he must give up his suit?"

"Tzuref, Tzuref, leave me be with that suit! I'm not the only lawyer in the world. I'll drop the case, and you'll get somebody who won't talk compromise. Then you'll have no home, no children, nothing. Only a lousy black suit! Sacrifice what you want. I know what I would do."

To that Tzuref made no answer, but only handed Eli his letters.

"It's not me, Mr. Tzuref, it's them."

"They are you."

"No," Eli intoned, "I am me. They are them. You are you."

"You talk about leaves and branches. I'm dealing with under the dirt."

"Mr. Tzuref, you're driving me crazy with Talmudic wisdom. This is that, that is the other thing. Give me a straight answer."

"Only for straight questions."

"Oh, God!"

Eli returned to his chair and plunged his belongings into his case. "Then, that's all," he said angrily.

Tzuref gave him the shrug.

"Remember, Tzuref, you called this down on yourself."

"*I* did?"

Eli refused to be his victim again. Double-talk proved nothing. "Goodbye," he said.

But as he opened the door leading to the hall, he heard Tzuref.

"And your wife, how is she?"

"Fine, just fine." Eli kept going.

"And the baby is due when, any day?"

Eli turned. "That's right."

"Well," Tzuref said, rising. "Good luck."

"You know?"

Tzuref pointed out the window—then, with his hands, he drew upon himself a beard, a hat, a long, long coat. When his fingers formed the hem they touched the floor. "He shops two, three times a week, he gets to know them."

"He *talks* to them?"

"He sees them."

"And he can tell which is my wife?"

"They shop at the same stores. He says she is beautiful. She has a kind face. A woman capable of love . . . though who can be sure."

"*He* talks about *us,* to *you?*" demanded Eli.

"You talk about us, to her?"

"Goodbye, Mr. Tzuref."

Tzuref said, "Sholom. And good luck—I know what it is to have children. Sholom," Tzuref whispered, and with the whisper the candles went out. But the instant before, the flames leaped into Tzuref's eyes, and Eli saw it was not luck Tzuref wished him at all.

Outside the door, Eli waited. Down the lawn the children were holding hands and whirling around in a circle. At first he did not move. But he could not hide in the shadows all night. Slowly he began to slip along the front of the house. Under his hands he felt where bricks were out. He moved in the shadows until he reached the side. And then, clutching his briefcase to his chest, he broke across the darkest spots of the lawn. He aimed for a distant glade of woods, and when he reached it he did not stop, but ran through until he was so dizzied that the trees seemed to be running beside him, fleeing not towards Woodenton but away. His lungs were nearly ripping their seams as he burst into the yellow glow of the Gulf station at the edge of town.

"Eli, I had pains today. Where were you?"

"I went to Tzuref."

"Why didn't you call? I was worried."

He tossed his hat past the sofa and onto the floor. "Where are my winter suits?"

"In the hall closet. Eli, it's May."

"I need a strong suit." He left the room, Miriam behind him.

"Eli, talk to me. Sit down. Have dinner. Eli, what are you doing? You're going to get moth balls all over the carpet."

He peered out from the hall closet. Then he peered in again—there was a zipping noise, and suddenly he swept a greenish tweed suit before his wife's eyes.

"Eli, I love you in that suit. But not now. Have something to eat. I made dinner tonight—I'll warm it."

"You've got a box big enough for this suit?"

"I got a Bonwit's box, the other day. Eli, *why?*"

"Miriam, you see me doing something, let me do it."

"You haven't eaten."

"I'm *doing* something." He started up the stairs to the bedroom.

"Eli, would you please tell me what it is you want, and why?"

He turned and looked down at her. "Suppose this time you give me the reasons *before* I tell you what I'm doing. It'll probably work out the same anyway."

"Eli, I want to help."

"It doesn't concern you."

"But I want to help *you*," Miriam said.

"Just be quiet, then."

"But you're upset," she said, and she followed him up the stairs, heavily, breathing for two.

"Eli, what now?"

"A shirt." He yanked open all the drawers of their new teak dresser. He extracted a shirt.

"Eli, batiste? With a tweed suit?" she inquired.

He was at the closet now, on his knees. "Where are my cordovans?"

"Eli, why are you doing this so compulsively? You look like you *have* to do something."

"Oh, Miriam, you're supersubtle."

"Eli, stop this and talk to me. Stop it or I'll call Dr. Eckman."

Eli was kicking off the shoes he was wearing. "Where's the Bonwit box?"

"Eli, do you want me to have the baby right *here!*"

Eli walked over and sat down on the bed. He was draped not only with his own clothing, but also with the greenish tweed suit, the batiste shirt, and under each arm a shoe. He raised his arms and let the shoes drop onto the bed. Then he undid his necktie with one hand and his teeth and added that to the booty.

"Underwear," he said. "He'll need underwear."

"Who!"

He was slipping out of his socks.

Miriam kneeled down and helped him ease his left foot out of the sock. She sat with it on the floor. "Eli, just lie back. Please."

"Plaza 9-3103."

"What?"

"Eckman's number," he said. "It'll save you the trouble."

"Eli—"

"You've got that goddam tender 'You need help' look in your eyes, Miriam, don't tell me you don't."

"I don't."

"I'm not flipping," Eli said.

"I know, Eli."

"Last time I sat in the bottom of the closet and chewed on my bedroom slippers. That's what I did."

"I know."

"And I'm not doing that. This is not a nervous breakdown, Miriam, let's get that straight."

"Okay," Miriam said. She kissed the foot she held. Then, softly, she asked, "What *are* you doing?"

"Getting clothes for the guy in the hat. Don't tell me why, Miriam. Just let me do it."

"That's all?" she asked.

"That's all."

"You're not leaving?"

"No."

"Sometimes I think it gets too much for you, and you'll just leave."

"What gets too much?"

"I don't *know,* Eli. Something gets too much. Whenever everything's peaceful for a long time, and things are nice and pleasant, and we're expecting to be even happier. Iike now. It's as if you don't think we *deserve* to be happy."

"Damn it, Miriam! I'm giving this guy a new suit, is that all right? From now on he comes into Woodenton like everybody else, is that all right with you?"

"And Tzuref moves?"

"I don't even know if he'll take the suit, Miriam! Why do you have to bring up moving!"

"Eli, I didn't bring up moving. Everybody did. That's what everybody wants. Why make everybody un*happy*. It's even a law, Eli."

"Don't tell me what's the law."

"All right, sweetie. I'll get the box."

"*I'll* get the box. Where is it?"

"In the basement."

When he came up from the basement, he found all the clothes neatly folded and squared away on the sofa: shirt, tie, shoes, socks, underwear, belt, and an old gray flannel suit. His wife sat on the end of the sofa, looking like an anchored balloon.

"Where's the green suit?" he said.

"Eli, it's your loveliest suit. It's my favorite suit. Whenever I think of you, Eli, it's in that suit."

"Get it out."

"Eli, it's a Brooks Brothers suit. You say yourself how much you love it."

"Get it out."

"But the gray flannel's more practical. For shopping."

"Get it out."

"You go overboard, Eli. That's your trouble. You won't do anything in moderation. That's how people destroy themselves."

"I do *everything* in moderation. That's my trouble. The suit's in the closet again?"

She nodded, and began to fill up with tears. "Why does it have to be *your* suit? Who are you even to decide to give a suit? What about the others?" She was crying openly, and holding her belly. "Eli, I'm going to have a baby. Do we need all *this?*" and she swept the clothes off the sofa to the floor.

At the closet Eli removed the green suit. "It's a J. Press," he said, looking at the lining.

"I hope to hell he's happy with it!" Miriam said, sobbing.

A half hour later the box was packed. The cord he'd found in the
kitchen cabinet couldn't keep the outfit from popping through. The
trouble was there was too much: the gray suit *and* the green suit, an
oxford shirt as well as the batiste. But let him have two suits! Let him
have three, four, if only this damn silliness would stop! And a hat—of
course! God, he'd almost forgotten the hat. He took the stairs two at a
time and in Miriam's closet yanked a hatbox from the top shelf. Scattering hat and tissue paper to the floor, he returned downstairs, where he
packed away the hat he'd worn that day. Then he looked at his wife,
who lay outstretched on the floor before the fireplace. For the third time
in as many minutes she was saying, "Eli, this is the real thing."

"Where?"

"Right under the baby's head, like somebody's squeezing oranges."

Now that he'd stopped to listen he was stupefied. He said, "But you
have two more weeks . . ." Somehow he'd really been expecting it was to
go on not just another two weeks, but another nine months. This led
him to suspect, suddenly, that his wife was feigning pain so as to get his
mind off delivering the suit. And just as suddenly he resented himself for having such a thought. God, what had he become! He'd been
an unending bastard towards her since this Tzuref business had come
up—just when her pregnancy must have been most burdensome. He'd
allowed her no access to him, but still, he was sure, for good reasons:
she might tempt him out of his confusion with her easy answers. He
could be tempted all right, it was why he fought so hard. But now a
sweep of love came over him at the thought of her contracting womb,
and his child. And yet he would not indicate it to her. Under such
splendid marital conditions, who knows but she might extract some
promise from him about his concern with the school on the hill.

Having packed his second bag of the evening, Eli sped his wife to
Woodenton Memorial. There she proceeded not to have her baby, but
to lie hour after hour through the night having at first oranges, then
bowling balls, then basketballs, squeezed back of her pelvis. Eli sat in
the waiting room, under the shattering African glare of a dozen rows of
fluorescent bulbs, composing a letter to Tzuref.

Dear Mr. Tzuref:

The clothes in this box are for the gentleman in the hat. In a life of
sacrifice what is one more? But in a life of no sacrifices even one is impossible. Do you see what I'm saying, Mr. Tzuref? I am not a Nazi who

would drive eighteen children, who are probably frightened at the sight of a firefly, into homelessness. But if you want a home here, you must accept what we have to offer. The world is the world, Mr. Tzuref. As you would say, what is, is. All we say to this man is change your clothes. Enclosed are two suits and two shirts, and everything else he'll need, including a new hat. When he needs new clothes let me know.

We await his appearance in Woodenton, as we await friendly relations with the Yeshivah of Woodenton.

He signed his name and slid the note under a bursting flap and into the box. Then he went to the phone at the end of the room and dialed Ted Heller's number.

"Hello."

"Shirley, it's Eli."

"Eli, we've been calling all night. The lights are on in your place, but nobody answers. We thought it was burglars."

"Miriam's having the baby."

"At home?" Shirley said. "Oh, Eli, what a fun-idea!"

"Shirley, let me speak to Ted."

After the ear-shaking clatter of the phone whacking the floor, Eli heard footsteps, breathing, throat-clearing, then Ted. "A boy or a girl?"

"Nothing yet."

"You've given Shirley the bug, Eli. Now she's going to have *our* next one at home."

"Good."

"That's a terrific way to bring the family together, Eli."

"Look, Ted, I've settled with Tzuref."

"When are they going?"

"They're not exactly going, Teddie. I settled it—you won't even know they're there."

"A guy dressed like 1000 B.C. and I won't know it? What are you thinking about, pal?"

"He's changing his clothes."

"Yeah, to what? Another funeral suit?"

"Tzuref promised me, Ted. Next time he comes to town, he comes dressed like you and me."

"What! Somebody's kidding somebody, Eli."

Eli's voice shot up. "If he says he'll do it, he'll do it!"

"And, Eli," Ted asked, "he said it?"

"He said it." It cost him a sudden headache, this invention.

"And suppose he doesn't change, Eli. Just suppose. I mean that *might* happen, Eli. This might just be some kind of stall or something."

"No," Eli assured him.

The other end was quiet a moment. "Look, Eli," Ted said, finally, "he changes. Okay? All right? But they're still up there, aren't they? *That* doesn't change."

"The point is you won't know it."

Patiently Ted said, "Is this what we asked of you, Eli? When we put our faith and trust in you, is that what we were asking? We weren't concerned that this guy should become a Beau Brummel, Eli, believe me. We just don't think this is the community for them. And, Eli, we isn't me. The Jewish members of the community appointed me, Artie, and Harry to see what could be done. And we appointed you. And what's happened?"

Eli heard himself say, "What happened, happened."

"Eli, you're talking in crossword puzzles."

"My wife's having a baby," Eli explained, defensively.

"I realize that, Eli. But this is a matter of zoning, isn't it? Isn't that what we discovered? You don't abide by the ordinance, you go. I mean I can't raise mountain goats, say, in my backyard—"

"This isn't so simple, Ted. People are involved—"

"People? Eli, we've been through this and through this. We're not just dealing with people—these are religious fanatics is what they are. Dressing like that. What I'd really like to find out is what goes on up there. I'm getting more and more skeptical, Eli, and I'm not afraid to admit it. It smells like a lot of hocus-pocus abracadabra stuff to me. Guys like Harry, you know, they think and they think and they're afraid to admit what they're thinking. I'll tell you. Look, I don't even know about this Sunday school business. Sundays I drive my oldest kid all the way to Scarsdale to learn Bible stories . . . and you know what she comes up with? This Abraham in the Bible was going to kill his own *kid* for a sacrifice. She gets nightmares from it, for God's sake! You call that religion? Today a guy like that they'd lock him up. This is an age of science, Eli. I size people's feet with an X-ray machine, for God's sake. They've disproved all that stuff, Eli, and I refuse to sit by and watch it happening on my own front lawn."

"Nothing's happening on your front lawn, Teddie. You're exaggerating, nobody's sacrificing their kid."

"You're damn right, Eli—I'm not sacrificing mine. You'll see when you have your own what it's like. All the place is, is a hideaway for people who can't face life. It's a matter of *needs*. They have all these superstitions, and why do you think? Because they can't face the world, because they can't take their place in society. That's no environment to bring kids up in, Eli."

"Look, Ted, see it from another angle. We can convert them," Eli said, with half a heart.

"What, make a bunch of Catholics out of them? Look, Eli—pal, there's a good healthy relationship in this town because it's modern Jews and Protestants. That's the point, isn't it, Eli? Let's not kid each other, I'm not Harry. The way things are now are fine—like human beings. There's going to be no pogroms in Woodenton. Right? 'Cause there's no fanatics, no crazy people—" Eli winced, and closed his eyes a second—"just people who respect each other, and leave each other be. Common sense is the ruling thing, Eli. I'm for common sense. Moderation."

"Exactly, exactly, Ted. I agree, but common sense, maybe, says make this guy change his clothes. Then maybe—"

"Common sense says that? Common sense says to me they go and find a nice place somewhere else, Eli. New York is the biggest city in the world, it's only 30 miles away—why don't they go there?"

"Ted, give them a chance. Introduce them to common sense."

"Eli, you're dealing with *fanatics*. Do they display common sense? Talking a dead language, that makes sense? Making a big thing out of suffering, so you're going oy-oy-oy all your life, that's common sense? Look, Eli, we've been through all this. I don't know if you know—but there's talk that *Life* magazine is sending a guy out to the Yeshivah for a story. With pictures."

"Look, Teddie, you're letting your imagination get inflamed. I don't think *Life's* interested."

"But I'm interested, Eli. And we thought you were supposed to be."

"I am," Eli said, "I am. Let him just change the clothes, Ted. Let's see what happens."

"They live in the medieval ages, Eli—it's some superstition, some *rule*."

"Let's just *see*," Eli pleaded.

"Eli, every day—"

"One more day," Eli said. "If he doesn't change in one more day. . . ."

"What?"

"Then I get an injunction first thing Monday. That's that."

"Look, Eli—it's not up to me. Let me call Harry—"

"You're the spokesman, Teddie. I'm all wrapped up here with Miriam having a baby. Just give me the day—them the day."

"All right, Eli. I want to be fair. But tomorrow, that's all. Tomorrow's the judgment day, Eli, I'm telling you."

"I hear trumpets," Eli said, and hung up. He was shaking inside— Teddie's voice seemed to have separated his bones at the joints. He was still in the phone booth when the nurse came to tell him that Mrs. Peck would positively not be delivered of a child until the morning. He was to go home and get some rest, he looked like *he* was having the baby. The nurse winked and left.

But Eli did not go home. He carried the Bonwit box out into the street with him and put it in the car. The night was soft and starry, and he began to drive the streets of Woodenton. Square cool windows, apricot-colored, were all one could see beyond the long lawns that fronted the homes of the townsmen. The stars polished the permanent baggage carriers atop the station wagons in the driveways. He drove slowly, up, down, around. Only his tires could be heard taking the gentle curves in the road.

What peace. What incredible peace. Have children ever been so safe in their beds? Parents—Eli wondered—so full in their stomachs? Water so warm in its boilers? Never. Never in Rome, never in Greece. Never even did walled cities have it so good! No wonder then they would keep things just as they were. Here, after all, were peace and safety—what civilization had been working toward for centuries. For all his jerkiness, that was all Ted Heller was asking for, peace and safety. It was what his parents had asked for in the Bronx, and his grandparents in Poland, and theirs in Russia or Austria, or wherever else they'd fled to or from. It was what Miriam was asking for. And now they had it—the world was at last a place for families, even Jewish families. After all these centuries, maybe there just had to be this communal toughness—or numbness—to protect such a blessing. Maybe that was the trouble with the Jews all along—too soft. Sure, to live takes guts . . . Eli was thinking as he drove on beyond the train station, and parked his car at the darkened Gulf station. He stepped out, carrying the box.

At the top of the hill one window trembled with light. What *was* Tzuref doing up there in that office? Killing babies—probably not. But studying a language no one understood? Practicing customs with origins long forgotten? Suffering sufferings already suffered once too often? Teddie was right—why keep it up! However, if a man chose to be stubborn, then he couldn't expect to survive. The world is give-and-take. What sense to sit and brood over a suit. Eli would give him one last chance.

He stopped at the top. No one was around. He walked slowly up the lawn, setting each foot into the grass, listening to the shh shhh shhhh his shoes made as they bent the wetness into the sod. He looked around. Here there was nothing. Nothing! An old decaying house—and a suit.

On the porch he slid behind a pillar. He felt someone was watching him. But only the stars gleamed down. And at his feet, off and away, Woodenton glowed up. He set his package on the step of the great front door. Inside the cover of the box he felt to see if his letter was still there. When he touched it, he pushed it deeper into the green suit, which his fingers still remembered from winter. He should have included some light bulbs. Then he slid back by the pillar again, and this time there was something on the lawn. It was the second sight he had of him. He was facing Woodenton and barely moving across the open space towards the trees. His right fist was beating his chest. And then Eli heard a sound rising with each knock on the chest. And it did all three to Eli, plus more. Some feeling crept into him for whose deepness he could find no word. It was strange. He listened—it did not hurt to hear this moan. But he wondered if it hurt to make it. And so, with only stars to hear, he tried. And it did hurt. Not the bumblebee of noise that turned at the back of his throat and winged out his nostrils. What hurt buzzed down. It stung and stung inside him, and in turn the moan sharpened. It became a scream, louder, a song, a crazy song that whined through the pillars and blew out to the grass, until the strange hatted creature on the lawn turned and threw his arms wide, and looked in the night like a scarecrow.

Eli ran, and when he reached the car the pain was only a bloody scratch across his neck where a branch had whipped back as he fled the greenie's arms.

The following day his son was born. But not till one in the afternoon, and by then a great deal had happened.

First, at nine-thirty the phone rang. Eli leaped from the sofa—where he'd dropped the night before—and picked it screaming from the cradle. He could practically smell the hospital as he shouted into the phone, "Hello, yes!"

"Eli, it's Ted. Eli, he *did* it. He just walked by the store. I was opening the door, Eli, and I turned around and I swear I thought it was you. But it was him. He still walks like he did, but the clothes, Eli, the clothes."

"Who?"

"The greenie. He has on man's regular clothes. And the suit, it's a beauty."

The suit barreled back into Eli's consciousness, pushing all else aside. "What color suit?"

"Green. He's just strolling in the green suit like it's a holiday. Eli . . . is it a Jewish holiday?"

"Where is he now?"

"He's walking straight up Coach House Road, in this damn tweed job. Eli, it worked. You were right."

"We'll see."

"What next?"

"We'll see."

He took off the underwear in which he'd slept and went into the kitchen where he turned the light under the coffee. When it began to perk he held his head over the pot so it would steam loose the knot back of his eyes. It still hadn't when the phone rang.

"Eli, Ted again. Eli, the guy's walking up and down every street in town. Really, he's on a tour or something. Artie called me, Herb called me. Now Shirley calls that he just walked by our house. Eli, go out on the porch you'll see."

Eli went to the window and peered out. He couldn't see past the bend in the road, and there was no one in sight.

"Eli?" He heard Ted from where he dangled over the telephone table. He dropped the phone into the hook, as a few last words floated up to him—"Eliyousawhim . . . ?" He threw on the pants and shirt he'd worn the night before and walked barefoot on to his front lawn. And sure enough, his apparition appeared around the bend: in a brown hat a little too far down on his head, a green suit too far back on the shoulders, an unbuttoned-down button-down shirt, a tie knotted so as to leave a two-inch tail, trousers that cascaded onto his shoes—he was shorter than that black hat had made him seem. And moving the clothes was that walk that was not a walk, the tiny-stepped shlumpy gait. He came round the bend, and for all his strangeness—it clung to his whiskers, signaled itself in his locomotion—he looked as if he belonged. Eccentric, maybe, but he belonged. He made no moan, nor did he invite Eli with wide-flung arms. But he did stop when he saw him. He stopped and put a hand to his hat. When he felt for its top, his hand went up too high. Then it found the level and fiddled with the brim. The fingers fiddled, fumbled, and when they'd finally made their greeting, they traveled down the fellow's face and in an instant seemed to have touched each one of his features. They dabbed the eyes, ran the length of the nose, swept over the hairy lip, until they found their home in the hair that hid a little of his collar. To Eli the fingers said, *I have a face, I have a face at least.* Then his hand came through the beard and when it stopped at his chest it was like a pointer—and the eyes asked a question as tides of water shifted over them. *The face is all right, I can keep it?* Such a look was in those eyes that Eli was still seeing them when he turned his head away. They were the hearts of his jonquils, that only last week had appeared—they were the leaves on his birch, the bulbs in his coach lamp, the droppings on his lawn: those eyes were the eyes in his head. They were his, he had made them. He turned and went into his house and when he peeked out the side of the window, between shade and molding, the green suit was gone.

The phone.

"Eli, Shirley."

"I saw him, Shirley," and he hung up.

He sat frozen for a long time. The sun moved around the windows. The coffee steam smelled up the house. The phone began to ring, stopped, began again. The mailman came, the cleaner, the bakery man, the gardener, the ice cream man, the League of Women Voters lady. A Negro woman spreading some strange gospel calling for the revision of the Food and Drug Act knocked at the front, rapped the windows, and finally scraped a half-dozen pamphlets under the back door. But Eli only sat, without underwear, in last night's suit. He answered no one.

Given his condition, it was strange that the trip and crash at the back door reached his inner ear. But in an instant he seemed to melt down into the crevices of the chair, then to splash up and out to where the clatter had been. At the door he waited. It was silent, but for a fluttering of damp little leaves on the trees. When he finally opened the door, there was no one there. He'd expected to see green, green, green, big as the doorway, topped by his hat, waiting for him with those eyes. But there was no one out there, except for the Bonwit's box which lay bulging at his feet. No string tied it and the top rode high on the bottom.

The coward! He couldn't do it! He couldn't!

The very glee of that idea pumped fuel to his legs. He tore out across his back lawn, past his new spray of forsythia, to catch a glimpse of the bearded one fleeing naked through yards, over hedges and fences, to the safety of his hermitage. In the distance a pile of pink and white stones—which Harriet Knudson had painted the previous day—tricked him. "Run," he shouted to the rocks, "Run, you . . ." but he caught his error before anyone else did, and though he peered and craned there was no hint anywhere of a man about his own size, with white, white, terribly white skin (how white must be the skin of his body!) in cowardly retreat. He came slowly, curiously, back to the door. And while the trees shimmered in the light wind, he removed the top from the box. The shock at first was the shock of having daylight turned off all at once. Inside the box was an eclipse. But black soon sorted from black, and shortly there was the glassy black of lining, the coarse black of trousers, the dead black of fraying threads, and in the center the mountain of black: the hat. He picked the box from the doorstep and carried it inside. For the first time in his life he *smelled* the color of blackness: a little stale, a little sour, a little old, but nothing that could overwhelm you. Still, he held the package at arm's length and deposited it on the dining room table.

Twenty rooms on a hill and they store their old clothes with me! What am I supposed to do with them? Give them to charity? That's where they came from. He picked up the hat by the edges and looked inside. The crown was smooth as an egg, the brim practically thread-bare. There is nothing else to do with a hat in one's hands but put it on, so Eli dropped the thing on his head. He opened the door to the hall closet and looked at himself in the full-length mirror. The hat gave him bags under the eyes. Or perhaps he had not slept well. He pushed the brim lower till a shadow touched his lips. Now the bags under his eyes had inflated to become his face. Before the mirror he unbuttoned his shirt, unzipped his trousers, and then, shedding his clothes, he studied what he was. What a silly disappointment to see yourself naked in a hat. Especially in that hat. He sighed, but could not rid himself of the great weakness that suddenly set on his muscles and joints, beneath the terrible weight of the stranger's strange hat.

He returned to the dining room table and emptied the box of its contents: jacket, trousers, and vest (*it* smelled deeper than blackness). And under it all, sticking between the shoes that looked chopped and bitten, came the first gleam of white. A little fringed serape, a gray piece of semi-underwear, was crumpled at the bottom, its thready border twisted into itself. Eli removed it and let it hang free. What is it? For warmth? To wear beneath underwear in the event of a chest cold? He held it to his nose but it did not smell from Vick's or mustard plaster. It was something special, some Jewish thing. Special food, special language, special prayers, why not special BVD's? So fearful was he that he would be tempted back into wearing his traditional clothes—reasoned Eli—that he had carried and buried in Woodenton everything, including the special underwear. For that was how Eli now understood the box of clothes. The greenie was saying, Here, I give up. I refuse even to be tempted. We surrender. And that was how Eli continued to understand it until he found he'd slipped the white fringy surrender flag over his hat and felt it clinging to his chest. And now, looking at himself in the mirror, he was momentarily uncertain as to who was tempting who into what. Why *did* the greenie leave his clothes? Was it even the greenie? Then who was it? And why? But, Eli, for Christ's sake, in an age of science things don't happen like that. Even the goddam pigs take drugs . . .

Regardless of who was the source of the temptation, what was its end, not to mention its beginning, Eli, some moments later, stood draped in black, with a little white underneath, before the full-length mirror. He had to pull down on the trousers so they would not show the hollow of his ankle. The greenie, didn't he wear socks? Or had he forgotten them? The mystery was solved when Eli mustered enough courage to investigate the trouser pockets. He had expected some damp awful thing to happen to his fingers should he slip them down and out of sight— but when at last he jammed bravely down he came up with a khaki army sock in each hand. As he slipped them over his toes, he invented a genesis: a G.I.'s present in 1945. Plus everything else lost between 1938 and 1945, he had also lost his socks. Not that he had lost the socks, but that he'd had to stoop to accepting these, made Eli almost cry. To calm himself he walked out the back door and stood looking at his lawn.

On the Knudson back lawn, Harriet Knudson was giving her stones a second coat of pink. She looked up just as Eli stepped out. Eli shot back in again and pressed himself agianst the back door. When he peeked between the curtain all he saw were paint bucket, brush, and rocks scattered on the Knudsons' pink-spattered grass. The phone rang. Who was it—Harriet Knudson? Eli, there's a Jew at your door. *That's me.* Nonsense, Eli, I saw him with my own eyes. *That's me, I saw you too, painting your rocks pink.* Eli, you're having a nervous breakdown again. Jimmy, Eli's having a nervous breakdown again. Eli, this is

Jimmy, hear you're having a little breakdown, anything I can do, boy? Eli, this is Ted, Shirley says you need help. Eli, this is Artie, you need help. Eli, Harry, you need help you need help . . . The phone rattled its last and died.

"God helps them who help themselves," intoned Eli, and once again he stepped out the door. This time he walked to the center of his lawn and in full sight of the trees, the grass, the birds, and the sun, revealed that it was he, Eli, in the costume. But nature had nothing to say to him, and so stealthily he made his way to the hedge separating his property from the field beyond and he cut his way through, losing his hat twice in the underbrush. Then, clamping the hat to his head, he began to run, the threaded tassels jumping across his heart. He ran through the weeds and wild flowers, until on the old road that skirted the town he slowed up. He was walking when he approached the Gulf station from the back. He supported himself on a huge tireless truck rim, and among tubes, rusted engines, dozens of topless oil cans, he rested. With a kind of brainless cunning, he readied himself for the last mile of his journey.

"How are you, Pop?" It was the garage attendant, rubbing his greasy hands on his overalls, and hunting among the cans.

Eli's stomach lurched and he pulled the big black coat round his neck.

"Nice day," the attendant said and started around to the front.

"Sholom," Eli whispered and zoomed off towards the hill.

The sun was directly overhead when Eli reached the top. He had come by way of the woods, where it was cooler, but still he was perspiring beneath his new suit. The hat had no sweatband and the cloth clutched his head. The children were playing. The children were always playing, as if it was that alone that Tzuref had to teach them. In their shorts, they revealed such thin legs that beneath one could see the joints swiveling as they ran. Eli waited for them to disappear around a corner before he came into the open. But something would not let him wait—his green suit. It was on the porch, wrapped around the bearded fellow, who was painting the base of a pillar. His arm went up and down, up and down, and the pillar glowed like white fire. The very sight of him popped Eli out of the woods onto the lawn. He did not turn back, though his insides did. He walked up the lawn, but the children played on; tipping the black hat, he mumbled, "Shhh . . . shhhh," and they hardly seemed to notice.

At last he smelled paint.

He waited for the man to turn to him. He only painted. Eli felt suddenly that if he could pull the black hat down over his eyes, over his chest and belly and legs, if he could shut out all light, then a moment later he would be home in bed. But the hat wouldn't go past his forehead. He couldn't kid himself—he was there. No one he could think of had forced him to do this.

The greenie's arm flailed up and down on the pillar. Eli breathed loudly, cleared his throat, but the greenie wouldn't make life easier for him. At last, Eli had to say "Hello."

The arm swished up and down; it stopped—two fingers went out after a brush hair stuck to the pillar.

"Good day," Eli said.

The hair came away; the swishing resumed.

"Sholom," Eli whispered and the fellow turned.

The recognition took some time. He looked at what Eli wore. Up close, Eli looked at what he wore. And then Eli had the strange notion that he was two people. Or that he was one person wearing two suits. The greenie looked to be suffering from a similar confusion. They stared long at one another. Eli's heart shivered, and his brain was momentarily in such a mixed-up condition that his hands went out to button down the collar of his shirt that somebody else was wearing. What a mess! The greenie flung his arms over his face.

"What's the matter . . ." Eli said. The fellow had picked up his bucket and brush and was running away. Eli ran after him.

"I wasn't going to hit . . ." Eli called. "Stop . . ." Eli caught up and grabbed his sleeve. Once again, the greenie's hands flew up to his face. This time, in the violence, white paint spattered both of them.

"I only want to . . ." But in that outfit Eli didn't really know what he wanted. "To talk . . ." he said finally. "For you to look at me. Please, just *look* at me . . ."

The hands stayed put, as paint rolled off the brush onto the cuff of Eli's green suit.

"Please . . . please," Eli said, but he did not know what to do. "Say something, speak *English*," he pleaded.

The fellow pulled back against the wall, back, back, as though some arm would finally reach out and yank him to safety. He refused to uncover his face.

"Look," Eli said, pointing to himself. "It's your suit. I'll take care of it."

No answer—only a little shaking under the hands, which led Eli to speak as gently as he knew how.

"We'll . . . we'll moth-proof it. There's a button missing"—Eli pointed—"I'll have it fixed. I'll have a zipper put in . . . Please, please —just look at me . . ." He was talking to himself, and yet how could he stop? Nothing he said made any sense—that alone made his heart swell. Yet somehow babbling on, he might babble something that would make things easier between them. "Look . . ." He reached inside his shirt to pull the frills of underwear into the light. "I'm wearing the special underwear, even . . . Please," he said, *"please, please, please"* he sang, as if it were some sacred word. "Oh, *please* . . ."

Nothing twitched under the tweed suit—and if the eyes watered, or twinkled, or hated, he couldn't tell. It was driving him crazy. He had dressed like a fool, and for what? For this? He reached up and yanked the hands away.

"There!" he said—and in that first instant all he saw of the greenie's face were two white droplets stuck to each cheek.

"Tell me—" Eli clutched his hands down to his sides—"Tell me, what can I do for you, I'll do it . . ."

Stiffly, the greenie stood there, sporting his two white tears.

"Whatever I can do . . . Look, look, what I've done *already*." He grabbed his black hat and shook it in the man's face.

And in exchange, the greenie gave him an answer. He raised one hand to his chest, and then jammed it, finger first, towards the horizon. And with what a pained look! As though the air were full of razors! Eli followed the finger and saw beyond the knuckle, out past the nail, Woodenton.

"What do you want?" Eli said. "I'll bring it!"

Suddenly the greenie made a run for it. But then he stopped, wheeled, and jabbed that finger at the air again. It pointed the same way. Then he was gone.

And then, all alone, Eli had the revelation. He did not question his understanding, the substance or the source. But with a strange, dreamy elation, he started away.

On Coach House Road, they were double-parked. The Mayor's wife pushed a grocery cart full of dog food from Stop N' Shop to her station wagon. The President of the Lions Club, a napkin around his neck, was jamming pennies into the meter in front of the Bit-in-Teeth Restaurant. Ted Heller caught the sun as it glazed off the new Byzantine mosaic entrance to his shoe shop. In pinkened jeans, Mrs. Jimmy Knudson was leaving Halloway's Hardware, a paint bucket in each hand. Roger's Beauty Shoppe had its doors open—women's heads in silver bullets far as the eye could see. Over by the barbershop the pole spun, and Artie Berg's youngest sat on a red horse, having his hair cut; his mother flipped through *Look*, smiling: the greenie had changed his clothes.

And into this street, which seemed paved with chromium, came Eli Peck. It was not enough, he knew, to walk up one side of the street. That was not enough. Instead he walked ten paces up one side, then on an angle, crossed to the other side, where he walked ten more paces, and crossed back. Horns blew, traffic jerked, as Eli made his way up Coach House Road. He spun a moan high up in his nose as he walked. Outside no one could hear him, but he felt it vibrate the cartilage at the bridge of his nose.

Things slowed around him. The sun stopped rippling on spokes and hubcaps. It glowed steadily as everyone put on brakes to look at the man in black. They always paused and gaped, whenever he entered the town. Then in a minute, or two, or three, a light would change, a baby squawk, and the flow continue. Now, though lights changed, no one moved.

"He shaved his beard," Eric the barber said.

"Who?" asked Linda Berg.

"The . . . the guy in the suit. From the place there."

Linda looked out the window.

"It's Uncle Eli," little Kevin Berg said, spitting hair.

"Oh, God," Linda said, "Eli's having a nervous breakdown."

"A nervous breakdown!" Ted Heller said, but not immediately. Immediately he had said "Hoooly . . ."

Shortly, everybody in Coach House Road was aware that Eli Peck, the nervous young attorney with the pretty wife, was having a breakdown. Everybody except Eli Peck. He knew what he did was not insane, though he felt every inch of its strangeness. He felt those black clothes as if they were the skin of his skin—the give and pull as they got used to where he bulged and buckled. And he felt eyes, every eye on Coach House Road. He saw headlights screech to within an inch of him, and stop. He saw mouths: first the bottom jaw slides forward, then the tongue hits the teeth, the lips explode, a little thunder in the throat, and they've said it: Eli Peck Eli Peck Eli Peck Eli Peck. He began to walk slowly, shifting his weight down and forward with each syllable: E–li–Peck–E–li–Peck–E–li–Peck. Heavily he trod, and as his neighbors uttered each syllable of his name, he felt each syllable shaking all his bones. He knew who he was down to his marrow—they were telling him. Eli Peck. He wanted them to say it a thousand times, a million times, he would walk forever in that black suit, as adults whispered of his strangeness and children made "Shame . . . shame" with their fingers.

"It's going to be all right, pal . . ." Ted Heller was motioning to Eli from his doorway. "C'mon, pal, it's going to be all right . . ."

Eli saw him, past the brim of his hat. Ted did not move from his doorway, but leaned forward and spoke with his hand over his mouth. Behind him, three customers peered through the doorway. "Eli, it's Ted, remember Ted . . ."

Eli crossed the street and found he was heading directly towards Harriet Knudson. He lifted his neck so she could see his whole face.

He saw her forehead melt down to her lashes. "Good morning, Mr. Peck."

"Sholom," Eli said, and crossed the street where he saw the President of the Lions.

"Twice before . . ." he heard someone say, and then he crossed again, mounted the curb, and was before the bakery, where a delivery man charged past with a tray of powdered cakes twirling above him. "Pardon me, Father," he said, and scooted into his truck. But he could not move it. Eli Peck had stopped traffic.

He passed the Rivoli Theater, Beekman Cleaners, Harris' Westinghouse, the Unitarian Church, and soon he was passing only trees. At Ireland Road he turned right and started through Woodenton's winding streets. Baby carriages stopped whizzing and creaked—"Isn't that . . ." Gardeners held their clipping. Children stepped from the sidewalk and tried the curb. And Eli greeted no one, but raised his face to all. He wished passionately that he had white tears to show them . . . And not till he reached his own front lawn, saw his house, his shutters, his new jonquils, did he remember his wife. And the child that must have been born to him. And it was then and there he had the awful moment. He could go inside and put on his clothes and go to his wife in the hospital. It was not irrevocable, even the walk wasn't. In Woodenton memories are long but fury short. Apathy works like forgiveness. Besides, when you've flipped, you've flipped—it's Mother Nature.

What gave Eli the awful moment was that he turned away. He knew exactly what he could do but he chose not to. To go inside would be to go halfway. There was more . . . So he turned and walked towards the hospital and all the time he quaked an eighth of an inch beneath his skin to think that perhaps he'd chosen the crazy way. To think that he'd *chosen* to be crazy! But if you chose to be crazy, then you weren't crazy. It's when you didn't choose. No, he wasn't flipping. He had a child to see.

"Name?"

"Peck."

"Fourth floor." He was given a little blue card.

In the elevator everybody stared. Eli watched his black shoes rise four floors.

"Four."

He tipped his hat, but knew he couldn't take it off.

"Peck," he said. He showed the card.

"Congratulations," the nurse said. ". . . the grandfather?"

"The father. Which room?"

She led him to 412. "A joke on the Mrs?" she said, but he slipped in the door without her.

"Miriam?"

"Yes?"

"Eli."

She rolled her white face towards her husband. "Oh, Eli . . . Oh, Eli."

He raised his arms. "What could I do?"

"You have a son. They called all morning."

"I came to see him."

"Like *that!*" she whispered harshly. "Eli, you can't go around like that."

"I have a son. I want to see him."

"Eli, why are you doing this to me!" Red seeped back into her lips. *"He's* not your fault," she explained. "Oh, Eli, sweatheart, why do you feel guilty about everything. Eli, change your clothes. I forgive you."

"Stop forgiving me. Stop understanding me."

"But I love you."

"That's something else."

"But, sweetie, you *don't* have to dress like that. You didn't do anything. You don't have to feel guilty because . . . because everything's all right. Eli, can't you see that?"

"Miriam, enough reasons. Where's my son?"

"Oh, please, Eli, don't flip now. I need you now. Is that why you're flipping—because I need you?"

"In your selfish way, Miriam, you're very generous. I want my son."

"Don't flip now. I'm afraid, now that he's out." She was beginning to whimper. "I don't know if I love him, now that he's out. When I look in the mirror, Eli, he won't be there . . . Eli, Eli, you look like you're going to your own funeral. Please, can't you leave well enough *alone?* Can't we just have a family?"

"No."

In the corridor he asked the nurse to lead him to his son. The nurse walked on one side of him, Ted Heller on the other.

"Eli, do you want some help? I thought you might want some help."

"No."

Ted whispered something to the nurse; then to Eli he whispered, "Should you be walking around like this?"

"Yes."

In his ear Ted said, "You'll . . . you'll frighten the kid . . ."

"There," the nurse said. She pointed to a bassinet in the second row and looked, puzzled, to Ted. "Do I go in?" Eli said.

"No," the nurse said. "She'll roll him over." She rapped on the enclosure full of babies. "Peck," she mouthed to the nurse on the inside.

Ted tapped Eli's arm. "You're not thinking of doing something you'll be sorry for . . . are you, Eli? Eli—I mean you know you're still Eli, don't you?"

In the enclosure, Eli saw a bassinet had been wheeled before the square window.

"Oh, Christ. . . ." Ted said. "You don't have this Bible stuff on the brain—" And suddenly he said, "You wait, pal." He started down the corridor, his heels tapping rapidly.

Eli felt relieved—he leaned forward. In the basket was what he'd come to see. Well, now that he was here, what did he think he was going to say to it? I'm your father, Eli, the Flipper? I am wearing a black hat, suit, and fancy underwear, all borrowed from a friend? How could he admit to this reddened ball—*his* reddened ball—the worst of all: that Eckman would shortly convince him he wanted to take off the whole business. He couldn't admit it! He wouldn't do it!

Past his hat brim, from the corner of his eye, he saw Ted had stopped in a doorway at the end of the corridor. Two interns stood there smoking, listening to Ted. Eli ignored it.

No, even Eckman wouldn't make him take it off! No! He'd wear it, if he chose to. He'd make the kid wear it! Sure! Cut it down when the time came. A smelly hand-me-down, whether the kid liked it or not!

Only Teddie's heels clacked; the interns wore rubber soles—for they were there, beside him, unexpectedly. Their white suits smelled, but not like Eli's.

"Eli," Ted said, softly, "visiting time's up, pal."

"How are you feeling, Mr. Peck? First child upsets everyone. . . ."

He'd just pay no attention; nevertheless, he began to perspire, thickly, and his hat crown clutched his hair.

"Excuse me—Mr. Peck. . . ." It was a new rich bass voice. "Excuse me, rabbi, but you're wanted . . . in the temple." A hand took his elbow, firmly; then another hand, the other elbow. Where they grabbed, his tendons went taut.

"Okay, rabbi. Okay okay okay okay okay okay. . . ." He listened; it was a very soothing word, that okay. "Okay okay everything's going to be okay." His feet seemed to have left the ground some, as he glided away from the window, the bassinet, the babies. "Okay easy does it everything's all right all right—"

But he rose, suddenly, as though up out of a dream, and flailing his arms, screamed: *"I'm the father!"*

But the window disappeared. In a moment they tore off his jacket—it gave so easily, in one yank. Then a needle slid under his skin. The drug calmed his soul, but did not touch it down where the blackness had reached.

SAUL BELLOW

FROM
THE ADVENTURES OF AUGIE MARCH

[CHAPTER V]

WILLIAM EINHORN WAS THE FIRST SUPERIOR MAN I
knew. He had a brain and many enterprises, real directing power,
philosophical capacity, and if I were methodical enough to take thought
before an important and practical decision and also (*N.B.*) if I were
really his disciple and not what I am, I'd ask myself, "What would
Caesar suffer in this case? What would Machiavelli advise or Ulysses
do? What would Einhorn think?" I'm not kidding when I enter Einhorn
in this eminent list. It was him that I knew, and what I understand of
them in him. Unless you want to say that we're at the dwarf end of all
times and mere children whose only share in grandeur is like a boy's
share in fairy-tale kings, beings of a different kind from times better
and stronger than ours. But if we're comparing men and men, not
men and children or men and demigods, which is just what would
please Caesar among us teeming democrats, and if we don't have any
special wish to abdicate into some different, lower form of existence
out of shame for our defects before the golden faces of these and other
old-time men, then I have the right to praise Einhorn and not care
about smiles of derogation from those who think the race no longer has
in any important degree the traits we honor in these fabulous names.
But I don't want to be pushed into exaggeration by such opinion,
which is the opinion of students who, at all ages, feel their boyishness
when they confront the past.

I went to work for Einhorn while I was a high-school junior, not
long before the great crash, during the Hoover administration, when
Einhorn was still a wealthy man, though I don't believe he was ever so

rich as he later claimed, and I stayed on with him after he had lost most of his property. Then, actually, was when I became essential to him, not just metaphorical right hand but virtually arms and legs. Einhorn was a cripple who didn't have the use of either, not even partial; only his hands still functioned, and they weren't strong enough to drive a wheel chair. He had to be rolled and drawn around the house by his wife, brother, relations, or one of the people he usually had on call, either employed by or connected with him. Whether they worked for him or were merely around his house or office, he had a talent for making supernumeraries of them, and there were always plenty of people hoping to become rich, or more rich if already well-to-do, through the Einhorns. They were the most important real-estate brokers in the district and owned and controlled much property, including the enormous forty-flat building where they lived. The poolroom in the corner store of it was owned outright by them and called Einhorn's Billiards. There were six other stores—hardware, fruit, a tin shop, a restaurant, barbershop, and a funeral parlor belonging to Kinsman, whose son it was that ran away with my cousin Howard Coblin to join the Marines against Sandino. The restaurant was the one in which Tambow, the Republican vote-getter, played cards. The Einhorns were his ex-wife's relatives; they, however, had never taken sides in the divorce. It wouldn't have become Einhorn Senior, the old Commissioner, who had had four wives himself, two getting alimony still, to be strict with somebody on that account. The Commissioner had never held office, that was just people's fun. He was still an old galliard, with white Buffalo Bill vandyke, and he swanked around, still healthy of flesh, in white suits, looking things over with big sex-amused eyes. He had a lot of respect from everyone for his shrewdness, and when he opened his grand old mouth to say something about a chattel mortgage or the location of a lot, in his laconic, single-syllabled way, the whole hefty, serious crowd of businessmen in the office stopped their talk. He gave out considerable advice, and Coblin and Five Properties got him to invest some of their money. Kreindl, who did a job for him once in a while, thought he was as wise as a god. "The son is smart," he said, "but the Commissioner—that's really a man you have to give way to on earth." I disagreed then and do still, though when the Commissioner was up to something he stole the show. One of my responsibilities in summer was to go with him to the beach, where he swam daily until the second week in September. I was supposed to see that he didn't go out too far, and also I handed him lighted cigarettes while he floated near the pier in the pillow striping of his suit with large belly, large old man's sex, and yellow, bald knees; his white back-hair spread on the water, yellowish, like polar bear's pelt, his vigorous foreskull, tanned and red, turned up; while his big lips uttered and his nose drove out smoke, clever and pleasurable in the warm, heavy blue of Michigan; while wood-bracketed trawlers, tarred on the sides, chuffed and vapored outside the water reserved for the bawling, splashing, many-actioned, brilliant-colored crowd; waterside structures and towers, and skyscrapers beyond in a vast right angle to the evading bend of the shore.

Einhorn was the Commissioner's son by his first wife. By the second or third he had another son who was called Shep or, by his poolroom friends, Dingbat, for John Dingbat O'Berta, the candy kid of city politics and friend of Polack Sam Zincowicz. Since he didn't either know or resemble O'Berta and wasn't connected with Thirteenth Ward politics or any other, I couldn't exactly say how he came by the name. But without being a hoodlum himself he was taken up with gang events and crime, a kind of amateur of the lore and done up in the gangster taste so you might take him for somebody tied in with the dangerous Druccis or Big Hayes Hubacek: sharp financial hat, body-clasping suit, the shirt Andalusian style buttoned up to the collar and worn without a necktie, trick shoes, pointed and pimpy, polished like a tango dancer's; he clumped hard on the leather heels. Dingbat's hair was violent, brilliant, black, treated, ripple-marked. Bantam, thin-muscled, swift, almost frail, he had an absolutely unreasonable face. To be distinguished from brutal—it wasn't that, there was all kind of sentiment in it. But wild, down-twisting, squint-eyed, unchangeably firm and wrong in thoughts, with the prickles coming black through his unmethodical after-shave talcum: the puss of an executioner's subject, provided we understand the prototype not as a murderer (he attacked with his fists and had a killer's swing but not the real intention) but as somebody intractable. As far as that goes, he was beaten all the time and wore a mishealed scar where his cheek had been caught between his teeth by a ring, but he went on springing and boxing, rushing out from the poolroom on a fresh challenge to spin around on his tango shoes and throw his tense, weightless punches. The beatings didn't squelch him. I was by one Sunday when he picked a fight with that huge Five Properties and thrust him on the chest with his hands, failing to move him; Five Properties picked him up and threw him down on the floor. When Dingbat came back punching, Five Properties grinned but was frightened and shied back against the cue rack. Somebody in the crowd began to shout that Five Properties was yellow, and it was thought the right thing to hold Dingbat back, by the arms, struggling with a blinded, drawn face of rage. A pal of his said what a shame that a veteran of Château Thierry should be shoved around by a greenhorn. Five Properties took it to heart and thereafter stayed away from the poolroom.

Dingbat had had charge of the poolroom at one time, but he was unreliable and the Commissioner had replaced him with a manager. Now he was around as the owner's son—racked up balls, once in a while changed color like a coal when a green table felt was ripped—and in the capacity of key-man and bravo, referee, bet-holder, sports expert, and gang-war historian, on the watch for a small deal, a fighter to manage, or a game of rotation at ten cents a ball. Between times he was his father's chauffeur. The Commissioner couldn't drive the big red Blackhawk-Stutz he owned—the Einhorns never could see anything in a small car—and Dingbat took him to the beach when it was too hot to walk. After all, the old man was pushing seventy-five and couldn't be allowed to risk a stroke. I'd ride with him in the back seat while Dingbat sat with mauled, crazy neck and a short grip on the wheel, ukelele and bathing suit on the cushion beside him; he was particularly sex-goaded when he drove, shouting, whistling, and honking after quiff, to the entertainment of his father. Sometimes we had the company of Clem or Jimmy, or of Sylvester, the movie bankrupt, who was now flunking out of his engineer's course at Armour Tech and talking about moving away to New York altogether. On the beach Dingbat, athletically braced up with belt and wristbands, a bandanna to keep the sand out of his hair when he stood on his head, streaked down with suntan oil, was with a crowd of girls and other beach athletes, dancing and striking into his ukelele with:

> Ani-ka, hula wicki-wicki
> Sweet brown maiden said to me,
> And she taught me hula-hula
> On the beach of Waikiki . . .

Kindled enough, he made it suggestive, his black voice cracking, and his little roosterish flame licked up clear, queer, and crabbed. His old sire, gruff and mocking, deeply tickled, lay like the Buffalo Bill of the Etruscans in the beach chair and bath towel drawn up burnoose-wise to keep the dazzle from his eyes—additionally shaded by his soft, flesh-heavy arm—his bushy mouth open with laughter.

"Ee-*dyot!*" he said to his son.

If the party began after the main heat of the day William Einhorn might come down too, wheel chair brought on the baggage rack of the Stutz, and his wife carrying an umbrella to shade them both. He was taken pick-a-back by his brother, or by me, from the office into the car, from the car to the right site on the lakeshore; all as distinguished, observing, white, untouched and nobiliare as a margrave. Quickeyes. Originally a big man, of the Commissioner's stature, well formed, well favored, he had more delicacy of spirit than the Commissioner, and of course Dingbat wasn't a patch on him. Einhorn was very pale, a little flabby in the face; considerable curvature of the nose, small lips, and graying hair let grow thickly so that it touched on the ears; and continually watchful, his look going forward uninterruptedly to fasten on subject matters. His heavy, attractive wife sat by him with the parasol, languorous, partly in smiles, with her free, soft brown fist on her lap and strong hair bobbed with that declivity that you see in pictures of the Egyptian coif, the flat base forming a black brush about the back of the neck. Entertained by the summer breeziness and the little boats on the waves and the cavorting and minstrelsy.

If you want to know what she thought, it was that back home was locked. There were two pounds of hotdogs on the shelf on the gas range, two pounds of cold potatoes for salad, mustard, a rye bread already sliced. If she ran out, she could send me for more. Mrs. Einhorn liked to feel that things were ready. The old man would want tea. He needed to be pleased, and she was willing, asking only in return that he stop spitting on the floor, and that not of him directly, being too shy, but through her husband, to him it was merely a joking matter. The rest of us would have Coca-Cola, Einhorn's favorite drink. One of my daily chores was to fetch him Cokes, in bottles from the poolroom or glasses from the drugstore, depending on which he judged to have the better mixture that day.

My brother Simon, seeing me carry a glass on a tray through the gathering on the sidewalk—there was always an overflow of businessmen in front of Einhorn's, mixing with the mourners from Kinsman's chapel and the poolroom characters—gave a big laugh of surprise and said, "So this is your job! You're the butler."

But it was only one function of hundreds, some even more menial, more personal, others calling for cleverness and training—secretary, deputy, agent, companion. He was a man who needed someone beside him continually; the things that had to be done for him made him autocratic. At Versailles or in Paris the Sun King had one nobleman to hand him his stockings, another his shirt, in his morning levee. Einhorn had to be lifted up in bed and dressed. Now and then it was I who had to do it. The room was dark and unfresh, for he and his wife slept with the windows shut. So it was sleep rank from nights of both bodies. I see I had no sense of criticism about such things; I got used to it quickly. Einhorn slept in his underwear because changing to pajamas was a task, and he and his wife kept late hours. Thus, the light switched on, there was Einhorn in his BVDs, wasted arms freckled, grizzled hair afly from his face that was inclined to flatness, the shrewd curved nose and clipped mustache. If peevish, and sometimes he was, my cue was to be quiet until he got back his spirits. It was against policy to be out of temper in the morning. He preferred to be jocular. Birdy, teasing, often corny or lewd, he guyed his wife about the noise and bother she made getting breakfast. In dressing him, my experience with George came in handy, but there was more style about Einhorn than I was used to. His socks were of grand silk, trousers with a banker's stripe; he had several pairs of shoes, fine Walkovers that of course never wrinkled below the instep, much less wore out, a belt with a gothic monogram. Dressed to the waist, he was lifted into his black leather chair and pulled on quaky wheels to the bathroom. At times the first settling in the chair drew a frown from him, sometimes a more oblique look of empoisoned acceptance; but mostly it was a stoical operation. I eased him down and took him, traveling backwards, to the toilet, a sunny room with an east window to the yard. The Commissioner and Einhorn, both rather careless in their habits, made this a difficult place to keep clean. But for people of some nobility allowances have always been made in this regard. I understand that British aristocrats are still legally entitled to piss, if they should care to, on the hind wheels of carriages.

There wasn't anything Mrs. Einhorn could do about the wet floor. Once in a while when Bavatsky the handyman was gone too long in Polack Town or drunk in the cellar, she asked me to clean up. She said she didn't like to impose on me because I was a student. Nevertheless I was getting paid. For unspecified work of a mixed character. I accepted it as such; the mixed character of it was one of the things I liked. I was just as varietistic and unfit for discipline and regularity as my friend Clem Tambow; only I differed from Clem in being a beaver, once my heart was attached to a work or a cause. Naturally, when Einhorn found this out, and he quickly did, he kept me going steadily; it suited him perfectly because of the great number of things he had to be done. Should he run out, my standing by made him invent more. So I didn't often get the toilet detail; he had too many important tasks for me. And when I did get it, why, what I had had under Grandma Lausch made an inconsiderable thing of it to be porter for an hour.

But now in the toilet with Einhorn: he kept me by him to read the morning headlines from the *Examiner,* the financial news, closing quotations from Wall Street and La Salle Street. Local news next, something about Big Bill Thompson, that he had hired the Cort Theatre, for instance, and presented himself on the stage with two caged giant rats from the stockyards whom he addressed by the names of Republican renegades—I came to know what items Einhorn would want first. "Yes, it's just as Thompson says. He's a big gasbag, but this time it's true. He rushed back from Honolulu to save what's-his-name from the penitentiary." He was long and well-nigh perfect of memory, a close and detailed reader of the news, and kept a file on matters of interest to him, for he was highly systematic, and one of my jobs was to keep his files in order in the long steel and wood cases he surrounded himself with, being masterful, often fussy for reasons hard to understand when I placed something before him, proposing to throw it away. The stuff had to be where he could lay his hands on it at once, his clippings and pieces of paper, in folders labeled Commerce, Invention, Major Local Transactions, Crime and Gang, Democrats, Republicans, Archaeology, Literature, League of Nations. Search me, why the League of Nations, but he lived by Baconian ideas of what makes the man this and that, and had a weakness for complete information. Everything was going to be properly done, with Einhorn, and was thoroughly organized on his desk and around it—Shakespeare, Bible, Plutarch, dictionary and thesaurus, *Commercial Law for Laymen,* real-estate and insurance guides, almanacs and directories; then typewriter in black hood, dictaphone, telephones on bracket arms and a little screwdriver to hand for touching off the part of the telephone mechanism that registered the drop of the nickel—for even at his most prosperous Einhorn was not going to pay for every call he made; the company was raking in a fortune from the coinboxes used by the other businessmen who came to the office—wire trays labeled Incoming and Outgoing, molten Aetna weights, notary's seal on a chain, staplers, flap-moistening sponges, keys to money, confidential papers, notes, condoms, personal correspondence and poems and essays. When all this was arranged and in place, all proper, he could begin to operate, back of his polished barrier approached by two office gates, where he was one of the chiefs of life, a white-faced executive, much aware of himself and even of the freakish, willful shrewdness that sometimes spoiled his dignity and proud, plaque-like good looks.

He had his father to keep up with, whose business ideas were perhaps less imaginative but broader, based on his connections with his rich old-time cronies. The old Commissioner had made the Einhorn money and still kept the greater part of the titles in his name, not because he didn't trust his son, but only for the reason that to the business community he was *the* Einhorn, the one who was approached first with offers. William was the heir and was also to be trustee of the shares of his son Arthur, who was a sophomore at the University of Illinois, and of Dingbat. Sometimes Einhorn was unhappy about the Commissioner's habit of making private loans, some of them sizable, from the bankroll he carried pinned inside the pocket of his Mark Twain suit. More often he bragged about him as a pioneer builder on the Northwest Side and had dynastic ideas about the Einhorns—the organizer coming after the conqueror, the poet and philosopher succeeding the organizer, and the whole development typically American, the work of intelligence and strength in an open field, a world of possibilities. But really, with all respect for the Commissioner, Einhorn, while still fresh and palmy, had his father's overriding powers plus something else, statesmanship, fineness of line, Parsee sense, deep-dug intrigue, the scorn of Pope Alexander VI for custom. One morning while I was reading from a column on the misconduct of an American heiress with an Italian prince at Cannes, he stopped me to quote, " 'Dear Kate, you and I cannot be confined within the weak list of a country's fashion. We are the makers of manners, Kate, and the liberty that follows our places stops the mouth of all find-faults. . . .' That's Henry Fifth for you. Meaning that there's one way for people at large and another for those that have something special to do. Which those at large have to have in front of them. It braces them up that there's a privilege they can't enjoy, as long as they know it's there. Besides, there's law, and then there's Nature. There's opinion, and then there's Nature. Somebody has to get outside of law and opinion and speak for Nature. It's even a public duty, so customs won't have us all by the windpipe." Einhorn had a teaching turn similar to Grandma Lausch's, both believing they could show what could be done with the world, where it gave or resisted, where you could be confident and run or where you could only feel your way and were forced to blunder. And with his son at the university I was the only student he had to hand.

He put on a judicious head, and things, no matter how they ran, had to be collared and brought to a standstill when he was ready to give out. He raised his unusable arms to the desk by a neat trick that went through several stages, tugging the sleeve of the right with the fingers of the left, helping on the left with the right. There wasn't any appeal to feelings as he accomplished this; it was only an operation. But it had immense importance. As a robust, full-blooded man might mount up to a pulpit and then confess his weakness before God, Einhorn, with his feebleness demonstrated for a preliminary, got himself situated to speak of strength, with strength. It was plenty queer to hear him on this note, especially in view of the daily drift of life here.

But let's take it back to the toilet, where Einhorn got himself ready in the morning. At one time he used to have the barber in to shave him. But this reminded him too much of the hospital, he said, where he had put in a total of two and one-half years. Besides he preferred to do things for himself as much as possible; he had to rely on too many people as it was. So now he used a safety razor stropped in a gadget a Czech inventor had personally sold him; he swore by it. To shave took better than half an hour, chin on the edge of the sink and hands in the water, working round his face. He fished out the washrag, muffled himself in it; I could hear him breathe through its papillae. He soaped, he rubbed and played, scraped, explored with fingers for patches of bristle, and I sat on the cover of the pot and read. The vapor woke up old smells, and there was something astringent in the shaving cream he used that cut into my breath. Then he pomaded his wet hair and slipped on a little cap made of an end of woman's hose. Dried and powdered, he had to be helped into his shirt, his tie put on, the knot inspected many times by his fingers and warped exactly into place with some nervousness about the top button. The jacket next, finished off with the dry noise of the whiskbroom. Fly re-examined, shoes wiped of water drops, we were all set and I got the nod to draw him into the kitchen for breakfast.

His appetite was sharp and he crowded his food. A stranger with a head on him, unaware that Einhorn was paralyzed, would have guessed he was not a well man from seeing him suck a pierced egg, for it was something humanly foxy, paw-handled, hungry above average need. Then he had this cap of a woman's stocking, like a trophy from another field of appetites, if you'll excuse a sporting reference, or martial one, on his head. He was conscious of this himself, for pretty much everything was thought of, and his mind in its way performed admirable work with many of the things he did; or did not care to stop himself from doing; or was not able to stop; or thought it only creaturely human nature to do; or enjoyed, indulged; was proud his disease had not killed his capacity for but rather left him with more capacity than many normal men. Much that's nameless to many people through disgust or shame he didn't mind naming to himself or to a full confidant (or pretty nearly so) like me, and caught, used, and worked all feelings freely. There was plenty to be in on; he was a very busy man.

There was a short executive period, after coffee, when Einhorn threw his weight around about household matters. Wrinkled, gloomy Tiny Bavatsky, string-muscled, was fetched up from the basement and told what he must do, warned to lay off the bottle till night. He went away, hitch-gaited, talking to himself in words of menace, to start his tasks. Mrs. Einhorn was not really a good housekeeper even though she complained about the floor of the toilet and the old man's spitting. But Einhorn was a thoughtful proprietor and saw to it that everything was kept humming, running, flushing, and constantly improved—rats killed, cement laid in the backyard, machines cleaned and oiled, porches retimbered, tenants sanitary, garbage cans covered, screens patched, flies sprayed. He was able to tell you how fast pests multiplied, how much putty to buy for a piece of glazing, the right prices of nails or clothesline or fuses and many such things; as much as any ancient senator knew of husbandry before such concerns came to be thought wrong. Then, when everything was under control, he had himself taken into his office on the specially constructed chair with cackly casters. I had to dust the desk and get him a Coke to drink with his second cigarette, and he was already on his mail when I got back with it. His mail was large—he had to have it so, and from many kinds of correspondents in all parts of the country.

Let it be hot—for I'm reporting on summers, during vacations, when I spent full time with him—and he was wearing his vest in the office. The morning, this early, was often gentle prairie weather, long before the rugged grind—like the naïveté you get to expect in the hardest and toughest-used when you've been with them long enough—I refer to business and heat of a Chicago summer afternoon. But it was breathing time. The Commissioner wasn't finished dressing yet; he went into the mild sun of the street in his slippers, his galluses hung down, and the smoke of his Claro passed up and back above his white hair, while his hand was sunk comfortable and deep below his waistband. And Einhorn, away back, the length of the office, slit open his letters, made notes for replies, dipped into his files or passed things on for me to check on—me, the often stumped aide, trying to get straight what he was up to in his numerous small swindles. In this respect there was hardly anything he didn't get into, like ordering things on approval he didn't intend to pay for—stamps, little tubes of lilac perfume, packages of linen sachet, Japanese paper roses that opened in water, and all the sort of items advertised in the back pages of the Sunday supplement. He had me write for them in my hand and gave fictitious names, and he threw away the dunning letters, of course, and said all of these people calculated losses into what they charged. He sent away for everything that was free: samples of food, soaps, medicine, the literature of all causes, reports of the Bureau of American Ethnology and publications of the Smithsonian Institution, the Bishop Museum in Hawaii, the *Congressional Record*, laws, pamphlets, prospectuses, college catalogues, quack hygiene books, advice on bust-development, on getting rid of pimples, on longevity and Couéism, pamphlets on Fletcherism, Yoga, spirit-rapping, anti-vivisection; he was on the mailing list of the Henry George Institute and the Rudolf Steiner Foundation in London, the local bar association, the American Legion. He had to be in touch with everything. And all this material he kept; the overflow went down to the basement. Bavatsky or I or Lollie Fewter, who came in three days a week to do the ironing, carried it below. Some of it, when it went out of print, he sold to bookstores or libraries, and some he remailed to his clients with the Einhorn stamp on it, for good will. He had much to do also with contests and entered every competition he got wind of, suggesting names for new products, slogans; he made up bright sayings and most embarrassing moments, most delightful dreams, omens he should have heeded, telepathic experiences, and jingles:

> When radio first appeared, I did rave,
> And all my pennies I did save,
> Even neglected to shave.
> I'll take my dear Dynamic to the grave.

He won the *Evening American*'s first prize of five dollars with this, and one of my jobs was to see that what was sent out to contests, anagrams on the names of presidents or on the capitals of states, or elephants composed of tiny numbers (making what sum?), that these entries were neat, mounted right, inside ruled borders, accompanied by the necessary coupons, boxtops, and labels. Furthermore, I had to do reference work for him in his study or at the library downtown, one of his projects

being to put out an edition of Shakespeare indexed as the Gideon Bible
was: Slack Business, Bad Weather, Difficult Customers, Stuck with
Big Inventory of Last Year's Models, Woman, Marriage, Partners. One
thousand and one catchpenny deals, no order too big, no sum too small.
And, all the time, talkative, clowning, classical, philosophical, homiletic,
corny, passing around French poses and imitation turds from the Clark
Street novelty stores, pornographic Katzenjammers and Somebody's
Stenog; teasing with young Lollie Fewter who was fresh up from the
coal fields, that girl with her green eyes from which she didn't try to
keep the hotness, and her freckled bust presented to the gathering of
men she came among with her waxing rags and the soft shake of her
gait. Yea, Einhorn, careful of his perch, with dead legs, and yet denying
in your teeth he was different from other men. He never minded talking about his paralysis; on the contrary, sometimes he would boast of it
as a thing he had overcome, in the manner of a successful businessman
who tells you of the farm poverty of his boyhood. Nor did he overlook
any chance to exploit it. To a mailing list he got together from houses
that sold wheel chairs, braces, and appliances, he sent out a mimeo-
graphed paper called "The Shut-In." Two pages of notices and essays,
sentimental bits cribbed from *Elbert Hubbard's Scrapbook*, tags from
"Thanatopsis." "Not like the slave scourged to his quarry" but like a
noble, stoical Greek; or from Whittier: "Prince thou art, the grown up
man/Only is Republican," and other such sources. "Build thee more
stately mansions, O my soul!" The third page was reserved for readers'
letters. This thing—I put it out on the mimeograph and stapled and
carried it to the post office—gave me the creeps once in a while, uneasy
flesh around the neck. But he spoke of it as a service to shut-ins. It was
a help to him as well; it brought in considerable insurance business, for
he signed himself, "William Einhorn, a neighborhood broker," and
various companies paid the costs. Like Grandma Lausch again, he knew
how to use large institutions. He had an important bearing with their
representatives—clabber-faced, with his intelligent bit of mustache and
shrewd action of his dark eyes, chicken-winged arms at rest. He wore
sleeve garters—another piece of feminine apparel. He tried to maneu-
ver various insurance companies into competitive bidding to increase
his commissions.

Many repeated pressures with the same effect as one strong blow,
that was his method, he said, aind it was his special pride that he knew
how to use the means contributed by the age to connive as ably as anyone else; when in a not so advanced time he'd have been mummy-

handled in a hut or somebody might have had to help him be a beggar in front of a church, the next to a *memento mori* or, more awful, a reminder of what difficulties there were before you could even become dead. Whereas now—well, it was probably no accident that it was the crippled Hephaestus who made ingenious machines; a normal man didn't have to hoist or jack himself over hindrances by means of cranks, chains, and metal parts. Then it was in the line of human advance that Einhorn could do so much; especially since the whole race was so hepped-up about appliances, he was not a hell of a lot more dependent than others who couldn't make do without this or that commodity, engine, gizmo, sliding door, public service, and this being relieved of small toils made mind the chief center of trial. Find Einhorn in a serious mood when his fatty, beaky, noble Bourbon face was thoughtful, and he'd give you the lowdown on the mechanical age, and on strength and frailty, and piece it out with little digressions on the history of cripples—the dumbness of the Spartans, the fact that Oedipus was lame, that gods were often maimed, that Moses had faltering speech and Dmitri the Sorcerer a withered arm, Caesar and Mahomet epilepsy, Lord Nelson a pinned sleeve—but especially on the machine age and the kind of advantage that had to be taken of it; with me like a man-at-arms receiving a lecture from the learned *signor* who felt like passing out discourse.

I was a listener by upbringing. And Einhorn with his graces, learning, oratory, and register of effects was not out to influence me practically. He was not like Grandma, with her educational seventy-fives trained on us. He wanted to flow along, be admirable and eloquent. Not fatherly. I wasn't ever to get it into my head that I was part of the family. There was small chance that I would, the way Arthur, the only son, figured in their references, and I was sent out when any big family deal began to throb around. To make absolutely sure I wouldn't get any such notions, Einhorn would now and then ask me some question about my people, as if he hadn't informed himself through Coblin, Kreindl, Clem, and Jimmy. Pretty clever, he was, to place me this way. If Grandma had ideas about a wealthy man who might take a fancy to us and make our fortune, Simon's and mine, Einhorn had the reverse. I wasn't to think because we were intimately connected and because he liked me that I was going to get into the will. The things that had to be done for him were such that anybody who worked for him was necessarily intimate with him. It sometimes got my goat, he and Mrs. Einhorn made so sure I knew my place. But maybe they were right; the old woman had implanted the thought, though I never entertained it in earnest. However, there was such a thought, and it bulged somewhat into my indignation. Einhorn and his wife were selfish. They weren't mean, I admitted in fairness, and generally I could be fair about it; merely selfish, like two people enjoying their lunch on the grass and not asking you to join them. If you weren't dying for a sandwich yourself it could even make a pleasant picture, smacking on the mustard, cutting cake, peeling eggs and cucumbers. Selfish, Einhorn was, nevertheless; his nose in constant action smelled, and smelled out everything, sometimes austerely, or again without manners, covert, half an eye out for observers but not to be deterred if there were any, either.

I don't think I would have considered myself even remotely as a legatee of the Commissioner if they hadn't, for one thing, underlined my remoteness from inheritance, and, for another, discussed inheritances all the time.

Well, they were steeped and soaked necessarily in insurance and property, lawsuits and legal miscarriages, sour partnerships and welshings and contested wills. This was what you heard when the connoisseurs' club of weighty cronies met, who all showed by established marks —rings, cigars, quality of socks, newness of panamas—where they were situated; they were classified, too, in grades of luck and wisdom, darkness by birth or vexations, power over or subjection to wives, women, sons and daughters, grades of disfigurement; or by the roles they played in comedies, tragedies, sex farces; whether they screwed or were screwed, whether they themselves did the manipulating or were roughly handled, tugged, and bobbled by their fates; their frauds, their smart bankruptcies, the fires they had set; what were their prospects of life, how far death stood from them. Also their merits: which heavy character of fifty was a good boy, a donor, a friend, a compassionate man, a man of balls, a lucid percentage calculator, a fellow willing to make a loan of charity though he couldn't sign his name, a giver of scrolls to the synagogue, a protector of Polish relatives. It was known; Einhorn had it all noted. And apparently everybody knew everything. There was a good circulation of frankness and a lot of respect going back and forth. Also a lot of despicable things. Be this as it might, the topic inside the railed space of benches or at the pinochle game in the side-office annex was mostly business—receiverships, amortizations, wills, and practically nothing else. As rigor is the theme of Labrador, breathing of the summits of the Andes, space to the Cornish miner who lies in a seam under the sea. And, on the walls, insurance posters of people in the despair of firetraps and the undermining of rats in the beams, housewives bringing down the pantry shelves in their fall. Which all goes to show how you couldn't avoid the question of inheritance. Was the old Commissioner fond of me? While Mrs. Einhorn was a kindly woman ordinarily, now and again she gave me a glance that suggested Sarah and the son of Hagar. Notwithstanding that there was nothing to worry about. Nothing. I wasn't of the blood, and the old man had dynastic ideas too. And I wasn't trying to worm my way into any legacy and get any part of what was coming to her elegant and cultivated son Arthur. Sure the Commissioner was fond of me, stroked my shoulder, gave me tips; and he thought of me no further.

But he and Einhorn were an enigma to Tillie. Her pharaoh-bobbed hair grew out of a head mostly physically endowed; she couldn't ever tell what they might take it into their minds to do. And especially her husband, he was so supple, fertile, and changeable. She worshipfully obeyed him and did his biddings and errands just as the rest of us did. He'd send her to City Hall with requests for information from the Recorder's Office of the License Bureau; he wrote notes, because she could never explain what he wanted, and she brought back the information written out by a clerk. To get her out of the way when he was up to something he sent her to visit her cousin on the South Side, an all-day junket on the streetcars. To be sure she'd be good and gone; and what's more, she knew it.

But now suppose we're at lunchtime, in Einhorn's specimen day. Mrs. Einhorn didn't like to bother in the kitchen and favored ready-made or easy meals, delicatessen, canned salmon with onion and vinegar, or hamburger and fried potatoes. And these hamburgers weren't the flat lunch-wagon jobs, eked out with cornmeal, but big pieces of meat souped up with plenty of garlic and fried to blackness. Covered with horseradish and chili sauce, they didn't go down so hard. This was the food of the house, in the system of its normalcy like its odors and furnishings, and if you were the visiting albatross come to light, you'd eat the food you ne'er had eat and offer no gripe. The Commissioner, Einhorn, and Dingbat asked no questions about it but ate a great deal, with tea or Coca-Cola as usual. Then Einhorn took a white spoonful of Bisodol and a glass of Waukesha water for his gas. He made a joke of it, but he never forgot to take them and heeded all his processes with much seriousness, careful that his tongue was not too coated and his machinery smooth. Very grave, he was sometimes, when he acted as his own physician. He liked to say that he was fatal to doctors, especially to those who had never given him much hope. "I buried two of them," he said. "Each one told me I'd be gone in a year, and before the year was out he croaked." It made him feel good to tell other doctors of this. Still, he was zealous about taking care of himself; and with this zeal he had a brat's self-mockery about the object of his cares, bottomless self-ribbing; he let his tongue droop over his lip, comic and stupid, and made dizzy crosses with his eyes. Nevertheless he was always thinking about his health and took his powders and iron and liver pills. You might almost say he followed assimilation with his thoughts; all through his body that death had already moved in on, to the Washington of his brain, to his sex and to his studying eyes. Ah, sure, he was still a going concern, very much so, but he had to take thought more than others did about himself, since if *he* went wrong he was a total loss, nowise justified, a dead account, a basket case, an en-cumbrance, zero. I knew this because he expressed everything, and though he wouldn't talk openly about the money he had in the bank or the property he owned, he was absolutely outspoken about vital things, and he'd open his mind to me, especially when we were together in his study and busy with one of his projects that got more fanciful and mud-dled the more notions he had about being systematic, so that in the end there'd be a super-monstrous apparatus you couldn't set in motion either by push or crank.

"Augie, you know another man in my position might be out of life for good. There's a view of man anyhow that he's only a sack of craving guts; you find it in *Hamlet,* as much as you want of it. What a piece of work is a man, and the firmament frotted with gold—but the whole *gescheft* bores him. Look at me, I'm not even express and admirable in action. You could say a man like me ought to be expected to lie down and quit the picture. Instead, I'm running a big business today"—that was not the pure truth; it was the Commissioner who was still the main wheel, but it wasn't uninteresting all the same—"while no-body would blame me for rotting in the back room under a blanket or for crabbing and blabbing my bitter heart out, with fresh and healthy people going around me, so as not to look. A kid like you, for instance, strong as a bronco and rosy as an apple. An Alcibiades beloved-of-man, by Jesus. I don't know what brain power you've got; you're too frisky yet, and even if you turn out to be smart you'll never be in the class of my son Arthur. You shouldn't be angry for hearing the truth, if you're lucky enough to find somebody to hear it from. Anyhow, you're not bad off, being an Alcibiades. That's already way and above your fellow creatures. And don't think they didn't hate the original either. All but Socrates himself, ugly as an old dog, they tell us. Nor just because that the young fellow knocked the dongs of the holy figures off, either, before he shipped for Sicily. But to get back to the subject, it's one thing to be buried with all your pleasures, like Sardanapalus; it's another to be buried right plunk in front of them, where you can see them. Ain't it so? You need a genius to raise you above it . . ."

Quiet, quiet, quiet afternoon in the back-room study, with an oil-cloth on the library table, busts on the wall, invisible cars snoring and trembling toward the park, the sun shining into the yard outside the window barred against house-breakers, billiard balls kissing and bounding on the felt and sponge rubber, and the undertaker's back door still and stiller, cats sitting on the paths in the Lutheran gardens over the alley that were swept and garnished and scarcely ever trod by the chin-tied Danish deaconesses who'd come out on the cradle-ribbed and always fresh-painted porches of their home.

Somewhat it stung me, the way in which he compared me with his son. But I didn't mind being Alcibiades, and let him be in the same bracket with Socrates in the bargain, since that was what he was driving at. We had title just as good as the chain-mail English kings had to Brutus. If you want to pick your own ideal creature in the mirror coastal air and sharp leaves of ancient perfections and be at home where a great mankind was at home, I've never seen any reason why not. Though unable to go along one hundred per cent with a man like the Reverend Beecher telling his congregation, "Ye are Gods, you are crystalline, your faces are radiant!" I'm not an optimist of that degree, from the actual faces, congregated or separate, that I've seen; always admitting that the true vision of things is a gift, particularly in times of special disfigurement and world-wide Babylonishness, when plug-ugly macadam and volcanic peperino look commoner than crystal—to eyes with an ordinary amount of grace, anyhow—and when it appears like a good sensible policy to settle for medium-grade quartz. I wonder where in the creation there would be much of a double-take at the cry "Homo sum!" But I was and have always been ready to venture as far as possible; even though I was never as much imposed on by Einhorn as he wanted me to be in his big moments, with his banker's trousers and chancellor's cravat, and his unemployable squiggle feet on the barber-chairlike mount of his wheeled contraption made to his specifications. And I never could decide whether he meant that he was a genius or had one, and I suppose he wanted there should be some doubt about the meaning. He wasn't the man to come out and declare that he wasn't a genius while there was the chance he might be one, a thing like that coming about *nolens volens*. To some, like his half-brother Dingbat, he was one. Dingbat swore up and down, "Willie is a wizard. Give him two bits' worth of telephone slugs and he'll parlay it into big dough." His wife agreed too, without reservations, that Einhorn was a wizard. Anything he did—and that covers a lot of territory—was all right with her. There wasn't any higher authority, not even her cousin Karas, who ran the Holloway Enterprises and Management Co. and was a demon moneymaker himself. Karas, that bad, rank character, cinder-crawed, wise to all angles, dressed to kill, with a kitty-cornered little smile and extortionist's eyes, she was in awe of him also, but he wasn't presumed to be in Einhorn's class.

But Einhorn wasn't exactly buried in front of his pleasures. He carried on with one woman or another, and in particular he had a great need of girls like Lollie Fewter. His explanation was that he took after his father. The Commissioner, in a kindly, sleepy, warm-aired, fascinated way, petted and admired all women and put his hands wherever he liked. I imagine women weren't very angry when he saluted them in this style because he picked out whatever each of them herself prized most—color, breasts, hair, hips, and all the little secrets and connivances with which she emphasized her own good things. You couldn't rightly say it was a common letch he had; it was a sort of Solomonic regard of an old chief or aged sea lion. With his spotty big old male hands, he felt up the married and the unmarried ones, and even the little girls for what they promised, and nobody ever was offended by it or by the names he invented, names like "the Tangerines," or "The Little Sled," "Madame Yesteryear," "the Six-Foot Dove." The grand old gentleman. Satisfied and gratified. You could feel from the net pleasantness he carried what there had been between him and women now old or dead, whom he recognized, probably, and greeted in this nose or that bosom.

His sons didn't share this quality. Of course you don't expect younger men to have this kind of evening-Mississippi serenity, but there wasn't much disinterestedness or contemplation in either of them. There was perhaps more of it in Dingbat than in his brother. There scarcely was a time when Dingbat wasn't engaged to a nice girl. He scrubbed himself and dressed himself to go see her in a desperate, cracked rage of earnest respect. Sometimes he would look ready to cry from devotion, and in his preparations he ran out of the perfumed bathroom, clean starched shirt open on his skinny hairiness, to remind me to fetch the corsage from Bluegren's. He could never do enough for these girls and never thought himself good enough for them. And the more he respected them the more he ran with tramps between times, whom he picked up at Guyon's Paradise and took to the Forest Preserves in the Stutz, or to a little Wilson Avenue hotel that Karas-Holloway owned. But Friday evenings, at family dinner, there was often a fiancée, now a piano teacher, now a dress designer or bookkeeper, or simply a home girl, wearing an engagement ring and other presents; and Dingbat with a necktie, tense and daffy, homagefully calling her "Honey," "Isabel, hon," "Janice dear," in his hoarse, thin black voice.

Einhorn, however, didn't have such sentiments at all, whatever sentiments he entertained on other scores. He took the joking liberties his father did, but his jokes didn't have the same ring; which isn't to say that they weren't funny but that he cast himself forward on them toward a goal—seduction. What the laugh was about was his disability; he was after a fashion laughing about it, and he was not so secretly saying to women that if they'd look further they'd find to their surprise that there was the real thing, not disabled. He promised. So that when he worked his wicked, lustful charm, apparently so safe, like a worldly priest or elderly gentleman from whom it's safe to accept a little complimentary badinage or tickle, he was really singlemindedly and grimly fixed on the one thing, ultimately *the* thing, for which men and women came together. And he was the same with them all; not, of course, foreseeing any great success, but hoping all the same that one of them—beautiful, forward, intrigued with him, wishing to play a secret game, maybe a trifle perverse (he suggested), would see, would grasp, would crave, burn for him. He looked and hoped for this in every woman.

He wouldn't stay a cripple, Einhorn; he couldn't hold his soul in it. Sometimes it was dreadful, this; he'd lose everything he'd thought through uncountable times to reconcile himself to it, and be like the wolf in the pit in the zoo who keeps putting his muzzle to the corners of the wall, back and forth, in his exhibition jail. It didn't happen often; probably not oftener than ordinary people get a shove of the demon. But it happened. Touch him when he was off his feed, or had a cold and a little fever, or when there was a rift in the organization, or his position didn't feel so eminent and he wasn't getting the volume of homage and mail he needed—or when it was the turn of a feared truth to come up unseen through the multitude of elements out of which he composed his life, and then he'd say, "I used to think I'd either walk or swallow iodine, and I'd have massages and exercises, and drills when I'd concentrate on a single muscle and think I was building it up by my will, and it was all the bunk, Augie, the Coué theory, etcetera. For the birds. And *It Can Be Done* and the sort of stuff that bigshot Teddy Roosevelt wrote in his books. Nobody'll ever know all the things I tried before I finally decided it was no go. I couldn't take it, and I took it. And I *can't* take it, yet I do take it. But how! You can get along twenty-nine days with your trouble, but there's always that thirtieth day when goddammit you can't, when you feel like the stinking fly in the first cold snap, when you look about and think you're the Old Man of the Sea locked around Sinbad's neck; and why should anybody carry an envious piece of human junk? If society had any sense they'd give me euthanasia or leave me the way the Eskimos do their old folks in an igloo with food for two days. Don't you look so miserable. Go on away. See if Tillie wants you for something."

But this was on the thirtieth day, or more seldom, because in general he enjoyed good health and looked on himself as a useful citizen and even an extraordinary one, and he bragged that there was hardly anything he couldn't bring off if he put his mind to it. And he certainly did some bang-up things. He'd clear us all out of the way to be alone with Lollie Fewter; he'd arrange for the whole lot of us to drive out to Niles Center and show the Commissioner a piece of property. Ostensibly getting ready to occupy himself with a piece of work while we were away —the files and information were laid out for him—he was unhurried, engaging, and smooth-tempered in his tortoiseshells, answering every last question in full and even detaining the excursion to have some last words with his father about frontages or improvements. "Wait till I show you on the map just where the feeder-bus comes through. Bring the map, Augie." He'd have me fetch it and kept the Commissioner till he became impatient, with Dingbat grinding the klaxon and Mrs. Einhorn already settled with bags of fruit in the back seat, calling, "Come, it's hot. I'm fainting here." And Lollie in the passage between the flat and the offices sauntered up and down with the dustmop in the polished dimness, big and soft, comfortable for the heat in a thin blouse and straw sandals, like an overgrown girl walking a doll and keeping a smile to herself about this maternal, matrimonial game, lazy and care-less and, you could say, saving force for the game to follow. Clem Tambow had tried to tell me what the score was but hadn't convinced me, not just because of the oddness of the idea, and that I had a boyish respect for Einhorn, but also because I had made a start with Lollie my-

self. I found excuses to be with her in the kitchen while she was ironing. She told me of her family in the Franklin County coal fields, and
then about the men there, and what they tried and did. She rolled me
in feelings. From suggestion alone, I didn't have the strength to keep
my feet. We soon were kissing and feeling; she now held off my hands
and now led them inside her dress, alleging instruction, boisterous that
I was still cherry, and at last, from kindness, she one day said that if I'd
come back in the evening I could take her home. She left me so horny
I was scarcely able to walk. I hid out in the poolroom, dreading that
Einhorn would send for me. But Clem came with a message from her
that she had changed her mind. I was bitter about that but I reckon I
felt freed, too, from a crisis. "Didn't I tell you?" said Clem, "You both
work for the same boss, and she's his little nooky. His and a couple of
other guys'. But not for you. You don't know anything and you don't
have any money."

"Why, damn her soul!"

"Well, Einhorn would give her anything. He's nuts about her."

I couldn't conceive that. It wouldn't be like Einhorn to settle his
important feelings on a tramp. But that exactly was what he had done.
He was mad for her. Einborn know, too, that he shared her with a few
hoodlums from the poolroom. Of course he knew. It wasn't in his life
to be without information; he had the stowage of an anthill for it, with
weaving black lines of approvisioners creeping into the crest from every
direction. They told him what would be the next turn in the Lingle
case, or what the public-auction schedule would be, or about Appellate
Court decisions before they were in print, or where there was hot
goods, from furs to school supplies; so he had a line on Lollie from the
beginning to the end.

Eleanor Klein asked me sentimental questions. Did I have a sweetheart yet? It was a thing I appeared ripe for. Our old neighbor, Kreindl,
asked me too, but in a different way, on the q.t. He judged I was no
longer a kid and he could reveal himself, his cockeyes turning fierce
and gay. "*Schmeist du schon*, Augie? You've got friends? Not my son.
He comes home from the store and reads the paper. *S'interesiert ihm
nisht.* You're not too young, are you? I was younger than you and
gefärlich. I couldn't get enough. Kotzie doesn't take after me." He
much needed to pronounce himself the better, and in fact the only,
man in his house; and he did look very sturdy when he massed up his
teeth and creased his out-of-doors, rugged face to smile. He saw a lot
of weather, for he went through the entire West Side on foot with his

satchel of samples. Because he had to count every nickel. And he had the patience and hardness of steady pavement going, passing the same lead-whited windows of a factory twenty times a month and knowing to the last dent every empty lot between him and a destination. Arriving, he could hang around hours for a six-bit commission or a piece of information. "Kotzie takes after my missis. He is *kaltblutig*." Sure I knew it was he himself that did all the trumpeting, screaming, and stamping down in his flat, throwing things on the floor.

"And how is your brother?" he said intriguingly. "I understand the little *maidelech* wet their pants for him. What is he doing?"

As a matter of fact I didn't know what Simon was up to these days. He didn't tell me, nor did he seem curious as to what was happening to me, having decided in his mind that I was nothing but a handyman at Einhorn's.

Once I went with Dingbat to a party one of his fiancées was giving, and I met my brother with a Polish girl in a fur-trimmed orange dress; he wore a big, smooth, check suit and looked handsome and sufficient to himself. He didn't stay long, and I had a feeling that he didn't want to spend his evenings where I did. Or maybe it was the kind of evening Dingbat made of it that didn't please him, Dingbat's recitations and hoarse parodies, his turkey girding and obscene cackles that made the girls scream. There were several months when Dingbat and I were very thick. At parties I horsed around with him, goofy, his straight man; or I hugged and pitched on the porches and in the backyards with girls, exactly as he did. He took me under his protection in the poolroom, and we did some friendly boxing, at which I was never much good, and played snooker—a little better—and hung about there with the hoods and loudmouths. So that Grandma Lausch would have thought that the very worst she had ever said about me let me off too light, seeing me in the shoeshine seat above the green tables, in a hat with diamond airholes cut in it and decorated with brass kiss-me pins and Al Smith buttons, in sneakers and Mohawk sweatshirt, there in the frying jazz and the buzz of baseball broadcasts, the click of markers, butt thumping of cues, spat-down pollyseed shells and blue chalk crushed underfoot and dust of hand-slickening talcum hanging in the air. Along with the blood-smelling swaggeroos, recruits for mobs, automobile thieves, stick-up men, sluggers and bouncers, punks with ambition to become torpedoes, neighborhood cowboys with Jack Holt sideburns down to the jawbone, collegiates, tinhorns and small-time racketeers and pugs, ex-servicemen, home-evading husbands, hackies, truckers and bush-

league athletes. Whenever someone had a notion to work out on me—
and there were plenty of touchy characters here to catch your eye in a
misconstrued way—Dingbat flew around to protect me.

"This kid is a buddy of mine and he works for my bro. Monkey with
him and you'll get something broke on your head. What's the matter,
you tough or hungry!"

He was never anything but through and through earnest when the
subject was loyalty or honor; his bony dukes were ready and his Cuban
heels dug down sharply; his furrowed chin was already feeling toward
its fighting position on the shoulder of his starched shirt, prepared to
go into his stamping dance and start slugging.

But there weren't any fights over me. If there was one doctrine of
Grandma Lausch's that went home, it was the one of the soft answer,
though with her this was of tactical not merciful origin, the dust-off for
heathen, stupes, and bruteheads. So I don't claim it was a trained spirit
turning aside wrath, or *integer vitae* (how could I?) making the wolves
respect me; but I didn't have any taste for the perpetual danger-sign,
eye-narrowing, tricky Tybalt all coiled up to stab, for that code, and
was without curiosity for what it was like to hit and so I refused all the
bids to outface or be outfaced.

On this I had Einhorn's views also, whose favorite example was his
sitting in the driver's seat of the Stutz—as he sometimes did, having
been moved over to watch tennis matches or sandlot games—and a coal
heaver running up with a tire tool because he had honked once or twice
for the Stutz to move and Dingbat wasn't there to move it. "What
could I do," said Einhorn, "if he asked me no questions but started to
swing or punch me in the face? With my hands on the wheel, he'd
think I was the driver. I'd have to talk fast. Could I talk fast
enough? What could make an impression on an animal like that?
Would I pretend to faint or play dead? Oh my God! Even before I was
sick, and I was a pretty husky young fellow, I'd do anything possible
before I started to trade punches with any sonofabitch, muscle-minded
ape or bad character looking for trouble. This city is one place where a
person who goes out for a peaceful walk is liable to come home with a
shiner or bloody nose, and he's almost as likely to get it from a cop's
nightstick as from a couple of squareheads who haven't got the few
dimes to chase pussy on the high rides in Riverview and so hang around
the alley and plot to jump someone. Because you know it's not the city
salary the cops live on now, not with all the syndicate money there is
to pick up. There isn't a single bootleg alky truck that goes a mile with-

out being convoyed by a squad car. So they don't care what they do. I've heard of them almost killing guys who didn't know enough English to answer their questions." And now, with eager shrewdness of nose and baggy eyes, he began to increase his range; sometimes, with that white hair bunched over his ears and his head lifted back, he looked grand, suffering more *for* than *from* something, relaxing his tense care of himself. "But there is some kind of advantage in the roughness of a place like Chicago, of not having any illusions either. Whereas in all the great capitals of the world there's some reason to think humanity is very different. All that ancient culture and those beautiful works of art right out in public, by Michelangelo and Christopher Wren, and those ceremonies, like trooping the color at the Horse Guards' parade or burying a great man in the Pantheon over in Paris. You see those marvelous things and you think that everything savage belongs to the past. So you think. And then you have another think, and you see that after they rescued women from the coal mines, or pulled down the Bastille and got ride of Star Chambers and *lettres de cachet,* ran out the Jesuits, increased education, and built hospitals and spread courtesy and politeness, they have five or six years of war and revolutions and kill off twenty million people. And do they think there's less danger to life than here? That's a riot. Let them say rather that they blast better specimens, but not try to put it over that the only human beings who live by blood are away down on the Orinoco where they hunt heads, or out in Cicero. But the best specimens always have been maltreated or killed. I've seen a picture of Aristotle mounted and ridden like a horse by some nasty whore. There was Pythagoras who got killed over a diagram; there was Seneca who had to cut his wrists; there were the teachers and the saints who became martyrs.

"But I sometimes think," he said, "what if a guy came in here with a gun and saw me at this desk? If he said 'Stick 'em up!' do you think he'd wait until I explained to him that my arms were paralyzed? He'd let me have it. He'd think I was reaching in a drawer or pushing a signal button, and that would be the finish of Einhorn. Just have a look at the hold-up statistics and then tell me I'm dreaming up trouble. What I ought to do is have a sign put up above my head saying 'Cripple.' But I wouldn't like to be seeing that on the wall all the time. I just hope the Brink's Express and Pinkerton Protective labels all over the place will keep them away."

He often abandoned himself to ideas of death, and notwithstanding that he was advanced in so many ways, his Death was still the old one in shriveling mummy longjohns; the same Death that beautiful maidens failed to see in their mirrors because the mirrors were filled with their white breasts, with the blue light of old German rivers, with cities beyond the window checkered like their own floors. A cheating old rascal with bones showing in his buckskin fringes, not a gentle Sir Cedric greeting young boys from the branches of an apple tree. Einhorn had no kind familiar thoughts of him, but superstitions about this frightful snatcher, and he only played the Thanatopsis stoic but maneuvered to beat this other, who had already gained so much on him. Who maybe was the only real god he had.

Often I thought that in his heart Einhorn had completely surrendered to this fear. But when you believed you had tracked Einhorn through his acts and doings and were about to capture him, you found yourself not in the center of a labyrinth but on a wide boulevard; and here he came from a new direction—a governor in a limousine, with state troopers around him, dominant and necessary, everybody's lover, whose death was only one element, and a remote one, of his privacy.

BERNARD MALAMUD

TAKE PITY

DAVIDOV, THE CENSUS-TAKER, OPENED THE DOOR WITH-
out knocking, limped into the room and sat wearily down. Out came his
notebook and he was on the job. Rosen, the ex-coffee salesman, wasted,
eyes despairing, sat motionless, cross-legged, on his cot. The square,
clean but cold room, lit by a dim globe, was sparsely furnished: the cot,
a folding chair, small table, old unpainted chests—no closets but who
needed them?—and a small sink with a rough piece of green, insitu-
tional soap on its holder—you could smell it across the room. The worn
black shade over the single narrow window was drawn to the ledge,
surprising Davidov.

"What's the matter you don't pull the shade up?" he remarked.

Rosen ultimately sighed. "Let it stay."

"Why? Outside is light."

"Who needs light?"

"What then you need?"

"Light I don't need," replied Rosen.

Davidov, sour-faced, flipped through the closely scrawled pages of
his notebook until he found a clean one. He attempted to scratch in a
word with his fountain pen but it had run dry, so he fished a pencil
stub out of his vest pocket and sharpened it with a cracked razor blade.
Rosen paid no attention to the feathery shavings falling to the floor.
He looked restless, seemed to be listening to or for something, although
Davidov was convinced there was absolutely nothing to listen to. It
was only when the census-taker somewhat irritably and with increasing
loudness repeated a question, that Rosen stirred and identified himself.
He was about to furnish an address but caught himself and shrugged.

87

Davidov did not comment on the salesman's gesture. "So begin," he nodded.

"Who knows where to begin?" Rosen stared at the drawn shade. "Do they know here where to begin?"

"Philosophy we are not interested," said Davidov. "Start in how you met her."

"Who?" pretended Rosen.

"Her," he snapped.

"So if I got to begin, how you know about her already?" Rosen asked triumphantly.

Davidov spoke wearily, "You mentioned before."

Rosen remembered. They had questioned him upon his arrival and he now recalled blurting out her name. It was perhaps something in the air. It did not permit you to retain what you remembered. That was part of the cure, if you wanted a cure.

"Where I met her—?" Rosen murmured. "I met her where she always was—in the back room there in that hole in the wall that it was a waste of time for me I went there. Maybe I sold them a half a bag of coffee a month. This is not business."

"In business we are not interested."

"What then you are interested?" Rosen mimicked Davidov's tone.

Davidov clammed up coldly.

Rosen knew they had him where it hurt, so he went on: "The husband was maybe forty, Axel Kalish, a Polish refugee. He worked like a blind horse when he got to America, and saved maybe two—three thousand dollars that he bought with the money this pisher grocery in a dead neighborhood where he didn't have a chance. He called my company up for credit and they sent me I should see. I recommended okay because I felt sorry. He had a wife, Eva, you know already about her, and two darling girls, one five and one three, little dolls, Fega and Surale, that I didn't want them to suffer. So right away I told him, without tricks, 'Kiddo, this is a mistake. This place is a grave. Here they will bury you if you don't get out quick!' "

Rosen sighed deeply.

"So?" Davidov had thus far written nothing, irking the ex-salesman.

"So?—Nothing. He didn't get out. After a couple months he tried to sell but nobody bought, so he stayed and starved. They never made expenses. Every day they got poorer you couldn't look in their faces. 'Don't be a damn fool,' I told him, 'go in bankruptcy.' But he couldn't stand it to lose all his capital, and he was also afraid it would be hard to find a job. 'My God,' I said, 'do anything. Be a painter, a janitor, a junk man, but get out of here before everybody is a skeleton.'

"This he finally agreed with me, but before he could go in auction he dropped dead."

Davidov made a note. "How did he die?"

"On this I am not an expert," Rosen replied. "You know better than me."

"How did he die?" Davidov spoke impatiently. "Say in one word."

"From what he died?—he died, that's all."

"Answer, please, this question."

"Broke in him something. That's how."

"Broke what?"

"Broke what breaks. He was talking to me how bitter was his life, and he touched me on my sleeve to say something else, but the next minute his face got small and he fell down dead, the wife screaming, the little girls crying that it made in my heart pain. I am myself a sick man and when I saw him laying on the floor, I said to myself, 'Rosen, say goodbye, this guy is finished.' So I said it."

Rosen got up from the cot and strayed despondently around the room, avoiding the window. Davidov was occupying the only chair, so the ex-salesman was finally forced to sit on the edge of the bed again. This irritated him. He badly wanted a cigarette but disliked asking for one.

Davidov permitted him a short interval of silence, then leafed impatiently through his notebook. Rosen, to needle the census-taker, said nothing.

"So what happened?" Davidov finally demanded.

Rosen spoke with ashes in his mouth. "After the funeral—" he paused, tried to wet his lips, then went on, "He belonged to a society that they buried him, and he also left a thousand dollars insurance, but after the funeral I said to her, 'Eva, listen to me. Take the money and your children and run away from here. Let the creditors take the store. What will they get?—Nothing.'

"But she answered me, 'Where will I go, where, with my two orphans that their father left them to starve?'

" 'Go anywhere,' I said. 'Go to your relatives.'

"She laughed like laughs somebody who hasn't got no joy. 'My relatives Hitler took away from me.'

" 'What about Axel—surely an uncle somewheres?'

" 'Nobody,' she said. 'I will stay here like my Axel wanted. With the insurance I will buy new stock and fix up the store. Every week I will decorate the window, and in this way gradually will come in new customers—'

" 'Eva, my darling girl—'

" 'A millionaire I don't expect to be. All I want is I should make a little living and take care on my girls. We will live in the back here like before, and in this way I can work and watch them, too.'

" 'Eva,' I said, 'you are a nice-looking young woman, only thirty-eight years. Don't throw away your life here. Don't flush in the toilet —you should excuse me—the thousand poor dollars from your dead husband. Believe me, I know from such stores. After thirty-five years' experience I know a graveyard when I smell it. Go better some place and find a job. You're young yet. Sometime you will meet somebody and get married.'

" 'No, Rosen, not me,' she said. 'With marriage I am finished. Nobody wants a poor widow with two children.'

" 'This I don't believe it.'

" 'I know,' she said.

"Never in my life I saw so bitter a woman's face.

" 'No,' I said. 'No.'

" 'Yes, Rosen, yes. In my whole life I never had anything. In my whole life I always suffered. I don't expect better. This is my life.'

"I said no and she said yes. What could I do? I am a man with only one kidney, and worse than that, that I won't mention it. When I talked she didn't listen, so I stopped to talk. Who can argue with a widow?"

The ex-salesman glanced up at Davidov but the census-taker did not reply. "What happened then?" he asked.

"What happened?" mocked Rosen. "Happened what happens."

Davidov's face grew red.

"What happened, happened," Rosen said hastily. "She ordered from the wholesalers all kinds goods that she paid for them cash. All week she opened boxes and packed on the shelves cans, jars, packages. Also she cleaned, and she washed, and she mopped with oil the floor. With tissue paper she made new decorations in the window, everything should look nice—but who came in? Nobody except a few poor customers from the tenement around the corner. And when they came? When was closed the supermarkets and they needed some little item that they forgot to buy, like a quart milk, fifteen cents' cheese, a small can sardines for lunch. In a few months was again dusty the cans on the shelves, and her thousand was gone. Credit she couldn't get except from me, and from me she got because I paid out of my pocket the company. This she didn't know. She worked, she dressed clean, she waited that the store should get better. Little by little the shelves got empty, but where was the profit? They ate it up. When I looked on the little girls I knew what she didn't tell me. Their faces were white, they were thin, they were hungry. She kept the little food that was left, on the shelves. One night I brought in a nice piece sirloin, but I could see from her eyes that she didn't like that I did it. So what else could I do? I have a heart and I am human."

Here the ex-salesman wept.

Davidov pretended not to see though once he peeked.

Rosen blew his nose, then went on more calmly, "When the children were sleeping we sat in the dark there, in the back, and not once in four hours opened the door should come in a customer. 'Eva, for Godsakes, *run away*,' I said.

" 'I have no place to go,' she said.

" 'I will give you where you can go, and please don't say to me no. I am a bachelor, this you know. I got whatever I need and more besides. Let me help you and the children. Money don't interest me. Interests me good health, but I can't buy it. I'll tell you what I will do. Let this place go to the creditors and move into a two-family house that I own, which the top floor is now empty. Rent will cost you nothing. In the meantime you can go and find a job. I will also pay the downstairs lady to take care of the girls—God bless them—until you will come home. With your wages you will buy the food, if you need clothes, and also save a little. This you can use when you get married someday. What do you say?'

"She didn't answer me. She only looked on me in such a way, with such burning eyes, like I was small and ugly. For the first time I thought to myself, 'Rosen, this woman don't like you.'

" 'Thank you very kindly, my friend Mr. Rosen,' she answered me, 'but charity we are not needing. I got yet a paying business, and it will get better when times are better. Now is bad times. When comes again good times will get better the business.'

" 'Who charity?' I cried to her. 'What charity? Speaks to you your husband's a friend.'

" 'Mr. Rosen, my husband didn't have no friends.'

" 'Can't you see that I want to help the children?'

" 'The children have their mother.'

" 'Eva, what's the matter with you?' I said. 'Why do you make sound bad something that I mean it should be good?'

"This she didn't answer. I felt sick in my stomach, and was coming also a headache so I left.

"All night I didn't sleep, and then all of a sudden I figured out a reason why she was worried. She was worried I would ask for some kind payment except cash. She got the wrong man. Anyway, this made me think of something that I didn't think about before. I thought now to ask her to marry me. What did she have to lose? I could take care of myself without any trouble to them. Fega and Surale would have a father he could give them for the movies, or sometime to buy a little doll to play with, and when I died, would go to them my investments and insurance policies.

"The next day I spoke to her.

" 'For myself, Eva, I don't want a thing. Absolutely not a thing. For you and your girls—everything. I am not a strong man, Eva. In fact, I am sick. I tell you this you should understand I don't expect to live long. But even for a few years would be nice to have a little family.'

"She was with her back to me and didn't speak.

"When she turned around again her face was white but the mouth was like iron.

" 'No, Mr. Rosen.'

" 'Why not, tell me?'

" 'I had enough with sick men.' She began to cry. 'Please, Mr. Rosen. Go home.'

"I didn't have strength I should argue with her, so I went home. I went home but hurt me my mind. All day long and all night I felt bad. My back pained me where was missing my kidney. Also too much smoking. I tried to understand this woman but I couldn't. Why should somebody that her two children were starving always say no to a man that he wanted to help her? What did I do to her bad? Am I maybe a murderer she should hate me so much? All that I felt in my heart was pity for her and the children, but I couldn't convince her. Then I went back and begged her she should let me help them, and once more she told me no.

" 'Eva,' I said, 'I don't blame you that you don't want a sick man. So come with me to a marriage broker and we will find you a strong, healthy husband that he will support you and your girls. I will give the dowry.'

"She screamed, 'On this I don't need your help, Rosen!'

"I didn't say no more. What more could I say? All day long, from early in the morning till late in the night she worked like an animal. All day she mopped, she washed with soap and a brush the shelves, the few cans she polished, but the store was still rotten. The little girls I was afraid to look at. I could see in their faces their bones. They were tired, they were weak. Little Surale held with her hand all the time the dress of Fega. Once when I saw them in the street I gave them some cakes, but when I tried the next day to give them something else, the mother shouldn't know, Fega answered me, 'We can't take, Momma says today is a fast day.'

"I went inside. I made my voice soft. 'Eva, on my bended knee, I am a man with nothing in this world. Allow me that I should have a little pleasure before I die. Allow me that I should help you to stock up once more the store.'

"So what did she do? She cried, it was terrible to see. And after she cried, what did she say? She told me to go away and I shouldn't come back. I felt like to pick up a chair and break her head.

"In my house I was too weak to eat. For two days I took in my mouth nothing except maybe a spoon of chicken noodle soup, or maybe a glass tea without sugar. This wasn't good for me. My health felt bad.

"Then I made up a scheme that I was a friend of Axel's who lived in Jersey. I said I owed Axel seven hundred dollars that he lent me this money fifteen years ago, before he got married. I said I did not have the whole money now, but I would send her every week twenty dollars till it was paid up the debt. I put inside the letter two tens and gave it to a friend of mine, also a salesman, he should mail it in Newark so she would not be suspicious who wrote the letters."

To Rosen's surprise Davidov had stopped writing. The book was full, so he tossed it onto the table, yawned, but listened amiably. His curiosity had died.

Rosen got up and fingered the notebook. He tried to read the small distorted handwriting but could not make out a single word.

"It's not English and it's not Yiddish," he said. "Could it be in Hebrew?"

"No," answered Davidov. "It's an old-fashioned language that they don't use it nowadays."

"Oh?" Rosen returned to the cot. He saw no purpose to going on now that it was not required, but he felt he had to.

"Came back all the letters," he said dully. "The first she opened it, then pasted back again the envelope, but the rest she didn't even open."

"'Here,' I said to myself, 'is a very strange thing—a person that you can never give her anything.—*But I will give.*'

"I went then to my lawyer and we made out a will that everything I had—all my investments, my two houses that I owned, also furniture, my car, the checking account—every cent would go to her, and when she died, the rest would be left for the two girls. The same with my insurance. They would be my beneficiaries. Then I signed and went home. In the kitchen I turned on the gas and put my head in the stove.

"Let her say now no."

Davidov, scratching his stubbled cheek, nodded. This was the part he already knew. He got up and before Rosen could cry no, idly raised the window shade.

It was twilight in space but a woman stood before the window.

Rosen with a bound was off his cot to see.

It was Eva, staring at him with haunted, beseeching eyes. She raised her arms to him.

Infuriated, the ex-salesman shook his fist.

"Whore, bastard, bitch," he shouted at her, "Go 'way from here. Go home to your children."

Davidov made no move to hinder him as Rosen rammed down the window shade.

HERBERT GOLD

ARISTOTLE AND THE HIRED THUGS

In 1933 my father had two mighty enemies. Against one of them he struggled all the long fruit-and-vegetable day, hoisting the crates and loading a top-heavy truck in early morning, at dawn, in his sheepskin jacket, then meeting the customers until evening in a store built narrow and dark in the alleyway between a bakery and a Peerless showroom. Against the other enemy he fought all night, tossing and groaning in his sleep, fierce with that strange nightmare which allows an angry man to be pursued without ever retreating.

His daytime adversary was one shared by most other Americans—the Great Depression. The one of his nights was that beast clanking and roaring in the streets of fantastic Deutschland. "Hitler!" he said at breakfast, shaking the sleep from his head. "I'm almost ashamed to be human. The other strawberries don't like the rotten strawberry, they blush rotten red if you don't pluck him out—"

"Have another cup of Wheatena for the strength in it," chanted my mother, grieving with him like a good wife because of the need for strength on a troubled planet.

"Sorry, no time—look at the clock!" He hadn't meant to complain; it was the only earth he knew. "The lettuce is in already, and the pascal comes with it." And standing up, jacketed in sheepskin, shod in Army-Navy boots, he drained his coffee, dropped the cup in the sink, and was off to the market downtown near the flats of Cleveland. Before light on a May morning, he fought the battered reconditioned motor of his third-hand truck, cursed, lifted the hood, wiped the wires and plugs. Mother opened the kitchen window to watch. Then fits and coughs, then action. Mother watched him go, and waved. *Action*—his pockets filled with knives, hammers, dollars, a deck of cards, and funny pictures to show his friends in the chill damp of a spring morning. Down the suburban streets, up the suburban highway he rattled; and through the sleeping city where the street lights abruptly died in the dawn; and only rare bedroom lamps and kitchen noises greeted him on his way.

But the Central Farmers' Market was a city in full life. Carloads of vegetables steamed with the haggle and babble of selling under corrugated zinc roofs and no roofs at all. Hot fat soup was sold from great tureens by farmers' wives—nickel soup for before the sale, coffee and steaming pies for later, ten cents, to be wolfed down whole by desperate eaters who could not remember whether this was their second or their third breakfast. My father paced the aisles of lettuce and tender peas, the green corridors of spinach, deep into silent back parlors of early fruit off the railway cars. Private, at one with food, he sniffed gratefully, at his ease, homely, taking the pleasures of business on his tongue and in his deep-breathing lungs. He went to the produce market as to worship—putting Hitler and bank holidays behind him in the glory of America's bounty. He squeezed a plum until the wine spurted. He wiped his eyes.

Joe Rini surprised him in his shadowy lair. "What you doing here, Sam?"

"Same as you! Good, eh?"

"But can we sell it? I still got last week's plums left over."

My father shrugged, the sheepskin ruffling against a crate. "They get soggy in the cooler. What else can we do?"

"Nothing—and these look like prime. Here, let me taste."

"Taste, go on. Me, I'd like to buy."

The fruitmen rivalled, of course, for the favor of the farmers, who were of another breed, not washing in those days as a protest against the cost of living. Their best produce many times rotted in the fields, and the farmers often suffered terrible bellyaches from the hopeless eating of an unbought crop. Even striated beefsteak tomatoes, warmed by sun and dusted with salt, can be too many! The farmers suffered from mortgages, skin diseases, unrepaired fences, chronically pregnant wives. Regularly removed from their lonely land to confront a crazy urban cackle, and perhaps returning without the profit of seed and fertilizer, they too passed cards among themselves.

The immigrant Italian and Jewish fruitmen, with their occasional

Greek and Negro colleagues, exchanged printed jokes and dirty pictures. They first competed and argued, then huddled for eat and gossip, sharing each other's hard times in the pleasure and intimacy of these early mornings. They left dawn with regret, jamming their trucks into gritty day.

The farmers' wives, bundled and red and unfragrant as men, dipped up the last coffee and watched without a word. Drops of fat cream whirled round like crazy fishlets in the tin cups. The farmers too had their whispered consultations, but these never ended in a burst of laughter as they got the point. Their little cards were other dreams, dreams of riding and hunting, gothic fantasies of ritual, celebration, and chastisement. The Black Legion haunted the countryside around Cleveland. It made contact with the Klan in Parma and the Bund in Lakewood, and there were histories of drilling in open fields, the youngsters standing guard with broomsticks. Their cards made them members together for sacred order and vengeance. Cousins who rarely came out saw each other on Sunday after church to listen to screaming harangues from the platforms of pickups. During the dark winter of 1933, some farmers discovered that they had the call—or at least as much a one as the man in blue serge sent down from Jackson, Michigan.

Al Flavin was a farmer with whom my father had dealt for almost ten years. They had never been friends, but my father gave as good a price as anyone and Flavin took good care of his lettuce; they met in commerce. An angry man who had sometimes wrestled at country fairs, a giant with magnificent hairy paws, he began to know glory for the first time since abandoning his boyish victories on sweaty canvas. Men listened to him. He became a Commander or a Knight or a Dragon, whatever the Black Legion name for it was. He could not pay off the loan on his greenhouse, but he could gather the legionnaires in before-dawn consultations at the edge of town.

It must have made Al feel distant from himself to break up the meeting, give the mystic handshake, crushing the wrists of men less mighty than he, climb into a truck with a load strapped on, and then go meekly off to do business with Sam Stein.

"All right, make it eleven crates for ten," my father said.

"Ten crates," Al repeated stubbornly.

"Eleven. Or ten and my last price."

"No. Ten crates. My price."

"Al, listen to me," my father said. "You *know* I can't buy it your way. Joe Rini will undersell me, he'll throw circulars on all the porches, and then where will I be? You got to make sense in business."

"You heard me."

"What's the matter, you don't feel good today, Al? Something hurting?"

"Joe Rini don't buy from me. I bring in first quality stuff."

"I know, I *know*, that's why I stand here and argue with you. I *want* your stuff, Al. I like it."

My father rocked, smiling. Al Flavin stood behind his barricade of lettuce. Patience, patience—the soul is tried on earth. At last they were agreed, some place between demand and offer, and then joining in the traditional aftermath of successful negotiation, the two of them completed their deal by hoisting the produce into my father's truck. Hot and sighing when this was done, the cash changing hands, usually they came to a moment of benevolent treaty, and the plump fruitman would light up with the burly, brooding farmer. Al Flavin was busy behind his squeezed-shut eyes trying to remember who he is, who other people are.

"Okay, Al," my father said, "have a cigar."

Now he remembered. He felt his card and sorted my father out: "*Kike!*"

"Wh-wh-wh," said my father.

Flavin's shoulder caught my father and halfspun him around as the man stamped off in the flapping galoshes which he wore almost into summer. My father stammered, wh-wh-wh, meaning *What?* and *Why?* First amazed, then stooped and solemn, pouting with thought. It was well past dawn now, but suddenly the nightmare toppled onto his daytime dream, and he was standing in the sad, crooked streets of old Nuremberg.

My father stopped dealing with Al Flavin. This did not put an end to it. He heard Flavin's word every market-day morning, first whispered, then called after him, twice a week. The single note grated on his nerves. The market is supposed to be a pleasure. My mother made him promise not to fight. Flavin, huge, profligate with his wrestler's flesh, yearning to brawl, would crush him in his paws. It was policy. Flavin was a Commander. He hoped to convert the waverers by rolling with Sam Stein in the running wash of the market gutters.

"I'd get him with the peen of my hammer first!" my father yelled.

"Sam, Sam, we don't want trouble."

"I'll break his head with the claw!"

Mother petted him, stroked him. "Think of your business. You got a family, Sam, you got to count them."

"*I'll Kill Him, Bella!*"

"Shush, you're making noise, the neighbors. You got to count me, too. No trouble, please, for your kids' sake."

"No, no, no." His eyes were red with sleepless thinking. There was an angry scratch in the tender eye-flesh. He breathed as if he were struggling for air. "No, you're right, Bella. But if he touches me one more time—"

That time came, however, on a morning during the dog days of July, when even at early market hours the men panted and sweated under the bloody-eyed sun before it reared up onto the exhausted city. Ice trickled through the crates of lettuce, rustling, and evaporated on cement still hot from the day before. The overfed market rats loped along on seared paws. Flavin sprang from behind a heap of crates, pretending to be in a hurry, and struck my father with his knee at the belly, so that he lost his balance and stumbled like a drunk. He grunted. He tried but could not quite sob out his breath. It was caught, trapped, exterminated some place within, and he lay sprawled on the soft market refuse while the little world of pain in his belly spun faster than the earth's turning, and only a moment later, when the hurtling agony at the center of his being slowed down to weakness, and the weakness to a sour sickness that drained into his mouth, did he remember again who he was. It's an assault against life that brings this gnawing, liver-eating agony upon a man gasping for his breath with his head against a crate of lettuce. The blood shrieked like eagles in his ears. It's a wish of murder—extermination. It's a terrible pain that makes a man forget he is Sam Stein.

Flavin roared, pushed the laughter forward with all his weight, and stood with his huge arms welcoming. Once taciturn, he had learned the tricks of oratory: "Looks drunk, don't he? Ain't he a rummy? Never did run into a rummy kike before, did you ever, boys?"

An offering of laughter. The rest would gather when the rich noise of brawling crashed out. Flavin was in boots, kicking free of a broken crate, ready.

Sam Stein pained badly in the gut. He climbed up dizzily and shook his head clear. He felt for the silver-pronged crating hammer in his back pocket. Flavin crouched, his long jaw twitching with desire. The buttons of his pants were stretched and a tab of shirt came out his fly.

Flavin could wait another moment to find and make himself real. The usual hubbub of commercial dispute hid them now; the life of the market swirled unknowing about the two men, food rising in great towers and vaults above them, around them, and only a couple of farmers watched. Joe Rini, terrified, blowing saliva, also watched.

My father had promised my mother.

He loved life and the right and *to win*.

Flavin might kill him.

My father walked away rapidly, hunched, turning red for shame and white for planning, and grabbed Joe Rini by the sleeve and took him with him. "Joe, Joe," he said, "I got to talk to you. I know you got friends. I got to talk to them, too."

"What you got to say, Sam?"

"Oh maybe I could kill him, but then again maybe not. It wouldn't be so good if he gave me a beating. Those other cossacks would feel too nice about it. Or worse. A bad precedent. No justice in that. So. . . ."

Eagerly Rini talked into the void. "So you know how they drink. They're drunkards. So don't raise your blood pressure." My father's eye made him stop. Rini agreed. My father decided slowly:

"The way things are going on the market now, Joe, it won't be safe for any of us soon."

"What you thinking, Sam?" Rini asked.

He was thinking, but in his own words: precedent, morale, example. This was a political question to be answered in the impure, compromising way of politics. A passionate answer—Sam Stein's face bloodied, a crowd secretly smiling over Sam Stein's fallen body, an inflamed Al finding his dream of power fulfilled—this was the worst possibility which my father's furious body had almost given him. The philosophical thing to do was to master that hot inner twitch, and then, only then, to think out how to discourage the cossack mob.

Job and Noah had patience; yet Job was permitted his anger. Not an educated man, my father knew that the patriarchs had even spoken for passion on earth, properly used. And he knew no other place for justice except here below, on earth, where he hoped to have more children.

He breathed deeply once, twice, again, that's better, and then thanked God for giving him a sense of responsibility. He thanked the Lord of Creation that his healthy, willing, complaining wife had come to mind. Wistfully he thanked the Almighty for prudence—and also for his friend Joe Rini. He said to Joe Rini: "You're going to help me now."

That very night Joe found the three young friends whom he had in mind and brought them to the house. My father wanted to meet them . . . "make your acquaintance." How formal we become under embarrassment. For fifty dollars he could buy a beating with any refinements he named. Except nothing vicious, of course—what do you think, they were queers? They were mere administrators.

"No, *no!*" my mother cried. "So then he'll kill you next, and what's the good? We can't afford it."

"We can't afford not to," my father said stonily. "We're going to do what the Frenchies won't do. When he makes his noise, we march into the Rhineland and stop it good. You don't have to listen to that noise. You stop it the best way you can. You stop it. You *stop* it."

"Sam, O Sam, it's dangerous, it's fifty dollars."

"It's the cost of living, Bella."

Joe Rini's friends, three young chaps with slicked-down hair, nervous hands, and old jokes, were very sociable. They jiggled and dandled and played beanbag with me, as if I were a baby, although I was eight years old already. They took time over the business because my father likes business. Also he wanted to be certain. Mother served liver *with,* the rich slabs covered by curly, glistening onions. How can businessmen discuss serious matters without keeping up their strength? Mugs of strong black coffee, too.

"For fifty dollars, Mr. Stein," said the leader of the group, "we can maybe kill him for you. It's no extra. We'll be working anyway. His truck has got to stop for a light on the edge of town, and there we are."

"No, no," my father said. "Put him in the hospital, that's all."

"Mr. Rini says he used to work in the commission house with you. He says you're buddies from way back. It's no trouble at all."

"No!" my father said. "The man has a wife and kids, just like me. His big boy is too dumb to run a farm by himself—"

"We got smart kids," my mother interrupted, smiling, politely patting with a napkin, pleased by their appetites. "My big boy, he gets such marks from his teacher—"

"Bella, shush. Go call up somebody on the telephone if you got to talk. Listen."

The businessmen shrugged apologetically, being brought up in a tradition which favors mothers, and turned regretfully back to hear out my father and his scrupling. They were unaccustomed to fine distinctions, but they came of devoted families: they enjoyed a mother's pride.

"So don't do that what you said there," my father repeated. "I just want him to learn a little, have time to think a little. The hospital."

"Okay," the leader of the trio said reluctantly, "you're the boss. You get a hold of us if you change your mind, will you? To you the price remains the same."

"The hospital," my father repeated, making them promise.

"Let us worry about the details, Mr. Stein. Fifty goes a long way these days."

My father arose angrily, sending his cup ringing against a platter. "I said the hospital!"

"The hospital, hospital," they intoned mournfully, and filed out.

The next morning Flavin did not show up at the market. It was so easy to follow him from the country in a flivver, stop with him at a red light, get rid of the cigarettes, and pile quickly onto his truck. So instead of Flavin, a weary, hardworking young thug appeared and nodded to Dad, saying that they had been careful, just as he said. But it would have been no extra trouble, in fact, the reverse.

My father was undelighted. By his veiled eyes he signalled regret at the weight of the world: he was obliged to send Flavin down to defeat without earning the kiss of victory. Life had provided him—as it does everyone—with one more little blemish on the ideal of brave perfection. He found it a necessary business, nothing more, a merely rational victory, and he foresaw the possibility of being ambushed in his turn by a man who might not bother to think of his wife and children. Nevertheless, reason consoled him.

"What if he does it to you now, Sam? Where will I and the kids be? Where will *you* be if you're dead?"

"Well, it's a risk. But in this life you have to take chances and defend yourself like you can. And now let me answer your question: If I'm dead, I'm no place."

He sent Flavin a five-dollar bouquet of flowers, followed the next morning by a two-dollar plant with thick wet leaves and a decorative sprinkle of spangles. Joe Rini approved. A friend who went to see Flavin in the hospital reported that they were the only flowers he received.

The moral which my father drew was one which he wanted to teach England and France in 1933 and after. Still strong and capable, Flavin came quietly to work in his bandages about ten days later. He sold tomatoes to my father, and they haggled like gentlemen over the price.

They mistered each other warily. There was further talk of the Black Legion, but not a gesture from Flavin. In a few years even the talk passed.

Sometimes my father thought that he might be beat up, but it never happened, although once he was robbed. That was not Flavin's work.

Flavin had taken instruction well, administered according to Aristotelean principles, with moderation, by a man whose fundamental passionate mildness led him to a reasonable strictness: the hospital for Flavin, nothing worse. Nightmares go on, but they have answers—albeit risky, rational, incomplete, and not ideally valorous. Poor Flavin, unused to surprises—he was discouraged.

And my mother was consoled. Dad made another fifty dollars to replace the ones spent in good works.

NORMAN MAILER

FROM
THE NAKED AND THE DEAD

A sturdy man about twenty-seven, perhaps, with blond straight hair and eager blue eyes. His nose is sharp, and there are deep sad lines which extend from his nose to the corners of his mouth. If it were not for this, he would look very young. His speech is quick and sincere and a little breathless as if afraid he will not be permitted to finish.

THE CANDY STORE IS SMALL AND DIRTY AS ARE ALL THE stores on the cobblestoned street. When it drizzles the cobblestones wash bare and gleaming on top, and the manhole covers puff forth their shapeless gouts of mist. The night fogs cloak the muggings, the gangs who wander raucously through the darkness, the prostitutes, and the lovers mating in the dark bedrooms with the sweating stained wall-paper of brown. The walls of the street fester in summer, are clammy in winter; there is an aged odor in this part of the city, a compact of food scraps, of shredded dung balls in the cracks of the cobblestones, of tar, smoke, the sour damp scent of the city people, and the smell of coal stoves and gas stoves in the cold-water flats. All of them blend and lose identity.

In the daytime, the peddlers stand at the curb and hawk their fruit and vegetables. Middle-aged women in black shapeless coats pluck at the food with shrewd grudging fingers, probing it to the narrow. Cautiously, the women step out from the sidewalk to avoid the water in the gutters, stare with temptation at the fish heads that the owner of the fish store has just cast into the street. The blood gives a sheen to the cobblestone at first, fades, becomes pink, and then is lost in the sewer water. Only the smell of fish remains together with the dung

104

balls, the tar, the rich uncertain odors of the smoked meats in the delicatessen windows.

The candy store is at the end of the street, a tiny place with grease in the ledges of the window, and rust replacing the paint. The front window slides open doubtfully to make a counter where people can buy things from the street, but the window is cracked and dust settles on the candy. Inside there is a narrow marble counter and an aisle about two feet wide for the customers who stand on the eroded oilcloth. In the summer it is sticky, and the pitch comes off on one's shoes. On the counter are two glass jars with metal covers and a bent ladling spoon containing essence of cherry, essence of orange. (Coca-Cola is not yet in vogue.) Between them is a tan moist cube of halvah on a block of wood. The flies are sluggish, and one has to prod them before they fly away.

There is no way to keep the place clean. Mrs. Goldstein, Joey's mother, is an industrious woman, and every morning and night she sweeps out the place, washes the counter, dusts the candy, and scrubs the floor, but the grime is too ancient, it has bedded into the deepest crevices of the store, the house next door, the street beyond, it has spread into the pores and cells of everything alive and unalive. The store cannot remain clean, and every week it is a little dirtier, a little more suppurated with the caries of the street.

The old man Moshe Sefardnick sits in the rear of the place on a camp stool. There is never any work for him to do and indeed he is too old for it, too bewildered. The old man has never been able to understand America. It is too large, too fast, the ordered suppressed castes of centuries wither here; people are always in flux. His neighbors become wealthier, move away from the East Side to Brooklyn, to the Bronx, to the upper West Side; some of them lose their little businesses, drift farther down the street to another hovel, or migrate to the country. He has been a peddler himself; in the spring before the First World War, he has carried his goods on his back, tramped the dirt roads through small New Jersey towns, selling scissors and thread and needles. But he has never understood it and now in his sixties he is prematurely senile, an old man relegated to the back of a tiny candy store, drifting in Talmudic halls of thought. (If a man hath a worm on his brain, it may be removed by laying a cabbage leaf near the orifice onto which the worm will crawl.)

His grandson, Joey, now seven, comes home from school weeping, a bruise on his face. Ma, they beat me up, they beat me up, they called me sheenie.

Who did, who was it?

It was the Italian kids, a whole gang, they beat me up.

The sounds move in the old man's mind, alter his thought stream. The Italians. He shrugs. An undependable people; in the Inquisition they let the Jews in at Genoa, but at Naples . . . Naples.

He shrugs, watches the mother wash the blood away, fit a patch of adhesive to the cut. Oh, mein Joey.

The old man laughs to himself, the delicate filtered laughter of a pessimist who is reassured that things have turned out badly. Nu, this American is not so different. The old man sees the goy faces staring at the victims.

Joey, he calls in a harsh cracked voice.

What is it, zaydee?

The goyim, what did they call you?

Sheenie.

The grandfather shrugs again. Another name. For a moment an ancient buried anger moves him. He stares at the unformed features of the boy, the bright blond hair. In America even the Juden look like goyim. Blond hair. The old man rouses himself to speech, talks in Yiddish. They beat you because you're a Jew, he says. Do you know what a Jew is?

Yes.

The grandfather feels a spasm of warmth for his grandchild. So handsome. So good. He is an old man and he will die soon, and the child is too young to understand him. There is so much wisdom he could give.

It's a difficult question, the meaning of a Jew. It's not a race, he says, it's not even a religion any more, maybe it will never be a nation. Dimly, he knows he has lost the child already, but he continues talking, musing aloud.

What is it, then? Yehudah Halevy said Israel is the heart of all nations. What attacks the body attacks the heart. And the heart is also the conscience, which suffers for the sins of the nations. He shrugs once more, does not differentiate between saying aloud what he thinks or merely moving his lips. It's an interesting problem, but personally I think a Jew is a Jew because he suffers. Olla Juden suffer.

Why?

So we will deserve the Messiah? The old man no longer knows. It makes us better and worse than the goyim, he thinks.

But the child must always be given an answer. He rouses himself, concentrates and says without certainty, It is so we will last. He speaks again, wholly lucid for a moment. We are a harried people, beset by oppressors. We must always journey from disaster to disaster, and it makes us stronger and weaker than other men, makes us love and hate the other Juden more than other men. We have suffered so much that we know how to endure. We will always endure.

The boy understands almost nothing of this, but he has heard the words and they engrave a memory which perhaps he will exhume later. He looks at his grandfather, at the wrinkled corded hands and the anger, the febrile intelligence, in his pale old-man's eyes. Suffer. It is the only word Joey Goldstein absorbs. Already he has forgotten most of the shame and fear of his beating. He fingers the plaster on his temple, wonders if he can go out to play.

The poor are the great voyagers. There are always new businesses, new jobs, new places to live, new expectations evolving into old familiar failures.

There is the candy store in the East Side, which fails, and another which fails, and still another. There are movements: to the Bronx, back to Manhattan, to candy stores in Brooklyn. The grandfather dies, and the mother is alone with Joey, settles at last in a candy store in Brownsville with the same front window that slides open painfully, the same dust on the candy.

By the time he is eight and nine and ten, Joey is up at five in the morning, sells the papers, the cigarettes, to the men going to work, leaves at seven-thirty himself for school, and is back in the candy store again until it is almost time for bed. And his mother is in the store almost all day long.

The years pass slowly in the work-vacuum, the lonely life. He is an odd boy, so adult, the relatives tell his mother. And he is eager to please, a fine salesman on the honest side, but there are no potentialities for the big operator, the con man. It is all work, and the peculiar intimate union between his mother and himself of people who work together for many years.

He has ambitions. During the time he is in high school there are impossible dreams about college, of being an engineer or a scientist. In his little spare time he reads technical books, dreams of leaving the candy store. But of course when he does it is to work in a warehouse as a shipping clerk while his mother employs a kid to do the work he has done formerly.

And there are no contacts. His speech is different, quite different from that of the men with whom he works, the few boys he knows on the block. There is virtually nothing of the hoarse rough compassionate accent of Brooklyn. It is like his mother's speech, slightly formal, almost with an accent, a loving use of bigger words than are really necessary. And when at night he sits on one of the stoops and talks to the youths with whom he grew up, whom he has watched play stick ball and touch foot-ball on the streets for many years, there is a difference between them and him.

Look at the knockers on her, Murray says.

A dish, Benny says.

Joey smiles uncomfortably, sits among the dozen other youths on the stoop, watches the foliage of the Brooklyn trees rustle in contented bourgeois rhythms over his head.

She got a rich father, Riesel says.

Marry her.

And two steps farther down, they are arguing about batting averages. Whatdeya mean? I know, ya wanta bet on it? Listen, that was the day I woulda made sixteen bucks if Brooklyn won. I had Hack Wilson picked for two for five to bring him up to .281 and Brooklyn to win, and he did three for four only they dropped it to the Cubs 7-2 and I lost. Whadeya handing me ya want to bet on it?

Goldstein's cheek muscles are tired from the stupid outsider grin.

Murray nudges him. How come you didn't go with us to the Giant doubleheader?

Oh, I don't know, somehow I never can concern myself properly with baseball.

Another girl wiggles by in the Brooklyn gloaming, and Riesel, the card, stalks after her, moving like an ape. Wheeeeeeh, he whistles, and her heels tap in the coquettish mating sounds of the bird flying away for only this night.

What bumpers on her.

You don't belong to the Panthers, do you, Joey? says the girl sitting next to him at the party.

No, but I'm familiar with them all, nice fellows, he says. In this

year, his nineteenth, out of high school, he is cultivating a blond
mustache which will not take.

I heard Larry is getting married.

And Evelyn too, Joey says.

Yeah, to a lawyer.

In the middle of the cellar, in the cleared place, they are dancing
sharpy style, their backsides out, their shoulders moving insolently. IS
IN THE STAR DUST OF A SONG.

You dance, Joey?

No. A momentary anger toward all the others. They have time to
dance, time to become lawyers, time to become smooth. But it passes, is
uncharacteristic, and he is merely uncomfortable again.

Excuse me, Lucille, he says to the hostess, but I have to go now,
got to get up early, convey my fondest apologies to your mother.

And back inside his house at the socially rejected hour of ten-thirty,
he sits with his mother, drinks a glass of hot tea on the eroded white
porcelain table, is obviously moody.

What's the matter, Joey?

Nothing. And it is unbearable that she knows. Tomorrow I got a
lot of work, he says.

At the shoe factory they should appreciate you more, all the work
you do.

He tilts the carton off the floor, gets his knee back of it, and zooms
it up over his head, lofting it onto the top of the seven-foot pile. Beside
him the new man is wrestling it up clumsily.

Here, let me show you, Joey says. You have to combat the inertia
of it, get it in momentum. It's very important to know how to lift these
things or you get a rupture, all kinds of physical breakdowns. I've
made a study of this. His powerful back muscles contract only slightly
as he flips up another carton. You'll get the hang of it, he says cheer-
fully. There are lots of things in this kind of work you have to study
about.

A lonely deal. Sad things, like leafing through the annual catalogues
sent out by MIT, Sheffield School of Engineering, NYU, and so on.

But there is a party at last, a girl to whom he can talk, a pretty dark-
haired little girl with a soft shy voice and an attractive mole on her
chin of which she is self-conscious. A year or two younger than he, just
out of high school, and she wants to be an actress or a poetess. She

makes him listen to the symphonies of Tchaikovsky (the Fifth is her favorite) and she is reading *Look Homeward, Angel,* works as a sales-girl in a woman's store.

Oh, it's not a bad job, I suppose, she says, but it's . . . the girls are not really high class, it's nothing special I could write a letter about. I'd like to do something else.

Oh, I would too, so much, he says.

You ought to, Joey, you're a finer-type person. I can see we're the only thinkers. (They laugh, suddenly and magically intimate.)

Soon they are having long conversations on the stuffed rigid cushions of a maroon sofa in the parlor of her house. They discuss marriage versus a career for her, academically, abstractly; of course it concerns neither of them. They are the thinkers, regarding life. And in the complicated, relished, introspective web of young lovers, or more ex-actly, young petters, they progress along the oldest channel in the world and the most deceptive, for they are certain it is unique to them. Even as they are calling themselves engaged, they are losing the details of their subtle involved pledging of a troth. They are moved and warmed by intimacies between them, by long husky conversations in the parlor, in inexpensive restaurants, by the murmurs, the holding of hands in the dark velvet caverns of movie houses. They forget most of the things that have advanced them into love, feel now only the effect of them. And of course their conversation alters, new themes are bruited. Shy sensitive girls may end up as poetesses or they may turn bitter and drink alone in bars, but nice shy sensitive Jewish girls usually marry and have children, gain two pounds a year, and worry more about refurbishing hats and trying a new casserole than about the meaning of life. After their engagement, Natalie talks over their prospects.

Oh, honey, you know I don't want to nag you, but we can't get married on the money you're making; after all, you wouldn't want me to live in a cold-water flat. A woman wants to fix up things and have a nice home, it's awfully important, Joey.

I understand what you mean, he answers, but, Natalie honey, it's not such an easy thing, there's been a lot of talk about a recession, and you can't tell, it might be a depression coming again.

Joey, it's not like you to talk like that, what I like about you is you're so strong and optimistic.

No, you make me that way. He sits there quite silent. You know, I'll tell you, I do have an idea, I've been thinking of going into welding, it's a new field but not so new that it isn't established. Of course I think that plastics or television is the thing to come, but it's undependable yet, and I don't have the education for that, I have to face it.

That sounds all right, Joey. She considers. It's not such a snooty profession, but maybe in a couple of years you'll be able to own a store.

A shop.

A shop, *shop,* that isn't anything to be ashamed of. You'd be a . . . a businessman then.

They discuss it, decide he must go to night school for a year until he is trained. The thought makes him moody. I won't be able to see you so much, maybe only a couple of nights a week, I'm wondering if that's such a healthy thing.

Oh, Joey, you don't understand me, when my mind is made up it's made up, I can wait, you don't have to worry about me. She laughs softly, warmly.

He begins a very hard year, working for forty-four hours in the warehouse, eating his quick supper, and striving to remain alert in the classrooms and workshops at night. He gets home at twelve, goes to bed, and drags himself up to meet the next morning. On Tuesday and Thursday nights he sees Natalie after class, staying up till two and three in the morning to the displeasure of her parents and the nagging of his mother.

They have fights over this.

Joey, I've got nothing against the girl, she's probably a very nice girl, but you're not ready to get married, for the girl's sake I don't want you to get married. She wouldn't want to live in a place not so nice.

But that's what you don't understand, that's where you underestimate her, she knows what we'll have to face, it isn't as if we're going into it blindfolded.

You're children.

Look, Mama, I'm twenty-one, I've been a good son to you, haven't I, I've worked hard, I'm entitled to a little pleasure, a little happiness.

Joey, you talk as if I begrudge it to you, of course you've been a good son. I want you to have all the joys in the world, but you're ruining your health, you're staying out late, and you're going to be taking on too much responsibility. Oh (tears form in her eyes), it's only your happiness I want, you should understand that. When the time comes I'll be happy for you to be married, and I only hope you should get a wife who deserves you.

But I don't even deserve Natalie.

Nonsense! Nothing is too good for you.

Mama, you got to face it. *I'm going to get married.*

She shrugs. Nu, you've got a half year yet, and then you got to find a job with this welding. I only want you should keep an open mind on the question, and when the time comes we'll see.

But my mind's made up. It's no longer an issue. I swear, Mama, you make me so upset.

She becomes silent, and they eat for a few minutes without speaking, both troubled, both absorbed with new arguments they are loath to use for fear of beginning it again. At last she sighs and looks at him.

Joey, you shouldn't say anything of what I said about Natalie, I've got nothing against her, you know that. Cautious, half convinced, she is beginning to hedge the bet.

He graduates from welding school, gets a job for twenty-five dollars, and they get married. The wedding presents come to almost four hundred dollars, enough for a bedroom set from a department store, and a couch and two chairs for the living room. They extend their furniture with a few pictures, an inaccurate calendar scene of cows in a pasture at sunset, a cheap reproduction of "The Blue Door" and a Maxfield Parrish from an advertisement. On an end table, Natalie puts their wedding pictures, joined like book covers in a double frame. His mother gives them a whatnot and a collection of tiny painted cups and saucers with plump nude angels chasing around the circumference. They settle down in their three-room flat, and are very happy, very warm and absorbed in each other. By the end of the first year he is making thirty-five a week, and they are moving through the regular ordained orbit of friends and relatives. Joey becomes adept at bridge. Their marital storms are infrequent and quickly lost, the memories of them buried in the avalanche of pleasant and monotonous trivia that makes up their life.

Once or twice there is some tension between them. Joey, they decide, is very virile and the knowledge that she wants him less often than he needs her is bitter and sometimes ugly. This is not to say that their matings always fail or that they even talk or brood about it a good deal. But still he is a little balked at times. He cannot understand her unpredictable coldness; during their engagement she had been so passionate in her petting.

After the boy is born there are other concerns. He is making forty dollars a week, and working as a soda jerk in the corner drug store on weekends. He is tired, often worried; her delivery is a Caesarean, and they go into debt to pay the doctor. Her scar troubles him; despite himself he looks at it with distaste and she notices that. She is completely involved with the child, content to stay at home for week after week. In the long evenings, he wants her very often and contains himself, sleeping irritably. One night their coupling ends in a quarrel.

He has a bad habit in the middle. Always, despite his injunctions, he must ask, are you warm? Her smile is so noncommittal; he is vaguely angered.

A little, she will say.

He slows himself, rests his head on her shoulder, relaxing, breathing deeply. Then he moves again.

How are you now? Are you close, Natalie?

Her smile again. I'm all right, Joey. Don't worry about me.

He glides through the passage of several neutral minutes, his mind far away, imagining another child. They had the last one after discussing it and agreeing that they wanted a baby, but now he cannot afford another one, and he is wondering if her diaphragm has been set properly. He thinks he can feel it, which worries him. Abruptly, he is conscious of the pressure in his loins, the perspiration on his back, and he halts roughly, relaxing again.

How close are you?

Don't worry about me, Joey.

He is angry suddenly. *Tell me, how close are you?*

Oh, darling, I won't be able to tonight, it's not important, go ahead, don't mind me, it's not important.

The bickering offends both of them, makes them cold. He dreads his tasteless isolated throe, knows suddenly that he cannot do it, cannot lie afterwards on his bed depressed with failure.

For once he swears. To hell with it. And he leaves her on the bed, and walks over to the window, staring at the drab parchment of the shade. He is trembling, partially from cold.

She comes up beside him, nuzzling her body against his to warm him. The caress is tentative, uncertain, and it offends him. He feels her maternalness. Go away, I don't want a . . . a mother, he blurts, feeling doubt and then dread at the awfulness of what he has said.

Her mouth forms in the blank smile, wrinkles suddenly into weeping. She cries on the bed like a little girl. He realizes abruptly after two and a half years of marriage that when she forms that smile she is close to hysteria and terror and perhaps even loathing. The knowledge freezes in his chest.

After a moment he flops down beside her, cushions her head, and tries to comfort her weeping, his numb hand moving over her fore-head and face.

In the morning none of it seems so awful, and by the end of a week he has nearly forgotten it. But on his side it marks the end or almost the end of one expectation from marriage, and for Natalie it means she must pretend excitement in order to avoid hurting him. Their marriage settles again like a foundation seeking bedrock. For them, that species of failure is not acute, not really dangerous. They ensconce themselves in their child, in adding and replacing furniture, in discussing insurance and finally buying some. There are the problems of his work, his slow advances, the personalities of the men in the shop. He takes to bowling with a few of them, and Natalie joins the sisterhood at the local temple, induces them finally to give courses in the dance. The rabbi is a young man, quite liked because he is modern. On Wednesday nights they have a baby sitter, and listen to his lectures on bestsellers in the social room.

They expand, put on weight, and give money to charitable organiza-tions to help refugees. They are sincere and friendly and happy, and nearly everyone likes them. As their son grows older, begins to talk, there are any number of pleasures they draw from him. They are content and the habits of marriage lap about them like a warm bath. They never feel great joy but they are rarely depressed, and nothing immediate is ever excessive or cruel.

The war comes and Joey doubles his salary with overtime and promo-tion. He is up before the draft board twice and is deferred each time, but in 1943 when they start drafting the fathers he does not try for an exemption because he is a war worker. There is a sense of guilt in all the familiar landscape of his home, there is the discomfort of walking the street in civilian clothes. More, he has convictions, reads *PM* from time to time, although he will say that it upsets him too much. He reasons it all out with Natalie, is drafted against the protests of his boss.

In the draft-board office on the early morning when he reports for induction he talks to a father like himself, a portly fellow with a mustache.

Oh, no, I told my wife to stay at home, Joey says, I figured it would be too upsetting for her.

I had an awful time, the other fellow says, settling everything, it was a crime what I had to take for my store.

In a few minutes they discover they know a few people in common.

Oh, yes, the new friend says, Manny Silver, nice fellow, we got along fine up at Grossinger's two years ago, but he travels in a crowd a little too fast for me. Nice wife, but she'd better watch her weight, I remember when they were married they were inseparable for a while, but of course you got to get out, meet people, it's bad for married people to stay alone together all the time.

Farewell to all this.

It has been lonely at times, empty, but still it has been a harbor. There are all the friends, all the people you understand immediately, and in the Army, in the bare alien worlds of the barracks and the bivouacs, Goldstein fumbles for a new answer, a new security. And in his misery the old habits wither away like bark in winter, and he is left without a garment. His mind searches, plumbs all the cells of his brain, and comes out with the concretion, the heritage, smudged for so long in the neutral lapping cradle of Brooklyn streets.

(We are a harried people, beset by oppressors . . . we must always journey from disaster to disaster . . . not wanted and in a strange land.)

We are born to suffer. And although he strains with the sinews of his heart and mind back toward his home, his cove, his legs are beginning to steady, his thighs to set.

Goldstein is turning his face to the wind.

PAUL GOODMAN

⚔⚔⚔⚔

A PRAYER FOR DEW

"And the offering of Judah and Jerusalem shall be a delight unto the Lord, as in days of old, as in ancient years."

With this ending of the great Standing-prayer, the congregation sat down.

It was Passover and a springtime thunder-shower was washing the windows of the synagogue, amid prolonged rumblings of thunder and many flashes of lightning. It was dark and all the electric lights had been turned on—by the Negro janitor (in accordance with the injunction, "On the first day shall be a holy convocation, ye [Jews] shall do no servile work").

Moonfaced Rabbi Horn stood up in front of the closed curtain of the Ark, adjusted his substantial sleeves, and said: "We come now to the most beautiful prayer of the day, *Tefilas Tal*, the Prayer for Dew. This prayer is said before the open Ark; it comes from the heart of springtime longing. What could man do without the rain? The rain falls in order to fill the rivers, and the rivers flow into the seas and lakes in order to evaporate into clouds. *Who* will give me fifteen dollars for the honor of opening the Ark for *Tal*, for *P'shichas Tal*, the opening of the Ark for *Tal*? What am I bid? Do I hear anybody bid fifteen dollars?"

"Four dollars for my son, in memory of my husband Isaac Podolnik," called down Mrs. Podolnik from the women's gallery.

"*Six* dollars!" said Mr. Brody with a quiet smile.

The Rabbi and the President, who wore a silk hat, looked up at the widow Podolnik.

116

"Just what," I turned round to my friend Leo, sitting behind me with his white-shawled father, "what is the *mitzvah* of a bid made in honor of somebody when it doesn't win the auction?" I was at that time a member of the skeptical and mocking fraternity.

"Seven dollars!" called a voice in the rear.

"Seven dollars is bid back here," said the beadle, hastening to the spot.

"What's the name please?" asked the Rabbi tending his large ear, that was like a handle to the moon.

"Thumim."

"Berman! Mr. Berman bids seven dollars."

"Seven-*fifty*," said Brody quietly.

"Seven-*fifty* is bid for the opening of the Holy Ark for the springtime Prayer for Dew," said Rabbi Horn.

Meantime the rain, not prayed for yet, thudded against the windows and on the skylight of green glass. The water could be heard busily flowing down the runnels and the drainpipes—a "pleasant noise of waters." A burst of lightning sharply silhouetted the old men near the window, with their fringes over their heads, and brightly illuminated the fringes.

"*Eight*-fifty!" said Mr. Thumim.

"Mr. Berman bids eight-fifty," said the Rabbi.

"Eight-seventy-five," said Brody.

"Nine!" cried Thumim excitedly.

"Nine and a half," said Brody.

There was a crack of thunder and one of the electric lights over the reading-table dimmed, and went dark.

"Nunny," said the President to his little son, "go call the *shfartse* to bring a new bulb."

Nunny ran down the aisle, bouncing a rubber ball on the red carpet.

Throughout the synagogue the conversation became general. Everywhere comments about the weather; and far in the rear a burst of laughter where some one had just told a new joke.

My friend Leo, the seminarian, at last gave an opinion on the status of the widow Podolnik's offer that had been outbid. "She fulfilled a commandment in starting the bidding off," he said in my ear. "It is a *mitzvah* to start something off. *Sof ma'aseh machshava tehila:* the end of the deed is the thought of the Beginning!—"

As if afire the Jewish joke progressed from bench to bench, greeted at each telling with a greater outburst of hilarity.

"*B'reshith*—in the *Beginning* God created the heavens and the earth."

"Shh! shh! this is a synagogue!" admonished the President pounding the palm of his hand loudly against his open prayer-book. The buzz fell an octave lower on the scale, as happens on a meadow in the month of August when the sun passes momentarily behind a cloud.

"Twelve dollars!" rang out the voice of Thumim in a last desperate raise.

"Twelve-fifty," said Brody.

"*For heaven's sake,* Marcus—" said Brody's brother-in-law, tugging wildly at his sleeve.

"So?" Brody turned to him with a bland smile. "Did I say I *want* the bid? I'm just—*raising* a little."

"Twelve-fifty is bid by Mr. Meyer Brody for the honor of opening the Ark for *Tal.*"

"*Fifteen dollars!*" thundered a new voice on the left.

"Ah," said the Rabbi, "now we're getting somewhere."

"Sixteen," said Brody.

"*Seventeen!*" boomed the voice.

"Seventeen *seventy-five,*" said Brody.

Preceded by Nunny, now bouncing a different ball, a small red ball at the end of an elastic string, Aaron, the grizzled-haired Negro janitor, came down the aisle carrying a ladder and a frosted bulb. He climbed on the ladder, stretching up his arm to unscrew the burnt-out light and the ladder began to wabble. The Reader lent his hand to hold it firm.

"The question is" I said to Leo, "whether he should even lend his hand to *hold* the ladder—"

"The answer is Yes," said Leo sharply. "This comes under the rubric of helping to preserve a man from injury."

"*Twenty dollars!*" said the booming voice on the left.

"Twenty dollars is bid!" cried Rabbi Horn joyously. "What is the name please?"

"Samuelson—Ely Samuelson."

"Ah, Mr. *Samuelson!*" exclaimed Rabbi Horn with the joyous and flattering quaver that he mostly reserved for weddings. "Mr. Samuelson is not a member of our Congregation," he explained to everybody. "He is a visitor from Providence, the capital of Rhode Island. His uncle, however, is our dear President, Mr. Sonnenschein; and I am sure that you will all join with me in telling Mr. Samuelson that he is just as much at home in this Congregation as in Providence, Rhode Island."

"I'll give just one more hike," said Brody quietly to us. "After such a build-up by the Rabbi, how can he get out of taking the bid? But why should I make him pay more than he can afford?"

"Twenty-three dollars," he called out after judicious consideration.

"*Twenty-five!*" said Mr. Samuelson, on the left.

"Good—take it," said Brody, and turned round to us triumphantly. "I bid them up all the way from four dollars to twenty-five!—After all, why shouldn't the money go to the synagogue? Have I been playing auction-pinochle for forty years for nothing? *Always* you can tell when you can bid them up and when there's nothing doing! Seventeen-seventy-five: *there* was a bid! Who could refuse to go at least to eight-een? But in a game of pinochle, never three-forty; always force them into it; then just drop your cards and say Good! take it!

"Sometimes in a game," said Brody, "they think that *they're* boosting *me*; but the fact is that *I'm* boosting *them*."

The pinochle-player of the Lord.

The Cantor and his choir of black-robed boys had begun to gather at the reading-table under the light that had been repaired (but it now shone dimly in the brightening space). Several of the young soprani were downstairs in the cellar playing punchball, and their piercing cries could be heard in the distance.

At last, after its triumphant progress from the rear of the room across the entire congregation to us in the front, the joke arrived at our bench; but it proved to be the antique story, that I have already set down elsewhere, about the little Jew in the crowded trolley-car who sings "Deedle-deedle-dee, it ain't my setchel."

"Look here, Brody," I said, "supposing the Rabbi decided to knock it down to *both* of you, and have both of you grasp the cord to open the curtain. Ha, then what?"

"It shouldn't happen on *Pesach*," said Brody, turning pale.

The Cantor, who had a white hat with a pom-pom, now stood up on a stool to tower, with his pom-pom, above the boys. For unfortunately, though he was very broad-shouldered and had a powerful black beard and a bass voice, he was only five feet high. Like Ulysses, "when he was seated he looked imposing, but when he rose to his feet you saw that he was of small stature." From the top of a stool he dominated the scene, and often, holding a long note, he would dart a sidewise and upwards glance at the women.

He smote the table with his little tuning-fork and held the sound to his ear, while the vibration welled out amongst us with the unpleasant ring of pure, colorless music. (At one time he had been accustomed to use a pitch-pipe, but this was considered by some of the orthodox as playing a musical instrument.) The choir, catching the note, sang an A-minor chord. And as if created out of nothing, the tranquillity of nature, the natural harmony, crowded into the corners of the space.

"Will the Congregation please rise," said Rabbi Horn, "for the repetition of the Amidah and the singing of *Tefilas Tal*. Mr. Samuelson, will you please come up and stand alongside me on the platform."

"Barukh . . . Blessed art Thou, O Lord, our God and God of our fathers—" began the Cantor in a deep voice, accompanied by a humming continuo of the boys.

"God of Abraham, God of Isaac and God of Jacob; great, strong and awful God, God most high, who grantest goodly favors and art the owner of all that is. Thou rememberest the piety of our fathers, and Thou wilt bring a redeemer to their children's children, for Thy name's sake, in love. King, Helper, Savior and Shield: Blessed art Thou, O Lord, the Shield of Abraham.

"Strong to eternity, O Lord, who quickenest the dead and art mighty to save."

The numerous and progressing chords of the choir, and the flowing line of the Cantor's voice, now baritone, penetrated every corner and we were (for the most part) still.

While Brody looked on with an ecstatic smile, Mr. Samuelson smartly pulled the cord of the curtain over the ark and disclosed the ranks of a dozen scrolls of the Law, dressed in white silk, wearing silver crowns.

The Congregation of Jews rose.

"Our God and God of our fathers, grant Dew!" said all.

"Grant dew, to quench the thirst of Thy land—" sang the Cantor alone, for all.

"In holy joy, sprinkle on us Thy blessing—
with quantity of wine and corn

established the City of Thy desire!"

"B'tal! . . . with Dew!" shouted all, while the choir gave voice to a loud paean.

Now the thunderstorm had moderated to a light steady rain, tapping on the skylight, flowing down all the drains. Meantime the space had become brighter, and the artificial lights shone dim and pale.

There were many stanzas to the poem, each comparing, in some trope or other, the state of the Jewish people in exile to that of a land thirsting and without water.

"With dew and contentment fill our barns—" sang the Singer of this agricultural people, accompanied by the continuo of the choir.

"Renew our days as of old—
Beloved, according to Thy valuation uplift our name—
make us like a garden well-watered—"

"B'tal!" shouted all.

". . . with Dew!"

ISAAC ROSENFELD

✟✟✟

KING SOLOMON

I. WITH HIS WOMEN

EVERY YEAR, A CERTAIN NUMBER OF GIRLS. THEY COME
to him, lie down beside him, place their hands on his breast and offer to
become his slaves.

This goes on all the time. "I will be your slave," say the girls, and no
more need be said. But Solomon's men, his counselors, can't bear it
—what is this power of his? Some maintain it is no power at all, he is
merely the King. Oh yes, admit the rest, his being the King has something to do with it—but there have been other kings, so it can't be
that. Nor is it anything else. Consider how unprepossessing he is, what
a poor impression he makes—why, most of the counselors are taller,
handsomer, and leaner than he. To be sure, he has an excellent voice.
But his voice comes through best on the telephone, and he has an
unlisted number which no one would give out. Certainly not, say the
men. Still the girls keep coming, and they lie down beside him with
their hands on his breast.

It is not enough to say the counselors are jealous. After all, there is
something strange here, the like of it has not been seen. But who shall
explain the King?

Solomon himself makes no comment, he does not speak of his personal affairs. He may drop a hint or two, but these hints are contradictory and vague, and he drops them only for his own amusement;
perhaps he, too, doesn't know. Every few years he publishes a collection
of his sayings, most of which he has never said, but the sayings have
little to do with the case, and their melancholy tone is held to be an

122

affectation. The wisest counselors pay no attention to his words. If anything is to be learned, the wise men say, it had better be sought among his girls.

But the girls also say nothing. The rejected go away in tears—in which case one cannot expect them to speak coherently or with regard for truth; or they are determined yet to win his love—and again they will tell lies. As for the women he accepts, they are useless. Almost at once they become so much like Solomon, adopting his mannerisms of gesture and speech and sharing his views of things, that they say only what he would say—and Solomon does not speak his heart.

So it has become the custom in the court to study Solomon's women in their work; perhaps the manner in which they serve him will make it clear. The counselors watch over the harem, each chooses a woman to follow about the palace, over the grounds and through the town. One woman . . . there she goes! . . . sets out early in the morning with a basket, trailed by a counselor. She makes her way to the largest and most crowded kosher market, where she will stand in line for hours, haggling and hefting, crying highway robbery! And what delicacies does she buy? Surely pickles and spices, the rarest and the best. . . . Not necessarily, it may even be noodles. So who is the wiser? And as for the obvious conclusion—that Solomon sets store by economy—this has long since been drawn. He even lunches on left-overs.

Others clean his shoes, open and sort the mail, tend the garden and the vineyards, keep his instruments polished and in tune: A few go to the well for water—a curious assignment, as the palace has had hot and cold running water for years. Perhaps he sends them to the well on purpose, to confuse the counselors. But if this occupation serves only to deceive, why not all the rest? This may well be the case. King Solomon has a staff of regular servants, quite capable of looking after his needs.

Therefore nothing has been learned. The counselors are always confronted by the same questions at nightfall, when their need to know the King is greatest. Much of the time, he sits quietly with a girl or two, pasting stamps in an album, while they massage his scalp. On festive nights, the counselors note the revelry and participate, when invited, in the dancing and carousing. Not that this enchants them; many counselors complain that the King has no taste in entertainment, that he relies, for instance, too heavily on tambourines, which he has his dancing girls flutter in their hands till the jingling gives one a headache; that much the same or better amusements can be had in the cabarets about the town which—so much for Solomon's originality—have been the source of many a spectacle of the King's court—and they even have newspaper clippings to prove the point. Nevertheless, they succumb to the King's merrymaking, and even if it makes them puke with disdain, still they lose the essential detachment. And then at the hour when the King retires to his chamber with his chosen love, all is lost, the counselors are defeated and go disgruntled to their own quarters, to lie awake or dream enviously through the night.

All the same a pertinacious lot. What stratagems, disguising themselves as eunuchs or hiding in vases or behind the furniture to learn what goes on at night! Here, too, they have been disappointed. Though Solomon burns soft lights beside his couch, no one has witnessed anything—or at least has ever reported what he saw. At the last moment the hidden counselors have shut their eyes or turned away; no one has dared look at the King's nakedness, dared to witness his love. Still, sounds have been heard floating in deep summer air over the garden and the lily pond, mingling with the voices of frogs—but the intrusion has been its own punishment, maddening those who have overheard the King and driving them wild with lust or despair. Sooner or later, the counselors have been compelled to stopper their ears. Now when these sounds issue from the King's apartments, the counselors take up instruments and play, softly but in concert, to hide his sounds within their own.

None has seen the King's nakedness; yet all have seen him in shirt sleeves or suspenders, paunchy, loose-jowled, in need of a trim. Often in the heat of the day he appears bareheaded, and all have looked upon his baldness; sometimes he comes forth in his bare feet, and the men have observed bunions and corns. When he appears in this fashion with, say, a cigar in his mouth and circles under his eyes; his armpits showing yellowish and hairy over the arm holes of his undershirt; his wrinkles deep and his skin slack; a wallet protruding from one hip pocket and a kerchief from the other—at such moments, whether he be concerned with issues of government or merely the condition of the plumbing, he does show himself in human nakedness after all, he is much like any man, he even resembles a policeman on his day off or a small-time gambler. And sometimes, unexpectedly, he summons the cabinet to a game of pinochle—then all are aware he has again transcended them.

Of late, King Solomon has turned his attention to the young. He has organized bicycle races for children, entertained them with magicians, taken them on picnics and excursions to the zoo. He loves to sit on a shady bench with a youngster on either knee, a boy and a girl, about four or five in age. They pull at his beard, tug at his ears, and finger his spectacles till he can no longer see through the smudges. Sometimes, the children are his own, more often not. It makes no difference, the King has many sons and daughters. He tells stories, not nearly so amusing as they should be, old stories which the children grew tired of in the nursery, or poor inventions, rather pointless on the whole. And he seldom finishes a story but begins to nod in the telling, his words thicken and stumble; eventually he falls asleep. Solomon is a disappointment to the young, seldom will children come twice to his garden. Yet for them he is truly a king: robed and gowned, golden-sandaled, wearing a crown, his hair trimmed, his beard washed lustrous, combed, and waved, and the hairs plucked out of his nostrils.

And in this splendor, in which he seldom appears, not even for the reception of ambassadors, he loves to bounce a rubber ball and play catch with the children. He is unskilled at these games, they call him butter-fingers. A man turning sixty, an aging king.

But how clear is the expression of his eyes as he plays with the children—if only one knew what it meant! Perhaps he longs to reveal himself but does not know how; or does not know that the people await this revelation; or is unable to see beyond the children, who are bored with him. Perhaps he has nothing to reveal, and all his wisdom lies scattered from his hand: he is merely this, that, and the other, a few buildings raised, roads leveled, a number of words spoken, unthinking, on an idle afternoon. Occasionally, when he recognizes the expectation of the people, he tries to remember an appropriate saying from one of the collections he has published. Most of the time, he is unaware of all this.

The children are fretful in the garden, they wait to be delivered. They have been brought by mothers, nurses, older sisters, who stand outside the gate, looking through the palings. The mothers and nurses whisper together, their feet and eyes and hands are restless, they look at his shining beard. Later in the afternoon, when the children have been led home, perhaps one of the older girls, one of the sisters, will enter the same garden, approach the spot where the King lies resting, lie down beside him, fold her hands upon his breast, and offer to become his slave.

II. THE QUEEN OF SHEBA

From all over they have come, and they keep coming, though the King is now an old man. It may be owing to his age that he has grown lenient, admitting women to concubinage whom, the counselors swear, he would have sent packing in the old days. He has reached the years when anything young looks good to him. This may not be true, there may be other reasons; but the counselors have a point in saying that the standards have fallen, and they tell the story of the Queen of Sheba.

A letter came, it was the first application to be received by mail. From a foreign country, the woman signed herself The Queen. She flattered Solomon's wisdom, word of which had reached her from afar; her own ears longed to hear his discourse, her own eyes, to behold his person. An unorthodox application, written in a powerful, forward-rushing though feminine hand on strangely scented paper: the King said it reminded him of jungles. He inspected the postmark, clipped off the stamp, and pasted it on a page by itself in his album. His expression was hidden in his beard.

The woman meant it. Boxes began to arrive, plastered with travel stickers. They came on sand-choked, sneezing camels, in long trains, attended by drivers, natives of the Land of Sheba. The next day, more boxes, and again on the third. Gifts of all description, of money and goods, spangles and bangles for the entire court. It made an excellent impression, but Solomon, who distributed the gifts, did not seem pleased. . . . Here the counselors pretend to know the King's mind. First of all, they say, he was annoyed at having to put up so many camels, whole droves of them—his stables were crowded, and there was a shortage of feed for his own animals. Then the camel drivers, rough and barbarous men, were inflamed by the sight of Solomon's women, and the King had to double the guard and pay overtime; this killed him. But their greatest presumption lies in saying that Solomon thought, "*Adonai Elohenu!* Is she coming to stay?" No one knows what the King thought.

He may well have been glad that the Queen was coming. No queen had ever before asked to be his slave—and she was a queen for sure, and of a rich country, think of the gifts she had sent. Solomon put his economists to work and they submitted a report: the financial structure was sound, and the country led in the production of myrrh, pepper and oil. Now to be sure, the Queen's letter made no direct application; apart from the flattery, it merely said, *coming for a visit*, as an equal might say. But the interpretation was clear. An equal would not come uninvited, only one who meant to offer herself would do so—unless the Queen was rude; but the gifts she had sent took care of that. Yet as a queen, writing from her own palace, she could not have expressed the intention, it would have been treason to her own people. Nevertheless, she had every intention: otherwise, why would she have gone to the trouble? The fact is, there was rejoicing in the palace, Solomon himself led the dancing, and he declared a holiday when the Queen of Sheba arrived.

She came in a howdah, on a camel, preceded by troops of archers and trumpeters. Solomon helped her down, and washed and anointed her feet in the courtyard. This didn't come off so well. Sheba used coloring matter on her toenails and the soles of her feet, and the coloring ran; Solomon was out of practice, he tickled her feet a few times and made her laugh. The ceremony was supposed to be a solemn one, the people took it very seriously, and they were offended by her toenails—feet were supposed to be presented dusty: as for the giggling, it was unpardonable, and the priests took offense. A poor set of omens.

Besides, Sheba was not quite so young as the autographed picture, which she had sent in advance to Solomon, would have led one to expect. Her skin was nearly black, and her black hair, which she had apparently made some effort to straighten, had gone frizzled and kinky again in the heat of the desert crossing. She wore anklets of delicate chain, gold bracelets all over her arms, and jewels in both obvious and unexpected places, so that the eye was never done seeing them; their light was kept in constant agitation by the massive rhythm of her breathing, which involved her entire body. A sense of tremendous power and authenticity emanated from her breasts. Some thought she was beautiful, others, not.

No one knows what the King thought; but he may well have felt what everyone else did who came to witness her arrival—drawn, and at the same time, stunned.

But the King is glad in his heart as he leads Sheba to the table, where he has put on a great spread for her. He is attended by his court and surrounded by his women—and how lordly are his movements as he eats meat and rinses his mouth with wine! At the same time he is uneasy in the Queen's presence—after all, this is no maiden lurking in the garden to trip up to him and fold her hands upon his breast. The meal goes well enough: Sheba asks for seconds, and seems impressed with the napkins and silverware. But suddenly, right in the middle of dessert, she turns to him and demands, in front of everyone and that all may hear, that he show her his famous wisdom. This comes as something of a shock. The implication is two-fold: that so far he has spoken commonplaces; and secondly, that he is to suffer no illusions, it was really for the sake of his wisdom that she made the difficult trip. The people turn their eyes on the King, who handles the awkward moment with skill; he clears his throat on schedule, and raises his hand in the usual gesture, admonishing silence. But nothing comes.

In the official account of the visit, which Solomon had written to order, he was supposed to have

. . . told her all questions: There was not anything . . . which he told her not. And when the Queen of Sheba had seen all Solomon's wisdom, and the house that he had built, and the meat of his table and the sitting of his servants . . .

etc.,

there was no more spirit in her. And she said to the King, It was a true report that I heard in mine own land, of thy acts and thy wisdom. Howbeit, I believed not the words, until I came and mine eyes had seen it; and behold, the half was not told me: Thy wisdom and prosperity exceedeth the fame which I heard. Happy are thy men . . . which stand continually before thee and that hear thy wisdom.

After which there was supposed to have been a further exchange of compliments and gifts.

Now this is not only a bit thick, it gets round the question of Solomon's wisdom. What *did* the King say, when put to it by the Queen? That there were so many feet in a mile? That all circles were round? That the number of stars visible on a clear night from a point well out of town was neither more nor less than a certain number? Did he advise her what to take for colds, give her a recipe for salad dressing, or speak of building temples and ships? Just what does a man say under the circumstances?

Certainly, he hadn't the nerve, the gall, to repeat the abominable invention to her face of the two women who disputed motherhood of a child. She would have seen through it right away. And surely he knew this was not the time to quote his sayings; besides, he always had trouble remembering them. Then what did he say?

His economists had worked up a report on the Land of Sheba. He may have sent for a copy; more likely, he knew the essential facts cold, and spoke what came to mind: industry, agriculture, natural resources. Of the financial structure, the public debt, the condition of business. Of the production of pepper, myrrh, and oil, especially oil. Grant him his wisdom.

Certainly, the Queen was impressed, but one need not suppose that the spirit was knocked out of her or that she said, "It was a true report that I heard in mine own land . . ." etc. Chances are, she paid no attention to his words (except to note the drift) but watched him as he spoke, taking in the cut of his beard, the fit of his clothes, and wondering, betimes, what sort of man he was. She saw his initial uncertainty give way and his confidence grow as he reached the meaty part of his delivery. And all along, she observed how he drew on the admiring glances of his girls, soaked up their adoration, as they lay open-mouthed on couches and rugs at his feet, all criticism suspended, incapacitated by love. Love ringed him round, love sustained him, he was the splendid heart of their hearts. She must have forgotten the heat and sand images of the desert crossing, she, too, lapped from all sides and borne gently afloat. . . .

So much, one may imagine. But the Queen spent a number of days or weeks, perhaps even a month or two in the King's company, and of what happened during the time of her stay, let alone the subsequent events of the first night, the official chronicles say nothing. A merciful omission, according to the counselors, who report that it went badly from the start. When the King had finished his discourse, they say the Queen felt called upon to answer. But words failed her, or she felt no need of words: she was the Queen. What she did was to lean forward and, in utter disregard of the company, take his head into her hands, gaze at him for a long time with a smile on her thick lips, and at last bestow on him a kiss, which landed somewhere in his beard.

Then she jumped onto the table, commanded music, and danced among the cups and bowls, the dishes and the crumpled napkins. The counselors were shocked, the girls smirked painfully, the servants held their breath. Nor was Sheba so slender as the autographed picture may have led one to believe. When she set her feet down, the table shook, and the carafes of wine and sweetened water swayed and threatened to topple. Solomon himself hastily cleared a way for her, pushing the dishes to one side; his hands were trembling. But she proceeded with the dance, the chain anklets tinkled, her fingers snapped, the many jewels she wore flashed wealthily. Her toes left marks on the tablecloth, as though animals had run there. And run she did, back and forth over the length of the table, bending over the counselors to tweak this one's nose and that one's ear. But always she glanced back to see if she had the King's eye.

She had it, darker than usual. To her, this meant that he was admiring her, gravely, as befits King and Queen, and her feet quickened. How stern she was! Already she felt the King's love, harder than any courtier's and so much more severe. She increased the tempo, the musicians scrambling to keep up with her, and whirled. Round and round she sped, drawing nearer the end of the table where the King sat. It was a dance in the style of her country, unknown in these parts, and she did it with the abandon of a tribesgirl, though one must assume she was conscious, in her abandonment, that it was she, the Queen, none other than Sheba, who abandoned herself to King Solomon. That was the whole point of it, the mastery of the thing. Pride did not leave her face, it entered her ecstasy and raised it in degree. Already cries, guttural, impersonal, were barking in her throat; then with a final whoop she spun round and threw herself, arms outstretched and intertwined, like one bound captive, to fall before him on the table where his meal had been.

It was a terrible mistake. The women and the counselors knew the King so much better than she, and their hearts went out in pity. The Queen had offered herself in the only way she knew—majesty, power, and reign implied—throwing herself prone with a condescending crash for the King to rise and take her. What presumption! He did not move. He sat infinitely removed, almost sorrowing over this great embarrassment. The music had stopped, there was an unbearable silence in the banquet hall. The King rumbled something deep in his beard; perhaps he was merely clearing his throat, preparatory to saying a few words (if only his wisdom did not fail him!). Some of the servants took it to mean more wine, others, more meat, still others, fingerbowls. They ran in all directions. Sheba lowered herself into her seat at the King's side. Her dark face burned. . . . Somehow the time went by, and the evening was over. Solomon led Sheba off to his chamber, as courtesy demanded. Even as she went with him, it was apparent that she still went in hope; even at the last moment. The older women wept.

Day by day, the strain mounted. Sheba was sometimes with the King, they played chess or listened to the radio, they bent their heads over maps, discussed politics, and played croquet. But there were no festivities and she did not dance again. She bore herself with dignity, but she had grown pale, and her smile, when she forgot herself, was cringing and meek. Sometimes, when she was alone, she was seen to run her finger over the table tops and the woodwork, looking for dust. She could not bear the sight of her waiting women—lest the revival of her hope, as they did her toilet, become apparent to them—and would chase them out of the room; only to call them back, and help her prepare for an audience with the King. Finally, she quarreled with some of the girls of the harem. And when this happened, Sheba knew that the day had come and she began to pack.

A pinochle game was in progress when the Queen of Sheba, unannounced and without knocking, came into the room to say she wanted a word with the King. He dismissed his counselors, but one of them swears he managed to hide behind the draperies, where he witnessed the scene.

The King was in his undershirt, smoking a cigar. He apologized for his dishevelment and offered to repair it. The affairs of state, he explained, were so trying lately, he found he worked better in dishabille. Had he been working? asked the Queen with a smile. She thought this was some sort of game, and she fingered the cards with pictures of kings and queens. Solomon, knowing that women do not play pinochle, told her the cabinet had been in extraordinary session, trying fortunes with the picture cards. The times were good, but one must look to the future, and he offered to show her how it was done.

"No, I don't want to keep you," said the Queen of Sheba, "I beg only a few words."

"Speak," said Solomon.

"Solomon, Solomon," said the Queen, "I am going away. No, don't answer me. You will say something polite and regretful, but my decision can only be a relief to you." She paused, taking on courage. "You must not allow this to be a disappointment to you, you must let me take the whole expense of our emotion upon myself. I did a foolish thing. I am a proud woman, being a Queen, and my pride carried me too far. I thought I would take pride in transcending pride, in offering myself to the King. But still that was pride, you did wisely to refuse me. Yes, you are wise, Solomon, let no one question your wisdom. Yours is the wisdom of love, which is the highest. But your love is love only of yourself; yet you share it with others by letting them love you—and this is next to the highest. Either way you look at it, Solomon is wise enough. Understand me—" She took a step forward, a dance step, as though she were again on the table top, but her eyes spoke a different meaning.

"I am not pleading with you that you love me or allow me to love you. For you are the King, your taking is your giving. But allow me to say, your power rests on despair. Yours is the power of drawing love, the like of which has not been seen. But you despair of loving with your own heart. I have come to tell the King he must not despair. Surely, Solomon who has built temples and made the desert flourish is a powerful king, and he has the power to do what the simplest slave girl or washerwoman of his harem can do—to love with his own heart. And if he does not have this power, it will come to him, he need only accept the love which it is his nature to call forth in everyone, especially in us poor women. This is his glory. Rejoice in it, O King, for you are the King!"

The counselor who hid behind the drapes said he regretted his action, to see how his King stood burdened before the Queen. His own heart filled with loving shame. Solomon looked lost, deprived of his power, as though the years in the palace and the garden had never been. He made an effort to stand dignified in his undershirt, he bore his head as though he were wearing the crown, but it was pitiful to see him.

"The Queen is wise," said he. Then he broke down, and the counselor did not hear his next words. He did hear him say that the Queen was magnificent, that she had the courage of lions and tigers . . . but by now his head was lowered. Suddenly, he clasped the Queen to his breast in an embrace of farewell, and the Queen smiled and stroked his curly beard. They did not immediately take leave of each other, but went on to speak of other matters. Before the Queen of Sheba left the country, King Solomon had leased her oil lands for ninety-nine years.

But on the day of her departure, he stood bareheaded in the crowded courtyard to watch her set out, with her trumpeters and archers mounted on supercilious camels. He extended his hand to help her up, and she, with her free hand, chucked him under the chin. Then she leaned out of the howdah to cry, "Long live the King!" King Solomon stood with bowed head to receive the ovation. Now more than ever they yearned for him.

When Sheba moved off, at the head of the procession, Solomon led the people onto the roof, to watch the camels file across the sand. He stood till evening fell, and the rump of the last plodding animal had twitched out of sight beyond the sand hills. Then he averted his face and wept silently lest the people see their King's tears.

III. WITH HIS FATHERS

So the counselors have a point when they say the standards have fallen. Once the Queen of Sheba herself was unable to make it; and now, look. But no wonder, her like will not come again, and besides, Solomon is old. He has been running the country forty years, and has begun to speak of retiring; but the people know he will never retire, and so they whisper, it is time for the King to die.

How does this strike him? To look at him—his beard is white, his spotted hands shake, he walks bent, his eyes are rheumy and dim—to look at him one would suppose he dwells on the thought of death. But he is no better known now than he was in his prime. The only certainty is that the King is old.

But what follows from this, how does it reveal him? Or this?—that he had an attack of pleurisy not long ago, and since then his side has been taped. And what does it mean to say that he now has more women than ever cluttering up the palace, one thousand in all, including seven hundred wives? (It is merely that the standards have fallen?) It was necessary to tear down the harem (while the women, to everyone's displeasure, were quartered in the town) and raise a new building, so large it has taken up ground formerly allotted to the garden. They are a great source of trouble to him, these women, and the counselors complain—that's where all the money is going, to support the harem. Harem? Why, it's a whole population, the country will be ruined! And the priests complain, every week they send fresh ultimatums, objecting to the fact that so many of Solomon's girls are heathen; they have even accused him of idolatry and threatened him with loss of the Kingdom and the wrath of God. And the people grumble, it's a shame, when they find his women loitering in beauty shops or quarreling right out in the open, as they have begun to do, in the very streets. But Solomon ignores the discontent and goes on collecting women as he once collected stamps.

Why? Or what does this mean?—that he seldom takes the trouble to interview applicants, but establishes a policy for several months, during which time the rule is, no vacancies. Then he will change the rule and take on newcomers by the dozen, most of whom he does not even see, the work being done by the counselors. And how complicated the work has become, compared with the old days, when all that was necessary was for a girl to lie beside the King with her hands upon his breast. Now there are forms to fill out and letters of recommendation to obtain, several interviews and a medical examination to go through, and even then the girls must wait until their references have been checked. The filing cabinets have mounted to the ceiling. What sense does it make?

And above all in view of the following? The counselors vouch for it, they swear they have seen the proof. That King Solomon now takes to bed, not with a virgin, as his father, David, did in his old age, or even with a dancing girl, but with a hot water bottle. If this report is true, then doesn't something follow? For this is the extreme, between life and death, where all thoughts meet; an extreme, not a mean; and a wrong guess is impossible, everything is true, as at the topmost point, where all direction is down. It follows that he warms his hands on the water bottle, presses it to his cheek, passes it down along his belly.

Now when he thinks of his pride, he of all men must wonder: what was the glory of the King? Who bestowed the power, and what did it consist in? When he had it, he did not consider, and now it is gone. Passing the rubber bottle down to his feet and digging with his toes for warmth, he sees he did everything possible in his life, and left no possibility untouched, of manhood, statesmanship, love. What else can a man do? There is no answer. Except to say, he was in God's grace then? And now no longer? Or is he still in a state of grace, witness the water bottle at his feet? And perhaps he is only being tried, and may look forward to even greater rewards? Such are the advantages of being a believer. If he were one, he would know—at least believe that he knew. But a man who knows only that once love was with him, which now is no more—what does he know, what shall he believe, old, exhausted, shivering alone in bed at night with a hot water bottle, when all's quiet in the palace? And if all's not quiet, that's no longer his concern.

No, if there were any rewards, he'd settle for a good night's sleep. But sleep does not come. He hears strange noises in the apartment, scratching. . . . Mice? He must remember to speak to the caretakers. . . . At last he drowses off, to sleep a while. And if he does not sleep? Or later, when he wakes, and it is still the same night? . . . Does he think of the Queen of Sheba and wonder, whom is she visiting now? Does he remember how she danced upon the table? Or the song he wrote soon after her departure, with her words still fresh in his mind, when he resolved to pour out his love for her, but from the very first line poured out, instead, her love for him? *Let him kiss me with the kisses of his mouth, for thy love is better than wine.* It has been years since he heard from her. . . .

Meanwhile, the bottle has grown cold. Shall he ring for another? He shifts the bottle, kneads it between his knees. *And be thou like a young hart upon the mountains of spices.* Look forward, look back, to darkness, at the light, both ways blind. He raises the bottle to his breast; it does not warm him. He gropes for the cord, and while his hand reaches, he thinks, as he has thought so many times, there is a time and a season for everything, a time to be born and a time to die. Is it time now? They will lay him out, washed, anointed, shrouded. They will fold his arms across his chest, with the palms turned in, completing the figure. Now his own hands will lie pressed to his breast, and he will sleep with his fathers.

GRACE PALEY

THE LOUDEST VOICE

THERE IS A CERTAIN PLACE WHERE DUMB-WAITERS boom, doors slam, dishes crash; every window is a mother's mouth bidding the street shut up, go skate somewhere else, come home. My voice is the loudest.

There, my own mother is still as full of breathing as me and the grocer stands up to speak to her. "Mrs. Abramowitz," he says, "people should not be afraid of their children."

"Ah, Mr. Bialik," my mother replies, "if you say to her or her father 'Ssh,' they say, 'In the grave it will be quiet.'"

"From Coney Island to the cemetery," says my papa. "It's the same subway; it's the same fare."

I am right next to the pickle barrel. My pinky is making tiny whirl-pools in the brine. I stop a moment to announce: "Campbell's Tomato Soup. Campbell's Vegetable Beef Soup. Campbell's S-c-otch Broth . . ."

"Be quiet," the grocer says, "the labels are coming off."

"Please, Shirley, be a little quiet," my mother begs me.

In that place the whole street groans: Be quiet! Be quiet! but steals from the happy chorus of my inside self not a tittle or a jot.

There, too, but just around the corner, is a red brick building that has been old for many years. Every morning the children stand before it in double lines which must be straight. They are not insulted. They are waiting anyway.

I am usually among them. I am, in fact, the first, since I begin with "A."

One cold morning the monitor tapped me on the shoulder. "Go

136

to Room 409, Shirley Abramowitz," he said. I did as I was told. I
went in a hurry up a down staircase to Room 409, which contained
sixth-graders. I had to wait at the desk without wiggling until Mr.
Hilton, their teacher, had time to speak.

After five minutes he said, "Shirley?"

"What?" I whispered.

He said, "My! My! Shirley Abramowitz! They told me you had a
particularly loud, clear voice and read with lots of expression. Could
that be true?"

"Oh yes," I whispered.

"In that case, don't be silly; I might very well be your teacher
someday. Speak up, speak up."

"Yes," I shouted.

"More like it," he said. "Now, Shirley, can you put a ribbon in
your hair or a bobby pin? It's too messy."

"Yes!" I bawled.

"Now, now, calm down." He turned to the class. "Children, not
a sound. Open at page 39. Read till 52. When you finish, start again."
He looked me over once more. "Now, Shirley, you know, I suppose,
that Christmas is coming. We are preparing a beautiful play. Most
of the parts have been given out. But I still need a child with a strong
voice, lots of stamina. Do you know what stamina is? You do? Smart
kid. You know, I heard you read 'The Lord is my shepherd' in Assem-
bly yesterday. I was very impressed. Wonderful delivery. Mrs. Jordan,
your teacher, speaks highly of you. Now listen to me, Shirley Abramowitz, if you want to take the part and be in the play, repeat after
me, 'I swear to work harder than I ever did before.'"

I looked to heaven and said at once, "Oh, I swear." I kissed my
pinky and looked at God.

"That is an actor's life, my dear," he explained. "Like a soldier's,
never tardy or disobedient to his general, the director. Everything,"
he said, "absolutely everything will depend on you."

That afternoon, all over the building, children scraped and scrubbed
the turkeys and the sheaves of corn off the schoolroom windows. Goodbye Thanksgiving. The next morning a monitor brought red paper
and green paper from the office. We made new shapes and hung them
on the walls and glued them to the doors.

The teachers became happier and happier. Their heads were ringing
like the bells of childhood. My best friend Evie was prone to evil, but
she did not get a single demerit for whispering. We learned "Holy

Night" without an error. "How wonderful!" said Miss Glacé, the student teacher. "To think that some of you don't even speak the language!" We learned "Deck the Halls" and "Hark! The Herald Angels". . . . They weren't ashamed and we weren't embarrassed.

Oh, but when my mother heard about it all, she said to my father: "Misha, you don't know what's going on there. Cramer is the head of the Tickets Committee."

"Who?" asked my father. "Cramer? Oh yes, an active woman."

"Active? Active has to have a reason. Listen," she said sadly, "I'm surprised to see my neighbors making tra-la-la for Christmas."

My father couldn't think of what to say to that. Then he decided: "You're in America! Clara, you wanted to come here. In Palestine the Arabs would be eating you alive. Europe you had pogroms. Argentina is full of Indians. Here you got Christmas. . . . Some joke, ha?"

"Very funny, Misha. What is becoming of you? If we came to a new country a long time ago to run away from tyrants, and instead we fall into a creeping pogrom, that our children learn a lot of lies, so what's the joke? Ach, Misha, your idealism is going away."

"So is your sense of humor."

"That I never had, but idealism you had a lot of."

"I'm the same Misha Abramovitch, I didn't change an iota. Ask anyone."

"Only ask me," says my mama, may she rest in peace. "I got the answer."

Meanwhile the neighbors had to think of what to say too.

Marty's father said: "You know, he has a very important part, my boy."

"Mine also," said Mr. Sauerfeld.

"Not my boy!" said Mrs. Klieg. "I said to him no. The answer is no. When I say no! I mean no!"

The rabbi's wife said, "It's disgusting!" But no one listened to her. Under the narrow sky of God's great wisdom she wore a strawberry-blond wig.

Every day was noisy and full of experience. I was Right-hand Man. Mr. Hilton said: "How could I get along without you, Shirley?"

He said: "Your mother and father ought to get down on their knees every night and thank God for giving them a child like you."

He also said: "You're absolutely a pleasure to work with, my dear, dear child."

Sometimes he said: "For God's sakes, what did I do with the script? Shirley! Shirley! Find it."

Then I answered quietly: "Here it is, Mr. Hilton."

Once in a while, when he was very tired, he would cry out: "Shirley, I'm just tired of screaming at those kids. Will you tell Ira Pushkov not to come in till Lester points to that star the second time?"

Then I roared: "Ira Pushkov, what's the matter with you? Dope! Mr. Hilton told you five times already, don't come in till Lester points to that star the second time."

"Ach, Clara," my father asked, "what does she do there till six o'clock she can't even put the plates on the table?"

"Christmas," said my mother coldly.

"Ho! Ho!" my father said. "Christmas. What's the harm? After all, history teaches everyone. We learn from reading this is a holiday from pagan times also, candles, lights, even Chanukah. So we learn it's not altogether Christian. So if they think it's a private holiday, they're only ignorant, not patriotic. What belongs to history, belongs to all men. You want to go back to the Middle Ages? Is it better to shave your head with a secondhand razor? Does it hurt Shirley to learn to speak up? It does not. So maybe someday she won't live between the kitchen and the shop. She's not a fool."

I thank you, Papa, for your kindness. It is true about me to this day. I am foolish but I am not a fool.

That night my father kissed me and said with great interest in my career, "Shirley, tomorrow's your big day. Congrats."

"Save it," my mother said. Then she shut all the windows in order to prevent tonsillitis.

In the morning it snowed. On the street corner a tree had been decorated for us by a kind city administration. In order to miss its chilly shadow our neighbors walked three blocks east to buy a loaf of bread. The butcher pulled down black window shades to keep the colored lights from shining on his chickens. Oh, not me. On the way to school, with both my hands I tossed it a kiss of tolerance. Poor thing, it was a stranger in Egypt.

I walked straight into the auditorium past the staring children. "Go ahead, Shirley!" said the monitors. Four boys, big for their age, had already started work as propmen and stagehands.

Mr. Hilton was very nervous. He was not even happy. Whatever he started to say ended in a sideward look of sadness. He sat slumped in the middle of the front row and asked me to help Miss Glacé. I did this, although she thought my voice too resonant and said, "Show-off!"

Parents began to arrive long before we were ready. They wanted to make a good impression. From among the yards of drapes I peeked out at the audience. I saw my embarrassed mother.

Ira, Lester, and Meyer were pasted to their beards by Miss Glacé. She almost forgot to thread the star on its wire, but I reminded her. I coughed a few times to clear my throat. Miss Glacé looked around and saw that everyone was in costume and on line waiting to play his part. She whispered, "All right . . ." Then:

Jackie Sauerfeld, the prettiest boy in first grade, parted the curtains with his skinny elbow and in a high voice sang out:

> "Parents dear
> We are here
> To make a Christmas play in time.
> It we give
> In narrative
> And illustrate with pantomime."

He disappeared.

My voice burst immediately from the wings to the great shock of Ira, Lester, and Meyer, who were waiting for it but were surprised all the same.

"I remember, I remember, the house where I was born . . ."

Miss Glacé yanked the curtain open and there it was, the house—an old hayloft, where Celia Kornbluh lay in the straw with Cindy Lou, her favorite doll. Ira, Lester, and Meyer moved slowly from the wings toward her, sometimes pointing to a moving star and sometimes ahead to Cindy Lou.

It was a long story and it was a sad story. I carefully pronounced all the words about my lonesome childhood, while little Eddie Braunstein wandered upstage and down with his shepherd's stick, looking for sheep. I brought up lonesomeness again, and not being understood at all except by some women everybody hated. Eddie was too small for that and Marty Groff took his place, wearing his father's prayer shawl. I announced twelve friends, and half the boys in the fourth grade gathered round Marty, who stood on an orange crate while my voice harangued. Sorrowful and loud, I declaimed about love and God and Man, but because of the terrible deceit of Abie Stock we came suddenly to a famous moment. Marty, whose remembering tongue I was, waited at the foot of the cross. He stared desperately at the audience. I groaned, "My God, my God, why hast thou forsaken me?" The soldiers who were sheiks grabbed poor Marty to pin him up to die, but he wrenched free, turned again to the audience, and spread his arms aloft to show despair and the end. I murmured at the top of my voice, "The rest is silence, but as everyone in this room, in this city—in this world —now knows, I shall have life eternal."

That night Mrs. Kornbluh visited our kitchen for a glass of tea.

"How's the virgin?" asked my father with a look of concern.

"For a man with a daughter, you got a fresh mouth, Abramovitch."

"Here," said my father kindly, "have some lemon, it'll sweeten your disposition."

They debated a little in Yiddish, then fell in a puddle of Russian and Polish. What I understood next was my father, who said, "Still and all, it was certainly a beautiful affair, you have to admit, introducing us to the beliefs of a different culture."

"Well, yes," said Mrs. Kornbluh. "The only thing . . . you know Charlie Turner—that cute boy in Celia's class—a couple others? They got very small parts or no part at all. In very bad taste, it seemed to me. After all, it's their religion."

"Ach," explained my mother, "what could Mr. Hilton do? They got very small voices; after all, why should they holler? The English language they know from the beginning by heart. They're blond like angels. You think it's so important they should get in the play? Christmas . . . the whole piece of goods . . . they own it."

I listened and listened until I couldn't listen any more. Too sleepy, I climbed out of bed and kneeled. I made a little church of my hands and said, "Hear, O Israel . . ." Then I called out in Yiddish, "Please, good night, good night. Ssh." My father said, "Ssh yourself," and slammed the kitchen door.

I was happy. I fell asleep at once. I had prayed for everybody: my talking family, cousins far away, passers-by, and all the lonesome Christians. I expected to be heard. My voice was certainly the loudest.

IVAN GOLD

✝✝✝

TAUB EAST

I

A THOUSAND YARDS SOUTH OF FENOLLOSA'S GRAVE IS A granite gas chamber too seldom and casually used to instil much terror, and four hundred yards to the northeast, down out of the hills, lies a white-washed chapel. This building is distinguished from fifteen others of similar appearance and size by the bronze crucifix rising thirty feet above the gabled doorway; also by proximity to the gym, the theater, and the service club. This last marks it as meant to see service during a leisure hour. The cluster of four buildings is separated from the workaday bulk of the camp by a closely cropped rectangular green, sometimes used as a parade field, and the whole nestles prim and swept at the foot of the tangled mountain. PX, bus depot, and BOQ lie across the road, escaping the orbit of the hills.

Dusk assaults Camp Hara as well as the town: charges down from the mountain, rolls in from the lake, and outflanks the daylight. Spidery foliage and black rooftops take on that diaphanous sheen recognizable from a thousand paintings and sometimes confused with technique, but it is something which happens to the air. Dusk covers the excursion boats moored at the lakeside pier, the high aluminum dome which makes an arcade of Hama-Hara's shopping street; it surrounds the radio tower and pummels the tiled roof of the chapel (for all camp buildings are topped off in local style); and dusk provides Taub a sign he relies on more closely than on his almanac; so he turns from his fat lawyer friend, Robert Helver, and clears his throat to greet the Sabbath Bride.

142

He has now been abetting her unorthodox entry into Hara for a little over a year.

Taub presides weekly with a poise and skill he once begrudged the congregation, not for being crumbs but lacking always two to three crumbs of a *Minyan*, the ten-man cachet. One does not hold eight-man services in Hassidic circles, nor even in Reformed; collects at least ten souls or regretfully, in time, disperses the flock to better-trafficked synagogues. But the Army at home and abroad is not the Bronx and the stylized tremolos he tickled from his chest, the sweet falsetto moan he tortured from his throat, he tickled and tortured (in any event) for the multitude: the unmarried and the undead and their relatives in heated temples and by windswept tombs at the thousand wakes and weddings that would one day turn upon his saucy baritone—laboring incidentally for the seven men who face his back this February night, restless eyes hindered by opaque saints from mingling with the dusk, scratching gibbon sides and waiting for the wine.

All the same, he is not undismayed; tonight as always he had personally corralled the light-headed seven behind him, combing barracks and day room and service club in the weekly cajoling burlesque, the doomed dutiful attempt to convene ten or more. So he is fortunate that his complex theology permits him (in his mind) to make the adjustment required.

"*Boey vshalom*," boomed Taub, and revolved to face them as the prayer required. "The congregation will please rise," he inserted with almost too much unction for his own taste in the circumstances; he was impelled to smile sweetly at Helver, and at Popkin by his side.

"He sings very nice," said the older man.

"He sings very nice? Jesus. He's practically a rabbi."

"I know that," said Popkin. "We sleep in the same lousy room."

And only the anonymous five are in any way genuine. Popkin was purchased. Helver is his friend.

"The concluding prayer over the wine, page 217," acquired from my own pocket and what all you *gonifs* came for; let them sip from the silver cup wrought for his grandfather in a dead city named Vilna; all dynasties end.

"Nice service, Lyle," said a man returning to the Zone of the Interior next week, which is home. "Thank you I was a trifle off," said Taub. "Howbeit I'm glad you enjoyed."

He is no malcontent; though life is a patchwork of surprises. Through the early months he shaped events and became chaplain's assistant in Georgia. He made inroads into the substantial civilian community in those parts until one day he was shipped out, eight thousand miles from Atlanta. He began again from scratch before he discovered there was no Jewish chaplain at Hara for him to be assistant to. Himself was put in charge, an additional duty without privilege, basically rewarding but different from what he had in mind.

"Come again," Taub whispers after the retreating tribe. "Next week, champagne."

But dusk succumbs rapidly too; the lake suddenly mirrors the mountains (if there is a moon), and only the twinkle and shimmer from the officers' club, up in the hills, between the gas chamber and the scholar's grave, can disturb E. Fenollosa's remains. There is one more ghost to lay, that not so simple: within the camp itself, between mess hall and dispensary, on a slight rise in a treed-in enclosure which is off limits to all military personnel, is buried a brief-tenured, legitimate seventh-century emperor and this man is bathed in light—from the mess hall, the barracks, the bowling alley, and his is the greater irony: for Fenollosa lies at last within easy reach of his own color and kind.

From a synagogue on Friday night a man ordinarily goes home to the evening meal and the dutiful wife who has prepared it, but (it is worth repeating) we are a long way from home. A rare enlisted man wins, or wages, a battle with the mess hall, and Taub ate prior to his service between the daylight hours of five and six with the rest of the troops and did not feel put-upon. The snack bar stayed open nightly until ten-thirty, serving outrageous food at impossible prices, but by seven-twenty Taub was on the rocky convex road, bouncing round the familiar turning across which the great bent tree threw its shadow, older than the town itself; accompanied by Helver, directed toward a home, a hearth, the heart of a low strange city where the Sabbath never touched.

"Kazuko expects us," Helver said.

"That's excellent," sonorous still; the numinous feeling ebbs slowly, confabulation with the Hebrew God. "And how is the shackrat's dream?"

"I worry," says Helver, and it's clear he worries, in his lardy, laughable body. "She's very possessive now, hardly lets me go anywhere." He worries, puffed with pride, this ugly, unlovable career man. Yet is he loved? No sweat, regard the girl. From the pits of a society whose pits

are slimier than our own. She loves him? She gets more from him each
month than a professor receives in a year. So she loves him. But irony,
contempt, are misplaced here, Helver is his friend.

"When is the wedding?" They moved past blind alleys, tinsel cabarets; a sweet shop, an old man glimpsed through a doorless doorway at
a cobbler's last, gray hair cropped close as Popkin's, over the ancient
bridge, the putrid canal, toward the house where Helver lived in sin
with an animal it was all too simple to explain. "When is the blessed
event?" pursues Taub.

"Who knows? It's not out of the question. I could do worse, I already have."

This he claims, impossible to love or not: he has been married before.

"You could," say Taub, but he does not believe it. This pig has
killed a man. In Washington, he was an MP then, guarding a prisoner
who reached into his pocket for a concealed weapon or a handkerchief
(Helver tells this story on himself). The criminal took eight slugs from
a carbine set on automatic in fleshy parts of the body, so face to the
ground clutched about in his pockets still; this wily wolf, fangs lost in
corpulence, reloaded in panic and pumped a few more in the back of
the head; emerged unjailed from a court-martial but was transferred
from the MPs to pursue the law career for which Wisconsin U. had
originally prepared him. Turned career man, stationed the past seven
years in Japan.

". . . don't let her do the laundry. I take it to the quartermaster, I
think she has enough work to do. So all that happens is she gets suspicious, she thinks I'm keeping another girl."

Butcher! You're kind, don't let your *kourve* do the laundry? "I'll tell
you a joke I just received from a friend in the States," say Taub. "It's
nicely apropos."

Once a GI is sent home unexpectedly from overseas. He is a New
Yorker of the Hebrew persuasion, who, on leaving the boat, phones up
home.

—Hello, Mom? It's Joe. I'm in New York.

—Joe, you're really in New York? Discharged? You're not hurt?
Come home!

—I'm on the way. Mom. There's just one thing I have to tell you
first.

—What is it sweetheart?

—I'm married. I married a girl overseas.

—Married? You didn't even write about it. You married a girl overseas? Wonderful. Come home with the wife.

—There's just one more thing. My wife is a Japanese.

—Yes, in the papers, I read about it all the time. Lots of youngsters, they go abroad, they're lonely, they marry Japanese girls. But you're all right, Joey? Back from China, and not hurt or anything? That's all that matters.

—I'm fine, Mom. I was hoping you'd feel this way.

—How else is there to feel?

—We've got a baby, a year old, a little girl.

—Naturally. With marriage comes children, this is news? Ach, a grandmother. Who would believe it? Come home now Joey, the entire family.

—Swell, Mom, right away. I haven't much money, no plans as yet, we were hoping we could stay with you for a while.

—*Stay* with us? This is how you talk? This is your home. You live here as long as you like. You and the wife take your old room, Papa stays where he is, and the baby sleeps in your Mama's room. No problem will present itself.

—Sounds all right, Mom, for Mariko and myself . . .

—Mariko? Your wife? A *sheina* name!

—But if the baby sleeps in your bed, where will you sleep?

—Yussel, love, don't be concerned. When we disconnect I'm going to shoot myself.

Helver had a live one, come to him two years earlier with a bed and household goods (she never claimed to be a virgin). He was a sergeant even then, and they added PX mirrors and chairs and a blond bureau bought in town. Kazuko, to the bargain, had a decorative eye. Taub had long before conceded, it was pleasant for a shack, as distinct from Popkin's frayed-mat, nightsoil-smelling place near the camp (but Popkin lived with an attractive girl). Helver made no bones about it, he loved his happy home. Taub lived in the barracks (he was in fact his "room sergeant") because he happened to prefer it, but he understood the shackers (raunchy slobs, lonely swine). Helver chuckled.

"That's a very Jewish joke."

"No doubt," Taub said, unflurried by the compliment.

They ascended the almost vertical stairway and popped into the cozy room.

"Please to see you," offers Kazuko to her man's companion. She is over the hill all right, but has never seen better days. In her wrinkled brownie's face Taub sees that, all things being equal, native politeness will just barely cloak her fondest wish: that Helver had come home alone.

"You bring sackey, *ne!*" says Buddha, with acquired Eastern bluster; creases his short legs and drops to the floor. He loosens his belt so his monstrous belly tumbles free; Kazuko is no lightweight too. Image of elephants doing it, the poor bed at night. Taub regards it, condoles.

"And what's new at Finance?" Helver asks.

"Popkin came in for an advance on tomorrow's pay this afternoon, but I couldn't help him. Lieutenant Frick left explicit orders."

"I gave him five hundred tonight."

"Popkin?"

"Yeah. He put the bite on me before the service."

The girl returned from below with a tray bearing *sake,* cups, peanuts and peas.

"*Sake* is an acquired taste," says Taub, handling the word with elaborate care (Helver murders it). "I don't believe I have ever really acquired it." He elevates the cup.

"*Kampai,*" he smiles, and clinks his own against Kazuko's thimble-sized cup.

"*Kampai,*" she toasts, and grimaces in turn, though she is too dense to be impressed by his respect for the idiom, to observe how much he has absorbed, in a year, of the culture and the tongue.

"I think he's a bit paranoid," Helver breaks in on the scene; "he's got the idea Frick is sleeping with his girl."

"You know for a fact Frick isn't?"

"It's highly unlikely. He's just been reprimanded by the colonel, I happen to know, for making the EM bar and whore circuit. He's apt to be being careful."

"Ah? Well. If Frick isn't, someone else probably is. Popkin has no luck. Drunk, misfit, he's the backbone of the Army. He must continually suffer, official and off-duty pain. The military *must,* to function, crucify its own."

Thesis, and image, are equally bold. Kazuko, the *sake* poured, sits dully and regards the floor.

"Why you no talk?" Helver asks. "You bashful? You know Lyle long time, he good *tomodachi.* You very quiet tonight, don't you."

Now she shows her teeth, food and dull gold.

"The cat's got her tongue," says Taub. He undoes his belt, gives his own belly room. But he is not really enjoying himself. The couple swap infantile, rapturous smiles. Lord, the slut must be thirty-five, three years Helver's senior (eleven his own). A pig in any tongue. "So close to the end of the month," he says, "I wonder, is it quiet in town?"

"More sackey, *ne?*" Helver prods her gently and she moves to obey. But she looks reproachfully at Taub; more than reproach, almost the opposite of love. Well she divines the tenor of his last remark (and well he knows she does, the bitch, pariahs understand each other—he does not shrink from this explanation of their mutual perspicacity).

Well she is absent now (but not for long) and he makes his move.

"Did you mean to sit up here all night?"

"Yeah, why? You restless?"

"Come. Jackie's for a beer. Amusement by Akemichan."

"Don't really need it. Kaz will blow her stack. I haven't any yen anyway, to coin a phrase." But he can be had, Taub believes: he can spoil the scene for the fat man by expressing displeasure.

"A ball and chain," he jokes weightily, "God help you. Poor *lansman,* traded in his freedom for a piece of ass."

Helver grins. Such language costs Taub an effort, he knows; he thinks he feels something of the host's onus, too.

"Well, maybe for a quick drink. If Kaz will lend me the yen. She doesn't like me out on the town."

"Naturally not," says Taub.

Up the stairs burdened by refreshments comes the ample peasant girl, barefoot, looking great from behind. Neither subtle nor delightful, she clatters the tray onto the low table, and only once in the next ten minutes will her black deadly eyes light on Taub.

"You go downtown?"

"Ears in the back of her head," says Helver, with an owner's love. "Yes honey, maybe I go with buddy catch one beer. Okay, *ne,* come back home soon. No have Japanese money, you lend me thousand yen, okay?"

"My no have," she says brightly. She will certainly use this unexpected luck.

"I could spare a hundred," Taub says doubtfully.

"Honey, you lie to me," Helver says gravely. "Yesterday I give you three thousand, impossible you already spend. You tell lie, I think. Lend me one thousand yen now, *ne!*"

"Why you want drink bar? Have plenty drink in house. I can go buy more."

Inviting praise, Helver cocks a brow at Taub; she's right, you know. "Kaz," he says, "no have to worry. *Shimpai nai.* You think I go whorehouse? That is what you think, *ne?* Never happen. I go have one drink cabaret, come back home."

"Why you want thousan, beer price hunner eighty. You go bar, I can go too."

"That would change the picture," laughs Taub, and it is here she nails him with her brilliant blackeyed rage.

"*Go men nasai,*" he says—he is more shaken than he shows. "But you must be aware of the feelings toward other females of the girls who work in bars."

"You give me five hundred yen," says Helver. "Maybe want drink *two* beers. *Hayaku!* I no go whorehouse, honey, honest to god. Only go have lousy beer."

A snicker comes from Taub.

Involving (she knows) Buddha's pride. "You come home soon?" she says bitterly.

"Honey you know it," Helver replies.

From her bosom she extracts a brown roll of notes from which she peels four which Helver presses to his lips, then counts. The girl anticipates: "Four hundred yen enough you can buy two beers." Helver is really touched by this. "Honey," he says, "you can give me four *thousand* yen, I no never go whorehouse."

Cumulative sentiment and syntax prove too much for Taub. "*Ojama shimashita,*" he says roundly, and makes to depart; he even bows a little. He has learned the right formulae in his time (he owns a text called *Japanese in a Hurry*), and truly, he thinks, he has committed a nuisance by luring her mate to face the ripe temptations of Hara's nighttime world. Poor girl, she is also luckless, he commiserates; shoeshiner for the Outcasts, awryly matched against their king.

On the cool road, under a sometime moon:

"Let me say this, Bob. She'll never learn English if you also use that horrible pidgin. Speak correctly, she'll start to do so too."

"Maybe," Helver grins. "But who knows how long we're going to live?"

II

The five hundred yen in PFC Popkin's pocket when he left the chapel that night was that much more than he thought he would need. While there was nothing he wanted to buy, an empty wallet made him feel naked, or out of uniform. That was why he applied for an advance at the Finance Office, that was also why he was refused. With the loss of three stripes and one hundred fifty dollars went certain less obvious humiliations. They knew what they were doing. After twenty-one years with the Army, three court-martials and countless instances of company punishment, Popkin knew what they were doing too. With Helver's help he thwarted them. They might bust him and levy a fine; they could not leave him naked while he still had a friend.

Popkin was fond of wine. Wine frequently undid him, but he learned nothing from punishment. He needed no capital tonight to satisfy his thirst, piqued pleasantly by the toast in the chapel. Three bottles of Akadama, a cheap port-type native brew, were stored beneath his and Reiko's bed, in the house along the blind dirt road which formed Camp Hara's northern boundary. He moved now toward this hoard, through the ragged gap in the wire fence behind the service club.

He felt no pain. The lake banked in to a point thirty yards from where he passed, and he sniffed the night air, rising to combat the dungy odors of the daylight. Out of the star-pricked sky that canopied the foreign night the Big Dipper rushed to meet him, balanced crazily on its head, like a man's close friend he has never seen drunk before. A PFC at forty-five, he was his own man still, in a strange, peacetime world. Up the road he had his grape and girl. Life was definitely bearable. On impulse, he retraced a few yards to a small shop. With the five hundred yen he bought a bottle of Ocean Whiskey, which he stuffed into his back pocket. Reiko didn't drink much, but liked whiskey when she did. So there was the borrowed money now, doing considerably more than soothing his pride; there was never a time when you couldn't hit on something useful to buy. The whiskey would be a peace offering. He wouldn't hand it over right away. First he would evoke the impassioned denials concerning her and Lieutenant Frick, only this time he would decide to believe her.

The house was in a clearing behind the road, led to by a narrow lane. It was ancient, smelly, in disrepair, but stocked for him with six months of memories. At the mouth of the alley squatted their neighbor, an old woman, blocking his passage, her kimono up about her ears. She ignored him until she was done. Then she stuggled upright and clutched his arm.

Reichan iahen yo." Her face worked wildly. "*Gō Kyoto tempurr.*"

"That's all right, so's you don't wet yourself." He pulled free and continued down the alley. The dark, sealed hulk lopped the warmth from him, a scythe-stroke he could almost hear.

She was not home. He had left his key inside. He drew close and yanked on the padlock, without hope. She knew his Friday schedule, she should have been home. He dropped onto a tree stump a few yards from the door. He knew he was wasting his time: if she was only shopping, or at the restaurant, she would not have locked up so completely, would have left a light burning inside. All the same he'd sit and wait a quarter of an hour.

The woman approached and gripped his arm. She croaked, *"Tempurr, tempurr."* She gestured vaguely toward the hills. She had something on her mind but he could not be bothered by her. She spoke no English, she was impossibly old. "Temper, temper," he aped. "Easy to give advice. But she ought to be home."

"Osō made kaette kiahen wa. Mattara akan." She grimaced; without teeth, or context, Popkin took it as a smile. He returned it. He took off his steel-rimmed spectacles, ran over the lenses with a khaki handkerchief. The whiskey made sitting uncomfortable. He drew it from his pocket. If there had been a way to get in the house, at the wine, he would not have minded this so much. He spun the bottle in his hand, ripped off the wrapping, and unscrewed the cap. He took a long pull. He wiped the neck with the handkerchief and handed the bottle to the woman, who squatted beside him.

She waved her hand in front of her face. *"Mamasan nomahen."*

"Just this once. A special favor. Don't make me drink this crud alone."

"Sukoshi itadakimasu." She received the bottle in two withered hands and raised it to her mouth. *"Oishikatta,"* she said, returning it. Her finger went to the single strip of cloth at his elbow; she tentatively brushed his steely crop. *"Kawaisō da, na,"* she said.

"No sweat, lady," Popkin said. "I've been better before. That's the story of my life in fact. I shuttle between private, sergeant first class."

"No spiku inlis," the old woman said.

"Maybe so," Popkin said. "But this time was different from the other times. It ain't that I was drunk on duty, I just never came in. I was completely covered so far as I knew. It was a midweek midnight shift, maybe three messages will arrive, nothin' goes out. Nance agrees to handle it all, the corporal, if I give him off next time we share mids. Naturally. I stay shacked and I rest up and drink my wine.

"So guess who is in the officers' club till two a.m.? Yessir, my buddy

Frick, sir. Plastered. Has a terrible urge to shoot the shit with the midnight crew, though he has never turned up after five-thirty before.
Naturally he wants the tricks chief, Nance says I'm out for coffee. He
waits. He sobers up. Boom, an AWOL charge."

"*Mō sukoshi kuremahen ka?*"

"What? This? *Dōzo.* Don't look like there's much left to celebrate
tonight." He gave her the whiskey, took it back and drank himself. It
scorched his throat, burned his belly, but was better than nothing at all.

"A special court. Not even a warning first. My first offense in this
country, and I got my last two stripes in frozen Chosen. (Our playboy
friend has never been to Korea.) Busted almost all the way down. They
don't even transfer me after. Hara needs its signal personnel; Frick
don't know ass from elbow. Son of a bitch. Reiko's friend."

She recalled her charge. "*Reichan kiahen wa,*" she whined. "*Gō
Kyoto tempurr.*"

"I don't know," Popkin said. "Naturally, she denies it. I was ready
to believe her. But if she ain't with him tonight, where in hell can she
be?"

The night he told her he was a PFC Reiko hit him, that was how
mad she was. "You a crazy old man! No care about me, about Army,
only care about wine."

"Now simmer down and take it easy. . . ."

"Take it easy? You like someone take it easy you better catch other
girl."

"It wasn't my fault. He didn't have to do it. I know for a fact now
there was no traffic that night. He was drunk, he had to feel his balls."

"Lutenan Frick do his job. When sergeant suppose to go work, he
go work. Not tell lie about night off, stay with me, get stinko, make
love. If now I go catch lutenan only one night, make more money,
deshō, than stay one month with you."

"Try it."

"I no scared of you. You think I scared? I know him longer time
than you, many time he come see me when I work in Pedro's bar."

"So you and he . . ."

"I know him long time before meet you," she said. "He not happy
with wife, come Pedro's bar. Why? You worry now? If still SFC, not
PFC, no have to worry. Now I must make money some way. So some
night you know why you come back here I not be home. . . ."

He damn well remembered this threat, she'd made it good, and all
the tears and denials in between made no difference. She was out with

Frick, "making money" tonight. A risky conclusion, he'd check it first. He corked the bottle, about half full, and stuffed it into his pocket.

"Excuse me. I might be back. I have a call to make."

He walked back through the ruined fence and into the service club. He dialed Dependents Housing. "Connect me with Lieutenant Frick's residence," he said.

A worried voice rasped in his ear, the john's gawky wife. "I'd like to speak to the lieutenant, please."

"I'm sorry, he's not in. Is there a message?"

"Uh no. Nothin' printable." He hung up the phone.

In the service club a horsey hostess with a portable mike led the troops and their friends through bingo. Most of the players were men of the bottom three grades. He looked over the shoulder of a private he knew. As SFC he had shared a room with two others, with a houseboy to keeep things tidy. The sergeants avoided bedcheck, and escaped most Saturday inspections. Now, he lived in a roomful of privates and PFCs. The household chores, the palaver of draftees, did not shake him up as much as one a.m. bedcheck, rigidly enforced by Taub, threatened to. If he and Taub had not finally worked this out between them, no knowing what would have happened to his home life, up the road.

But that was all fouled up anyway. His phone call did not exactly prove that Reiko was with Frick—but one more piece dropped into place. They were probably holed up in one of Hara's thousand cheap hotels, or maybe even further afield in the plush Kyoto Hotel. Or maybe they were not. In the end, she had only gone shopping, or visiting, and she was home waiting for him now. While he spent time twisting the knife kibitizing a bingo game. He started back for the house, the liquor taking hold, having one more pull at the start of the alleyway; remembering still why he had bought it but at once sickeningly certain he would not find her home.

It seemed the old lady had not moved in all this time. She squatted in the same position, her hands on the stump. She looked up as he approached. She was, he could tell, even drunker than he was, and he scolded her, to keep his thoughts from the bleak house behind.

"You're crocked. Don't think I ought to let you have no more."

"Anta mada hayai zo," she reproved in turn. "Sonna ni hayō kaette kiehen. Kitto jū ni ji made go tempurr."

"Jews need nothing," he said, "that somebody else don't need as well. That's from the horse's mouth, I'm half-Jewish myself. The rabbi though is a special case. He needs one extra thing, bodies. Hey, you know this story?" For she scratched her head, rose, and walked away. *"Chotto matte, ne,"* she called.

"Sure," he said; he understood this phrase. "I ain't goin nowhere."

The Popkins had Taub over for dinner the day Taub hinted at a way round bedcheck, more from perversity than gratitude. Taub was a crud; the Army were worse cruds; Taub might give him a chance to get back at the Army. To order Reiko to produce a meal on short notice was part of it too: if the house was crumbling he was still its master, he could still bring an honored buddy home for chow.

"Superb *sukiyaki*," Taub had said. "She can cook to the bargain."

"What do you mean, to the bargain?"

"I mean she's a fine-loking woman, hardly run-of-the-mill."

"Yeh. About bedcheck, what's on your mind?"

"You understand my position. I'm in charge of the room. I must see to it that it's ready for inspection, I must hand in a list of all parties not in bed by one. Needless to say, I don't relish the job, I certainly didn't request it. Personally, I couldn't care less who does what all night, but I'm forced to protect myself. If a man's name is missing from the bedcheck list and he is afterwards apprehended off the post, or if Beddoes or the captain pull a surprise check at four a.m., my ass is personally in the sling."

"It's a tough life."

"That may be. You know, I consider it a shame about your court-martial. Absolutely uncalled for."

"That's the truth."

"Company punishment perhaps, maybe the loss of a stripe, but not broken to PFC and then having to pay a fine."

"Miscarriage of justice," said Popkin, not anxious to discuss it with this chickenshit two-year man.

"You're Jewish, aren't you."

"On my father's side."

"On your father's side. Forgive my asking: do you think of yourself as a Jew?"

"What's the angle?"

"I'm thinking of sticking my neck out. If you're qualified and interested. I conduct Jewish services on the post, as you might know. The attendance is poor, despite the fact that twenty or more Jews are stationed on the post, and I'd like to increase it."

"I've never been to a service."

"No time like the present. If you care to attend, I guarantee the name Popkin never appears on the bedcheck list. You work in Signal, at odd hours: I need only say, if they check, I thought you had duty that night. It's a risk I'm willing to take in exchange for one hour a week of your time. You could return here each night to your charming girl as you're accustomed to."

"I'd be honored to attend the Jewish service," Popkin said.

"Superb. You might even find it rewarding." He looked at Reiko, bent over the stove. Her coal hair down her face, her rear etched against the PX navy blue. "I assume you know that Lieutenant Frick, while married, runs around in town."

"I've heard about this."

"His persecution of you," Taub went on. "I wonder if it's gratuitious, or stems from resentment that an EM lives with such a lovely girl. Could there be, frankly, anti-Semitism involved. But listen, however that may be: if my immediate superior were a vindictive *vonce* like Frick, and to the bargain I lived with a *shtik fleish* like yours, I'd keep up my guard."

"Maybe," Popkin said. He tried to drum up some warmth for Taub. He knew no Yiddish, supposed Taub did him a favor by assuming he did. Still, the drift was clear. It echoed his private suspicions. He'd make good use of the time he gained.

And he did. By attending the service four weeks running, he was able to sleep with Reiko three nights out of every four, excepting the one when he went to work at midnight. So he was three-quarters sure that, despite her early, since-repudiated threat, she had not tried to screw him, with Frick or anybody. Yet he made her sweat the twenty-five per cent, the nagging doubts, until he bought the whiskey tonight on borrowed money to announce the reconciliation. And she wasn't home.

"*Kore mi na,*" the old woman said. She held a flashlight and a photograph, the photo bright before his eyes. Popkin focused on a Buddhist temple. "Very nice. A house of worship. I have just come myself from the synagogue."

"*Reichan tempurr e ikahatta,*" she said. "*Otōsan shinda kara.*"

"You want a drink?" But she thrust the bottle away.

"*Bakayarō!*" she croaked, when he brought the bottle to his lips. "*Baka!*" she yelled, and held the picture, the light, a few inches from his nose. Popkin pushed them away. "You're mad as a loon," he said gently. "You've had a hard life. I need to take a little walk." He pushed off from the stump and staggered to the road, turned off it onto the main road which split Camp Hara in two. He made his way in toward the town.

III

We seek a wraith through Hara's dowdy night with the morals of a maniac; luckier than she, we mean her no harm. Akemi Yamada is her name, Shiga her birthplace, she's spindle-thin with the face (says Taub) of an angel; he means by this she resembles the petite Miss Rheingold of a recent year. But this is no merely cute, exotic night-child; this is much more than an ill-starred *objet d'art*. Akemi is wit and raconteur, and these are the aspects that lure him. She represents his only link with the GI-Japanese underworld.

What Taub doesn't know, or admit, is that her friends fall into two categories even if he withholds his appreciation: these have included, at their extremes, the rotund Korean doyen of an Osaka dope ring, and a U.S. major with a degree on the arts side from Cornell. (There's an overlap, too: she has been known to vamp the high IQs and she can entertain, if she chooses, almost anyone across a table.) He's unaware of this, or overlooks it anyway. To his mind only he strains past her lecherous frailty to glimpse the queen behind; the *kourve* is a Dorothy Parker at times. With her doings after closing, for bread or kicks, he's unconcerned. This is between herself, and the cops, and her imported pagan gods.

On her part Akemi is all heart and half curiosity; there's space in her ridiculous bosom for Taub. In her time she has known variations, subtle and not, on almost every attitude, but she has never before been patronized. This is why she permits, occasionally even encourages, his generosity and attention—so long as the bar is not full, and she is not in conversation with a blond, twentyish member of the Military Police (of which there are several at Hara, with whom she is collectively and seriously in love)—on those infrequent occasions when Taub stops by. He buys her a screwdriver, beer for himself, and they shoot the breeze; she flies off *sans* ceremony when her drink is gone, when others arrive, or if she is not being entertained. Generally, Taub is unperturbed by her frank (if un-Japanese) rudeness. He knows she is the only employee at Jackie's Bar whose drinks are not watered (this is by her own request), and too much alcohol usually brings out the worst in people. So that while he counts drinking among the milder of

her aberrations, he allows it to explain the volatile nature of their ur-
bane, innocent, cerebral affair.

He knows a thing or two more. Unmarked by countless crises, a life
of continual debauch, she will look twenty when closer to twice that
age, but the fact is that in February 1954 (this data can be checked at
the Judge Advocate's Office) Akemi has just put her twenty-eighth
birthday behind.

"I am terribly sorry, no. Not one is immune. It's simply a matter of
degree, and three cover the field."

"I doubt that," Helver said. "Suppose we consider . . ."

"Now listen to me a second. You'll cite exceptions? Do so. I say
only this. That everyone you want to mention fits into Category Three.
In this group you find it deep, perhaps it never surfaces. Such people
might live a lifetime voting the liberal ticket, calling your attention to
Einstein and Freud; they're not even aware they loathe the Jews. That's
perhaps a trifle strong, maybe not *loathe,* but they know him to be in
their hearts a lower form of life. So when Freud turns up it amounts
almost to mutation, you cite the case to show how unbigoted you are.
These people are as guilty as the rest."

Helver shook his head. "You leave no space for argument."

"Exactly the point. Let's proceed to Group Two, where feelings are
nearer the surface, but still unimplemented without outside aid. They
are waiting for Hitler. They need a leader to confirm them: not only
is the Jew a lower form of life, he is an evil force. Thank God in our
country there has been nothing quite like that up to now, but this
breed of *goyim* says, McCarthy? G. L. K. Smith? This is a free country, Ikey, they have rights to their opinions too. Sure. As thieves have
to steal, murderers to kill. About the third group, even you don't want
to debate. Here are the active *anti-Semiten,* who murder you. The
momsers who implement their hate, cause the real, not merely subtle
distress. Am I wrong?"

"Things all over have been worse than they are."

"And *last,* we have the group which is in some ways worst of all,
the anti-Semite Jews. But this of course is a class apart from the main
stream."

"You mean me?"

"No no you have guilt feelings?" Taub clapped the back of the gross,
good-natured man; in a hostile world, it is good to be with a friend.

Even with one so refractory; for where else lies the meaning of friendship? His good qualities are many, but he is not precisely an intellect, Helver, he has not breathed four years running the heady involuted air of the highest-priced college in New York. Taub is warm and compassionate as they near Jackie's Bar. The skinny sprite waits ahead, the depressing scene, the lumpish Kazuko, have been shunted behind.

"It follows," the lawyer persists, "that the Japanese are anti-Semites too."

"You think not? Permit an illustration. I was having coffee in the snack bar the other day with Nakamura, who works over at Finance. He's a *Tōdai*—Tokyo University—graduate, fairly bright. He wants to buy a house. He goes to an agent. The agent asks too much. Nakamura says, 'I tried to jew him down.' Now what are you bursting to say: merely an expression he picked up on post, doesn't even know what it means? I say you're wrong. I say, even if you're right, it won't be long before he finds out what it means, and I guarantee his attitude to me will alter when he learns I'm Jewish, if his knowing this was not why he made the remark in the first place. All prejudice is learned. Here they know the American white thinks Asians are inferior, they resent it. Yet they admire and envy the white man. They jump at the chance to take over his outgroups. They already hate blacks, you know. When it comes to bigotry, we have nothing to teach the sons and daughters of Amaterasu. You know what they feel toward Koreans, and their own so-called outcast class, the *eta*; all they need do is read a history of anti-Semitism in the West, they'll adapt quick enough."

"So you modify the original proposition. All non-Jews do not hate the Jews by definition. First they have to hear about them. The Buddhist and Hindu worlds are still only potential."

"Hairsplitter!" booms Taub affectionately. "You'll make a good shyster lawyer someday."

The bar was just beneath the arcade, at the mouth of the main shopping street, invisible behind a restaurant which was sandwiched between a haberdasher and a *geta* shop. A narrow corridor to the left of the restaurant led back to the bar. Jackie was a fortyish fullback of a woman who had it both ways. She did a roaring shoppers' trade up front in daylight hours (and lured the movie crowd at night), and the rear cabaret was one of the most popular GI spots in town. As our warriors near this site, their alien parley lost amidst the squawks and murmurs of oblivious passers-by, they're hailed by a countryman, concealed in a knot of bedizened strollers some way up the road. He's merely among them, not of them, breaks through presently with shaky strides, hatless, khaki-clad, no taller than the population at large.

"What's the action?"

"You're drunk, Lester," Helver says. "You're out of uniform."

"I mean besides that," Popkin says. "You join the MPs?"

"No, look. It was a special court. I did better than I should have keeping you out of jail. You shouldn't take chances so soon. Why don't you stay at home?"

"You know," says Taub, for the man's own good, "you endanger me too."

"Christ, is it one a.m.?" He checks his watch, with aghast, elaborate civility.

Helver says, "Put your hat on at least. It would be dumb to get picked up for something like that. Do you have to be out tonight?"

"Bob, I tell you honestly, I would rather be home. I would much rather be home. But I can't get in the goddamn house. Nobody home. I have the idea she's laying Frick, what's your opinion of that idea?"

"Now Pop," Helver says. "We've discussed this before. Every troop with a shack has a similar idea. I have it myself sometimes. It's an occupational hazard."

"You mean you don't think she is."

"No."

"Frick ain't home."

"Very likely. As usual, he's at the officers' club. Look, we're going in here for a drink. Come along."

"To chat," adds Taub, "with the witty Akemichan. Nothing more ambitious is contemplated. Do you know Akemi?"

"Know her? I fucked her. Long time ago when I was still a free agent. Much too skinny for my taste."

To Helver, Taub says, "Shall we proceed inside?"

"Proceed," Popkin says. "Enjoy hell out of yourself. I'm going home like Bob suggests. Perhaps developments. Toodleloo."

He dons the hat; he lurches on. From his back pocket the bottle protrudes. "He'll find trouble," Helver says. "Or it him."

"I hope you're wrong," says Taub. "The unhappy slob."

Thirteen hours to payday—the service club is full tonight, there are very few troops in town. Jackie is up front among the Japanese, and only a girl named Tomiko, on duty since the afternoon, decorates the gloom behind. As they enter she puts aside her *True Story* in translation and flicks on the colored lights and the phonograph. The noisy hybrid of hillbilly and rock-and-roll elicits from Taub an involved cross between a pout and a frown.

"Please!" he yells. "No music, please."

The girl looks shocked, but complies. She flops over leisurely, rests her knuckles on the table. "You want two beer?"

"If it's not too much trouble. Two Kirin, please."

She goes to the bar and returns with the beer.

Taub asks: "Where's Akemi?"

"Come later maybe eight ten o'clock. Too early now. Maybe no come."

"*Yasumi ka?*"

"What you say?"

So she ruins herself: that close to being requested to partake, to sit with the pair.

"I said," said Taub, " '*Yasumi ka?*', which translated from the original yields the meaning, Is it her day off?" He's infuriated when they pretend not to understand. His grammar is passable, his accent fair. They treat their language like a sacred cow, the outsider cannot touch.

"*Ah so,* you say '*Yasumi ka.*' No, not today, but sometime end of month she go way, no come till late," and she flashes a ribald, toothy smile.

"I see," he says, indulging the rare impulse to judge this undelicate and (when all is said) chief side of Akemichan.

After pouring their beer she says, "May I sit down?"

"No!" Taub snaps, but fabricates, "*Yōji ga arimasu kara* . . . we want to talk."

"Shit," she says, and shuffles back to her magazine.

"A delicate creature," says Taub.

Helver shrugs. "What's so pressing to talk about?"

"You have funds?"

"Two-twenty yen."

"Ah. Nor am I a millioniare. If she sits, she must be entertained. When Akemi comes in, I'm out the price of a screwdriver. Call the *tuchess* back if you want to underwrite her."

"You go for Akemi in a big way," Helver says.

"It's platonic," Taub begins, but sees he is twitted by the fat man. "Oh yes," he says. "Why not a double wedding in the spring."

"Your pass was approved, I saw it in the orderly room. Where you headed for?"

"The Inland Sea. One of the beauty spots I've missed. It's easy to grow fond of this country. A man does not learn much by sleeping with a nation's prostitutes, despite the theory to the contrary."

"Never heard of that one."

"Come now. You've been here five years. You know the military mind. Surely . . ." but he's cut off: a tremulous love song floats down the corridor (at times Taub is struck by the similarity between certain Japanese and Hebrew melodies, as well as techniques of voice control; could they be after all, as a closely written book in the post library suggests, the Thirteenth Lost Tribe?), and the clack of *geta,* and Akemi, flushed and lovely, stands in the doorway. She wears a red sweater, a tartan skirt, and her legs are bare over the clogs. She's not herself; she's herself rather plus hemp, liquor, or both. She's giggly, and her eyes are on fire.

"*Ohayō,*" Tomiko greets her. "*Kaerusan ga iru,*" and returns to the magazine. The sprite squints into the gloom, and locates Taub. "Ah, *Kaeru,*" she says (which never ceases to annoy: why, even in jest, he does not resemble one, does she call him Mr. Frog?). "*Comment ça va?*"

"*Ça va,*" says Taub, and he thinks that this exchange, in spite of all, establishes the proper mood. He has taught it to her himself.

Yet she flits past their booth and drops down next to Tomiko.

"*Kita?*"

"*Dare ga?*"

"*Karwairashii MP, kinō kita no.*"

"*Mada kiahen.*"

"*Kuso!*" says Akemi, and stamps on the floor.

"Dung!" translates Taub. "My cute MP has not yet been in tonight." Akemi turns. "*Wakatta?*" she says, with only half-feigned admiration. "You understand like native, no can say nothing round here."

She knows the tortuous route to the cantor's buttressed heart.

"I get by," says Taub. "Come and join us for the usual."

"Need a double tonight," Akemi says.

"A double! Well all right then. And bring us two more Kirin beers."

"*Arigatō,*" she replies. She pours a glassful of vodka (Jackie is up front, the bartender is late), opens the beer, and joins the pair.

"What did you do today," asks Taub, "to make you look so fiery-eyed?"

She giggles self-indulgently. "*Tsumaranai koto:* not worth your attention."

"Doubtless; who with?"

"*Nan da,* don't worry your fat head," and pats him on the crown.

"Too much grease," she decides, but he grabs her hand before she wipes it on his trousers.

"You're *taihen* rude tonight," he scolds; she's so much more than this she's nearly out of hand. "Perhaps you shouldn't drink any more."

"This is first drink I have all day," she says to Helver. "Skinpop." She flexes her skinny arm.

"They'll slap you in jail again," Helver says.

"No skin from your nose, *Debuchan*. Anyway, no GI involved." She has met the lawyer in his professional capacity before. She laughs wildly.

"You know what I do today? I make love in Blue Sky Hotel. First time this year."

This surprises Helver (a hotel in the environs of which he has not heard?) and depresses Taub; he has heard the bit before.

But Helver asks, "Where's the Blue Sky Hotel?"

Her head arches, she laughs like a child.

"She refers to the great outdoors," inserts Taub. "Like beasts, in bushes, under trees. It's her notion of a joke I believe." He lofts his beer.

"I see," Akemi says, "you not in very good mood tonight."

"I'm fine," he assures her; he has seen the possibility of four hundred yen disappearing with total lack of recompense. "But I have heard that joke before."

"You *takusan* egoist. You never think of other people."

"I apologize, Akemi. From now on I will think of other people."

"In a pig's ass," she says.

Helver, wittingly, delays catastrophe: "Your English has improved, Akemi."

"Thank you," she says, really pleased. "Only rude, broken GI English I learn working here, but sometimes study on the side."

"What are you reading these days, Akemi?" Taub labors to keep them on the firmer ground.

"Reading *ka!* I read Shakespeare *no Hamuretto*," and she is tickled by the affinities this has with "omelet" in the Japanese. Her laugh once more dances through the clubby darkness, then burbles into the vodka, which she is drinking straight. She has never been quite this far out in Taub's memory; the evening, he fears, will not be a success. He talks to Helver: "I was strolling in the hills behind the camp the other day, and I came across something interesting."

"What did you came across?" Akemi pounces on his lead—immediately she yells at Tomiko, "Phonograph *kakete kurehen?*" Tomi does, and the strident sounds once more fill the room.

"A grave," shouts Taub. "This man Fenollosa, very interested in Japanese art. The Japanese government sent a warship to pick up his body when he died. I had no idea he was buried here. *Gaijin no gakusha no baka o mitsuketa,*" he adds, so she too may understand.

"Never heard of him," mumbles Helver, staring hard at Akemi, who sits across from him adjoining Taub.

"Admired by Ezra Pound," Taub says. "But we needn't hold that against him. Need we." He turns to smile broadly at Akemichan.

Who has rolled up her sweater, unhooked her brassiere, and is studying a tiny breast. "*Okashii, na,*" she says with wonderment.

Taub's jaw drops, his body recoils.

"What in God's name are you up to now?"

"Very odd," she says. "Since week ago I find here something look like milk, there is no reason for. *Kore goran,*" she orders, turns, makes the bub convenient to the cantor's eyes. Helver leans forward. She applies pressure. A cloudy liquid appears. She looks amazed. "*Hen da, ne,*" she says to Helver, whose mien accords.

"What you think of that?" she says to Taub. "I have milk, but no damn babysan."

Jackie now enters the bar, counterfeits horror at the tableau, and goes to talk with Tomiko.

"We must go," Taub starts to rise. "She's not herself tonight."

"Where you off to?" She smiles suddenly at a secret thought, scratches her bare belly.

"I, back to camp." He looks at Helver. "Come."

"Okay, I'll make it back too. Kaz will be pleasantly surprised."

"Why you running off, *Kaerusan,*" she repeats, but still does not sound awfully concerned.

"Because," Taub says slowly, "you are behaving like an ill-mannered slut tonight."

"*Hommae,* that's me all over." She drops the sweater and glances at Jackie, who has placed her stout frame behind the bar. This, she realizes, cuts off her illegal liquor supply. "Before you go you buy me one more vodka, *nee.* It just now begins to feel real good."

"Sorry," says Taub.

"Don't be *kechimbō,*" she enjoins. "Next time you come in I buy you a drink. *Katte okure, Kaerusan.*"

"I'm sorry, if you'll let me get by."

"Certainly." She slides her legs to the side of the bench, giving him room. As he inches past she yanks at the seat of his trousers. "Buy me drink, corporal make good pay."

"Out of the question," says Taub.

"Go to hell," she says without rancor. "You a cheap stingy Jew."

Helver is almost to the door, but he turns at this, sees Taub lumber about and lift his hand. Christ he'll hit her, he thinks; he already envisions the trial.

"Now you *shut up!*" Taub croaks. "You *whore,* just keep your mouth closed." His face is different shades of pale beneath the over-head revolving rainbow. Helver starts back but Taub drops his hand, moves past Helver and down the corridor.

"*Sayonara. Odaiji ni!*" Akemi calls, through immediately forgotten surprise. But she has had a quick vision of meaning in the world. She giggles softly, looks dolefully at Jackie. With sudden hope she peers down the corridor, but no MPs, blond or otherwise, are in sight. If one or another of them fails to appear, or anyone else, which is possible, the evening threatens dry, unspeakable boredom. To turn her mind from this she rolls up her sweater, and once more scrutinizes the mystery fluid she loves to squeeze from her pageboy's supple barren form.

As a gesture of solidarity and probably superfluous caution, Helver accompanied Taub from the door of Jackie's to Camp Hara's snack bar, where coffee and cheese on rye, and a buoying piece of inside intelligence, restored Taub to something like pre-Akemi form. Helver divulged that the post commander had decided to run HQ Company the following morning through the gas chamber up in the hills. This was in line with a standing order to keep chairborne Far East troops on a nodding acquaintance with combat conditions. All men below the rank of sergeant would mask; enter, by twos, the fume-filled chamber; make their way to a point near the exit where the first sergeant waited; remove masks, recite name rank and serial number; stagger out into the air. Helver's rating spared him; Taub would evade the small ordeal by means of his three-day pass.

The cantor safe, Helver started homeward, choosing a route through the back streets of the town. More than an hour had passed since the pair left the bar. He walked slowly past the small silent cluster of moonlit brick dwellings of Hama-Hara's well-to-do, from here to the one street which was its pleasure quarter, the row of shops and bars and houses seeming to have sucked in the noise and population of the surrounding countryside, past it to the decrepit bridge, pressing himself to the railing as the big Army bus lumbered by. He did not trouble to unfreeze, although he could have left the narrow bridge in time. The white convertible was thirty yards to the rear of the bus and not moving fast. Laziness kept him there, astonishment drove it out; the split-second panic when the car came toward him, for him, fled in turn before the reflexes that once, in Washington, D.C., had been too quick for all concerned: he was able to reach over the driver's chest after saving himself and grab futilely at the wheel. The car was committed by then. He watched it smash the rail, dive with massive grace into the shallow canal. He rushed to the earth embankment and waded into the stew. For some moments (just long enough) he was the only other person on the scene.

IV

While not the world's most serious Buddhist, making peace with piety in general by infrequent trips to *Inari,* patron goddess of the working girl, Reiko felt moved to leave Hara on the seventh anniversary of her father's death and visit the family temple. Her mother dunned her by letter for the six weeks preceding the day, but she might have remembered anyway. She had behaved badly since his death, working in bars and cabarets, contracting unsavory relationships with GIs from her native Kyoto to as far south as Beppu, and this propitiatory gesture to her father's ghost and her mother's anxiety made good sense, since she lived now no more than an hour's ride from where she was born. The round trip to Kyoto, in all, should have taken under five hours.

She knew well in advance she would make the journey, but she put off telling Popkin when their trouble came. The old *sukebei* would not have believed her. On the morning of the day she thought she noticed a softening in his attitude, but was unwilling to test it with what struck even her (in the circumstances) as a fabrication. She decided to say nothing and risk returning in time. Shortly before she left, around noon, she had second thoughts—what if she was delayed?—but he was probably in or on the way to the mess hall, and there was no way to reach him. She could not write in English. She taught Obaachan an English phrase: "Reiko go Kyoto to temple," having the old lady repeat it several dozen times. Then she gave her a hundred yen, locked up the house, and caught the rickety electric train.

Near Sanjo Station, in Kyoto, she had two straight whiskies to nerve herself. She boarded a bus for Demachiyanagi. She was, or so she felt, too chicly dressed to be anything but what she was. They stared at her and judged her, these alien hard-eyed Japanese. Slightly drunk, she could return or ignore the glances. At Demachiyanagi she took still another electric train, bound for the suburbs. The monstrous machine with the wasplike undercarriage rattled her home. Her mother and young sister met her at the station, a five-minute walk from the temple. Afterwards they went to a small noodle shop, and her mother invited her home. It was difficult to refuse. At six-thirty she slipped out and phoned the barracks, but remembered before the call went through that he would not be there. He went to church Friday nights, his part of the bargain with his room sergeant. When she returned to the house the sleeping mats were spread. Her mother made a tearful appeal. It was hours before she got away. She caught the last train from Sanjo, arrived at Hama-Hara at twelve-fifteen and phoned the comcenter from a tobacconist. Popkin wasn't there. He was working mids, and she began to worry; worried even more when she did not find him at the house, drunk, asleep, as she expected to; remained uneasy through the following week without a clear idea of what had taken place, until events engulfed the wino and there was nothing left to be concerned about.

Taub returned from the Inland Sea on Monday, in time for the evening meal. He learned almost at once that Popkin was in trouble, although no one seemed to know exactly what the poor bastard had done. It seemed right for him to be in trouble, it gave Taub a sense of clairvoyance (although it was Helver, not he, who had predicted this). Helver came into the mess hall and Taub moved to join him. The lawyer would have the inside scoop. Taub found him by and large uncommunicative.

"But what's the upshot?"

"Everything's under control. He didn't take it, he wasn't driving. He'll get off lightly, I think, off post without a pass. Unless," he said, more to himself, "Akemi screws us up."

"Akemi! What's she got to do with it?"

"She was in the car. That's all I can tell you."

"What do you mean by screw us up? What can she do?"

Helver shrugged. "Excuse me, Lyle, I've got to take Kaz to the movies."

He was annoyed first with Helver, then with Akemi, who seemed responsible for Helver's reticence. His dislike for Popkin faded in front of the larger thing, the girl's seeming ability to cause disaster. Her Friday outrage burned anew in him; he had done less than justice, at the time, to its enormity.

Well, he was still on pass; he'd go see Akemi. Maybe he could play a role in saving the old man's luckless part-Jewish hide.

Around the corner from Jackie's Bar Friday night Popkin fell into a concrete ditch running parallel to the road. The right trouser leg of his khakis was wet through to the thigh, he scraped some skin from the side of his calf, but was not otherwise damaged. As he picked himself up an MP patrol jeep turned the corner, pulled up and stopped beside him.

"Need any help?"

"No," Popkin said. He knew better than accept favors from snot-nosed MPs. He walked with dignity back toward the camp, his eyes fixed on the chimney top straight ahead. Now a house loomed. That he walked at a sixty-degree angle to the road he discovered by tripping over the ditch on the other side and sprawling into the underbrush. He let the MP grip his shoulder.

"No sweat Jack, a free ride back home."

"All right then," Popkin said. "If it gives you pleasure."

The MP, as he said, simply meant to take the rummy home. His buddy, a lean, young blond, seemed to disapprove of the operation but said nothing. Popkin was sure he smelled liquor on his breath.

"Where you been drinkin'?"

"What?"

"Man you reek. Drinkin' on duty. Serious offense. You better kill it with this." The bottle had somehow survived; he pulled it from his back pocket and thrust it, from the back of the jeep, across the blond MP's chest. The MP pushed it away.

"Don't wise off, Pop," the boy said. He added, "We went off duty five minutes ago." Then he said, "Dad, let's see your pass."

So the first interior Popkin visited was not HQ Company's barracks (if he had planned returning there) but the desk sergeant's office. The desk sergeant scowled at Popkin until they were alone.

"Goddamn it, a man your age leaving post without his pass."

"Now wait up, Frank. How in hell old you think I am?"

"Look, Lester, you're crocked."

"No argument."

"You just been in trouble recently. If I write you up, it might go hard with you. I make you an offer. Go straight back and hit the sack, in the barracks I mean. Stay put there until the morning. And this little incident dies right here. But if I let you off, and you're seen again offpost tonight . . ."

"I'm a reasonable man," Popkin said. "Anyway, I go on duty at midnight. Till then, I could damn well use couple hours sleep."

"All right, get the hell out now. Just remember what I said."

Popkin went outside. The MPs who brought him in had gone. He wobbled smartly toward the barracks, counting cadence, across the parade field. He entered the barracks and left at once through the rear door. He stared at the cross above the chapel, at the service club, at the not yet visible jeep-sized hole in the fence beyond.

When she was not home now, the third time, he decided to go to bed. It was ten-fifteen, and an hour's sleep or so before going on mids was, as he told the desk sergeant, reasonable. The CQ was not in the orderly room. Awaiting his return, to ask to be wakened at twenty to twelve, Popkin succumbed to the telephone. In the midst of his call the CQ returned.

"Is Lieutenant Frick over there?"

"I'm sorry, he hasn't come in yet. I believe he's working late tonight. Who's calling, please?"

"This here is Major Dawes."

"This is his wife, Major. Did you ring earlier in the evening?"

"No, I'm a busy man."

"Is there a message?"

"No message," Popkin said. He smiled at the CQ, who waited to pounce: "Major Dawes," he said, "you're Popkin?"

"That's it."

"I got a call from the desk sergeant a couple of minutes ago that you're supposed to be in bed. I have just come down from your room."

"I was making my toilet," Popkin said. "But I'm retiring now."

"You'd best be. I'll be up for a look in five minutes' time."

"*Daijobe,*" Popkin said. "You're only doin' your job."

Despite the rush, climbing the stairs, of fatigue-banishing resentment, Popkin loved the Army: he proved this, after changing his trousers in the darkened room, by propping pillow and spare blanket and underclothes under the covers in a shape vaguely like a man's. He thumped down the stairway and into the night. Behind the barracks a rocky footpath lost itself in the hills. He followed it. He planned, after a while, to sit in the cool, silent darkness, inside the camp yet out of it. But the trail curved sharply after thirty yards and led him out into the clearing occupied by the officers' club.

Popkin sighed. A man could not escape the brass, even during off-duty hours. The silence which had misled him was suddenly shattered by a tinny rendering of "Sentimental Reasons," a halfnote away from the true melody. He watched couples rise and move out to the dance floor. According to Helver, Frick was in there too, no more with Reiko than Popkin was himself; but he knew better now. Great invention, the telephone. But he had not wanted to think about this again until he had to, which was why he wandered up into the mountain.

The smooth, green lawn lured him. He sat in its center, drained the whiskey bottle and tossed it in a high arc off toward the side of the building. A second later it crashed on chrome and steel. Popkin lay back on the grass. He moaned, "Why did I down all that rotgut at one time."

Lying down only made the world spin round. He staggered off to where the bottle had smashed and relieved himself. He bent to inspect the damage done by the bottle and found only a small scratch on the right rear fin. It was a cream-colored convertible, a beautiful car. He had not seen it at Hara before. Doubtless it belonged to a light-bird or above, and as he had nothing against light-birds and above, he was glad he had not damaged it much. He walked clear around it twice. The third time the button clicked smartly under his thumb, the door swung gently open, and Popkin lowered himself into the driver's seat.

Probably, if the key had not been in the ignition, he would not have thought to take it for a spin. The last time he had driven a car was four years ago, and he never felt easy behind a wheel. But this was a magic machine: to turn the key started it up, the power steering moved to a touch. "Lights," he said, fiddling with the dash until the lights came on. He spun the big car around to face the roadway. He kept it moving at a careful ten to fifteen miles an hour. It nosed into camp between the barracks and the snack bar. He ducked low as two signal men came out of the snack bar. At the main gate he straightened and returned a salute from an imaginary MP as he glided past the empty booth. "I'll be in the area all day," Popkin said. "Make way for General Dawes."

The *densha* rattled by just as the Cadillac turned onto the road. It was surprisingly quick, the ancient, two-car electric train, and he abandoned the contest after a hundred yards because of how hard it was to keep the car on the left side of the road. Got to obey that assbackwards law, he thought; for your own safety as well. A traffic light checked him on the camp side of the canal. Waiting, he put on his glasses and inspected the dashboard. He found the knob he wanted, pushed, and the top slid smoothly down. On green he jolted across the bridge, along the route he had followed earlier in the evening. This brought him onto the shopping street, a strictly pedestrian thoroughfare. There was barely any clearance as he eased the huge car down the bumpy road. He pulled up outside the flickering neon sign which spelled out Jackie's Bar.

Once, pre-Reiko, he had been fairly friendly with Akemi, but would not have gone to see her now had the meeting with Taub and Helver, in front of the bar, not planted the name in his mind. He craved uncritical company, to make a nice appearance in the front seat of the general's car. He had no money left, but once more there was nothing he wanted to buy.

Akemi was one of two girls in the bar. The other slept over a magazine; Akemi was occupied. She sat next to a burly blond in civvies who appeared unconscious. His cheek rested on the tabletop. To his profile she applied the business end of a cigarette. Occasionally he groaned and slapped his face. When she had to she removed his hand and patiently, gingerly resumed.

Popkin slid into the seat opposite and watched for a time.

"What the hell you doing, Akemi."

She glanced up.

"Hello, Pop. Why you don't mind your own business, *ne?*"

"Sorry."

She relented: "I give MP Mickey Finn. Now I write Japanese word for butterfly because I think he step out on me this week. He is a no good son of a bitch."

Suddenly the troop bolted upright, as if shamming all the time. But his eyes betrayed him. Popkin recognized the face of the snotnose who asked him for his pass (a lightning change into civilian clothes), life's stinking little ironies.

"I'm a no good son of a bitch," the MP said.

"That's all right," Popkin said. "So long as you know about it."

"A son of a bitch," he repeated, his face banging forward on the tabletop. Akemi reached into his shirt pocket for the cigarettes. She lit one, puffed it to a rosy glow, resumed.

While the scene was not without interest, Popkin felt moved to intervene. This he did carefully.

"I think you should knock off, Akemi, and come riding in my new car."

She paused. "You have convertible?"

"Bet your ass. Go take a look outside."

"A good idea," she said. "Jackie already go home, so no sweat. Okay, if he can come too."

"Him?"

"Him, yes, my boy friend, butterfly MP. We drive very fast, open door, drop him into fucking lake."

"Well now." He appeared to think this over. "We don't want no trouble now."

"If he come I come," Akemi said. "Or the whole world stay here."

"Ah hell, he can come."

They got the MP to his feet, moaning and blowing out his crimson cheek, and maneuvered him into the front seat of the car. "Where you steal this car, old man?" she asked cannily. "You're wrong about that, Akemi, the general lend it to me." She sat between them, the MP slumped heavily on her shoulder. "Drive that way." She pointed toward the camp. "That way is Tokyo." "Jesus," Popkin said, "a gallon of black coffee now would suit me fine."

The contents of the glove compartment had spilled into the front seat, where the MP had been. So Helver learned almost immediately whose car it was. Akemi sprawled on her belly across the hood, her hands locked protectively behind her head. The MP lay face upward in the dirty shallows. Popkin sat, as he had been, in the driver's seat, his hands gripping the wheel.

"Why'd you take his car?" Helver said. "What did that accomplish?"

"You think I did it on purpose?" Popkin said. "I been havin' this trouble all night, which way is straight ahead. But I was doin' fairly well until now."

"You're not driving," Helver said. "You're not even here. You've been with me. Now come, come." With strong, chubby arms he hoisted Popkin toward him, out of the driver's seat.

"Where you think you going, *Debuchan?*" She rolled onto her side, supporting herself on an elbow. "That old man son of a bitch spoil my new skirt. Look, I think MP is dead."

"He's breathing," Helver said. "How would you like ten thousand yen for a new dress?"

"You pull my leg, *ne?*"

"Listen closely," Helver said. "The MP was driving. Do you understand me? They will ask you who drove the car and you will say it was the MP. For ten thousand yen in cash. Will you do it?"

"If I say MP drive car you give me ten thousand yen? When you pay?"

"Tomorrow morning," Helver said. "Believe me, Akemi. Listen to me. You and Popkin were sitting in Jackie's. The MP came and picked you up in the car. Do you have that?" he hissed at Popkin, who looked up with horror and unbelief from the white laminated card. "My god, it's Frick's. But I didn't take it. I wasn't driving." He stared slackmouthed with shock and gratitude. *Good,* Helver thought. *So he does not screw himself.* He went to drag the slim blond boy out of the water just as a Japanese policeman and two MPs began to descend the embankment.

V

Unreasonable to hold the four who turned up responsible for the others' defection, but he couldn't help it: hate welled in him for Frankel, Teller, Michaelson, and Bernstein, caused him to falter in a treble, sputter off into silence on the word *Adonai.* Because twenty men had shipped home the day before, including a regular and two possibles (with one of whom he'd had frequent success); since he felt fairly certain of his half-dozen, and expected, at this point needed no more; Taub had omitted the pre-service ritual, the whimsical search for the Jews. So reaped his reward now, this anaemic quartet behind him. Failing to meet even his own adjusted minimum, the fruits of compromise, six skull-capped men without *talaisim* in worse than an empty room, a barely converted heathen temple. Yet he had gone ahead, with loathing, less for the absentees than for Frankel, Teller, Michaelson, and Bernstein, who looked up with interest and a trace of critical surprise when he faltered and stopped in the midst, at the height of a prayer.

He did not resume. In his shoulders and the back of his head they might read, if they were able, the persecuting weight of centuries, rabbinical prodigies of patience and mute despair. But when he turned, with a weary smile, he had molded a thing to be, from the stuff of dignity, disgust, and fellowship.

"Gentlemen. Your forbearance. I consider it pointless to continue. Where I erred, doubtless, was in beginning with less than a quorum; I was under the misapprehension that one or two more would drift in before we moved too far along. Under the circumstances . . . I suggest we follow the custom, each man praying silently at his own speed until he concludes."

It took them by surprise. "Tie it up, Lyle," Bernstein said (New York humor, guying common sense). "We have enough *frumkeit* here for ten."

Taub smiled. "I would rather we stopped. We could continue, but my heart would not be in it. If one of the congregation is willing or able to take over, naturally I raise no objection," since things can become no more farcical than they are. "No volunteers? *Lachah dodee lekras kalah,*" he sang, turned and unhinged his knees, signaling the abrupt plunge into the ultimate acreage of private, silent prayer.

Popkin's heart wasn't in it either fifteen minutes earlier when he took the shortcut behind the service club, his hands deep in his pockets, whistling tonelessly, so much out of it in fact that he questioned his own sanity. *This is no good either,* he thought; *I'm going to ruin myself,* walking too casually through the dusk past countless windows, visible to anyone inside who might want to reflect, "Popkin? Restricted indefinitely to the post? Courting trouble still another time?" and yet be unaware, this observer, that for three hours past, since Helver yanked him away from the day-room pool table, gave him the news as the pink, fat color faded from his face, the issue was merely would he seek trouble, or would he wait around and let it find him. But no one saw Lester Popkin from the service-club or library windows.

At first he had waited, as Helver had not even had to advise; shot pool by himself from two to five-thirty waiting for his name through the loudspeaker, refusing to think of what Helver had told him or what he, in a matter of moments, could say to Frick; blanked his mind to the new, deeper trouble. By five-forty-five, when he had still not been called, he put down his cue and went to the snack bar. Here, unable to eat, he succumbed to the hopelessness, gave in to the old impotent rage at their trickery. The old rage came on him, for Frick, sleek and plotting, like the goddamn Gestapo, waiting to haul him in at midnight maybe, or the day after, or the day after that, when his guard was down, at their leisure, because Pop? Restricted to the post forever, he ain't going nowhere.

This was what incensed him: that despite knowing all, they used the fact of his restriction to dawdle over punishment. The restriction itself, imposed one week before, he never objected to—a chronic offender caught off post without his pass, he had been liable, even for that small offense, to much graver penalties. (The MP, elected by a three-fourths majority as driver of the stolen car, remembering nothing and having said as much, awaited court-martial and the completion of Frick's investigations in Camp Hara's makeshift jail.) Restriction had not even inconvenienced him much. The good things came to him. Every night at eight Reiko (known now to be innocent; bringing wine) came on post and met him outside the enlisted men's club. After a couple of drinks there they walked back across the road and climbed into the hills, behind the barracks. Here, on a GI blanket, to background music from the officers' club, on a gentle slope, he drank wine and they made love. She was due this evening as well. But tonight, Popkin thought, we'll dance in bed; I've had it either way, I ain't going to hang around. He bolted his coffee, walked swiftly to the barracks, changed into a Hawaiian sport shirt and light blue trousers. I'm out of my mind, he thought, nearing the wire fence (after all, there are degrees of misfortune)—but he did not turn back; instead he adopted a comical (should anyone have seen), a much too casual air.

At which moment Taub's under-populated Friday service began. Now it nears its abortive end: "Git Shabbus," says Bernstein, first and too loudly, announcing his disenchantment and his reading speed. Taub smiles privately, without real pleasure. He prays on. Though he has abdicated the headship he remains at a height up front, his rear parts toward the group. These he manipulates with fresh violence, cheeks jutting toward the first row, where Frankel and Teller sit—this signifies that he too nears the end. "Gut Shabbus, gut Shabbus," at last he turns. Bernstein has made for the door, the others mill about with no real hope. Taub thinks: the shnurrers, but contains himself. There will be other Fridays, larger turnouts than this one in his remaining twelve weeks at Hara, if he does not alienate this trio here. "I think we'll skip the kiddush, gentlemen, since this is something less than an official gathering and," he smiles, "I honestly forgot the wine. By next week things ought to be back to normal. Which reminds me. Has anyone seen Helver, or Popkin? I'm amazed that neither turned up tonight."

But no one has. Taub lags behind, collects the prayer books, switches off the lights. He steps out and locks the door. Twelve weeks—he has not really considered how close he is to going home. To his parents, to a last year of rabbinical training, to familiar things. His spirits lift. He walks slowly along the base of the mountain, and from somewhere drums up an inkling of regret. They have not been bad, his sixteen months in this part of the world—no reasonably sensitive person who has lived there can help feeling deeply for Japan. Already he feels nostalgia, what will be nostalgia, as he sits at the kitchen table on Jerome Avenue and tries to re-create, for parochial family and friends, sixteen months in the Far East. He will not dwell long on the clichés, cherry blossoms, geisha, sacred mountain, but instead . . . on the other things. They'll be there when he needs them, in perspective and retrospect, the many things he has observed and learned which, immersed as he is in them still, are now not so easy to isolate. In spite of his initial chagrin at being expelled from Georgia, he must now feel something like gratitude toward the Army for sending him overseas.

Gratitude. That slob Popkin showed gratitude by missing the service tonight—but this Taub must dismiss. For Popkin cannot yet know he has real cause to be grateful. He is unaware that Taub has suffered in pride, pocket, and time; so he cannot have stayed away through thanklessness. Perhaps he'll never know, Taub thinks, or I at least will never tell him—a kindness in a case like this is its own best reward.

It begins to rain as he comes even with the barracks. His thoughts have turned him restless; he'll pick up his pass, his bamboo and oil-paper umbrella, catch the bus to Kyoto, and walk the streets awhile. He's fond of the city, redolent of ancient glory, although turning a face to the uninitiate of modernity and noise, cars and cabarets. He'll go in and feel the centuries pulse around him. There are so many temples, gardens, shrines he still has not seen. He'd use his time more wisely, given a second chance. All the same, he wishes he were going home soon, tomorrow, now. The foretaste of nostalgia grips him more.

The imponderables complicate thought, so he hums a little. He's almost wholly in the dark, recall, and she might not even be there. Or there and bleary-eyed, there hating his soul. Pathetic, ruined, and bad: once he ignored these things because of wit, but were they the price she paid for being so *amusante?* The necessary foil for her to seem to be? Likely, very likely. Although—he's no hypocrite—abominat-

ing her now, he need not scourge himself for admiring her once.
She was truly entertaining, in his partial knowledge. But now, her
badness threatens change. Helver told him. He plans to ascertain,
by whatever means (the imponderables complicate thought), that she
bring no harm, through malice or carelessness, to one of his own. And
he hates her all right. He will not neglect the chance, should it arise
(he hums a little), to crush her too.

It's soon after the supper hour, and a Monday, but a half-dozen
GIs are in the cabaret. This is Standard Operating Procedure near
payday. Some have been there most of the day, others, less lucky,
have come straight from work, bypassing the mess hall for the fried
rice and friendship that money can buy. Jackie's staff is ten strong
for all of this week which means that four girls, as Taub enters,
are not occupied. One rises, comes up and reaches for his hand.
Doubtless a new *kourve*, or she'd know the score and leave him alone.
This is how things are in bars: once you make your choice you've
made it, for better or worse, and even if your girl is busy while others
are not you'll be left alone until she's able or chooses to join you.
"You come sit down?" says the tart. Taub is not unkind. "I'm a
friend," he says, "of Akemi. Excuse me. Sorry." He disengages himself
and walks to the bar. Jackie is there, guarding the bottles and the
unoccupied stools. Taub sits. *"Konban wa,"* he says.

"Good evening," Jackie replies, "how you? Akemichan!" she yells
over the music's roar. "A beer, please," says Taub. *"Nani?"* Akemi
calls. Jackie inclines her head toward Taub. Taub can make out no
reply.

"Let's dance, Akemi," says someone, and there is shuffling behind
him on the dance floor. Naturally he doesn't expect her to join him
at once; Jackie has merely alerted her, if she cares, that the last arrival
is one of her own. Still, she should acknowledge him, Taub feels,
angry or not. But he does not turn round. Jackie pours his beer.
She reminds him of a football player he sat next to in a History of
Religion course. He looks away, toward the back of the room. Now
he can see her dancing from the corner of his eye. Recalling his
mission, he feels superior to the game. He turns and stares.

Over her partner's shoulder she smirks at him; more this, he decides,
than a scowl or a frown. *"Kaerusan,"* she says, *"kechinbō,"* and whispers something in the GI's ear. He spins her around and his tough,
dull eyes take in Taub. He laughs. "Naw," he says. "He don't look
like one to me."

Taub turns back around. Control, he thinks, a duty to perform. Sticks and stones, he thinks, but his pulse smacks in his temples. There's a shriek from the floor, followed by a giggle, then the voice of the leprechaun: "Son of a bitch. You goose me in public. Cost you five hundred yen."

"Naw, Akemi. You ain't got enough tail make it worth while."

"Then you buy me drink."

"Just bought you one. You drink 'em too fast. All water anyway."

One second later she stood by Taub, her bony elbows on the bar. "*Konban wa, Kaerusan. Comment allez-vous?*"

"Hello, Akemi."

She squeezed his upper arm.

"You feel like beat me up again tonight?"

"I never touched you, Akemi. I hope that's clear in your mind."

"*Dorinku katte kurehen?*"

Taub nods.

"Vodka collins, *chōdai,*" she says to Jackie, who mixes and serves.

"Come sit in booth," Akemi says. Same price. We shoot the shit awhile."

Three large, boisterous troops enter the bar.

"I want to talk to you, Akemi, but preferably outside."

"Outside? What for? Nothing to drink outside."

"Then finish up your drink and we'll go somewhere else. It's too crowded here."

"*Detara akan,*" Jackie says. "Very busy now. She must work here."

"Just for ten minutes," Taub says.

"*Dekimahen.* She work here till eleven. Then she can go where she want."

In his hand he clutches eight hundred yen, his change from a thousand-yen note. He pockets the three hundreds, carefully folds the five-hundred-yen note in four. He places this unsmiling near Jackie's hand.

"*Sore wa nan desu no?*" She is arch.

"*Presento.* If she can come outside for twenty mintues."

"*Sore dake?*" the fullback flashes him a golden smile. "*Happyaku en nara, nan toka,*" she says.

All right. The hungry whore. $2.22 more. He takes out the three hundred yen, places it with the five on the bar. With amazement, Akemi has watched this odd exchange.

"What's up, *Kaeru?* For my part, I don't want to go anywhere."

Ah God, no trouble with her, Taub pleads.

"Suppose we sit up front then in the restaurant. Believe me, Akemi, it's highly important."

"*Shōchi shimasu,*" she says. "*Itte kimasu,*" she calls to the group. She picks up her drink and leads the way.

A family of four sits toward the front of the restaurant. They eat ice cream. The two small children regard the materialized Taub with amazement, tug at mother's kimono sleeve. Taub lowers himself deliberately at a rear table, nearest to the bar. Akemi sits opposite. He waves the waiter away, stares the adults (but not the children) down. Music is audible, from the world inside, but not disturbing. He looks a long while at Akemi (he has her now) with humor, compassion, understanding, hatred, love.

She breaks it up: "You feel hot to go?"

"No," Taub says. He even smiles. "I'd like to know, first of all, what you whispered, concerning me I think, to the friend you were just dancing with. You know I'm interested in your strange little mind."

"*Are!*" she says. "Of course." She thinks. "I said to him . . . *chotto matte, ne* . . . I said, 'You see fat ugly troop sit at bar?' "

Taub waits.

" 'He number one muffdiver in Japan.' Now you know I can go back to bar, *ne?*"

"Wait!" Taub says. He reaches out and encircles her wrist. "We're not finished. That was incidental. Something totally different is on my mind."

"*Ah sō ka.* Must be *takusan* important, too, you pay eight hundred yen."

"You can be sure it is. Please pay careful attention to what I say. It's about Popkin and your accident Friday night. And the matter of the stolen car." He gropes for knowledge as he sets the scene. Helver is once more inwardly cursed for leaving him so deeply in the dark. Akemi and Popkin and an unidentified thief-driver crash in Frick's car sometime Friday night after Taub and Helver leave Jackie's Bar; and Akemi is not trusted to give an accurate account of the scene. This last part he can fasten on, how well he conceives it to be true.

"What accident?"

"Akemi, act your age. I know all about the accident so I ask you, don't play games."

"Nobody got hurt," she said. "Very small accident."

"The Army takes a different view," said Taub. "Stealing an officer's car is a serious offense, let alone smashing it up. The guilty party will be heavily punished."

"You break my heart."

"All right. He doubtless deserves it. That's precisely why we have to guard against mistakes. So that the right man receives his punishment."

She looks surprised. "You know MP?"

"What MP?"

"Corporal Baker, you jerk, we all go for ride in convertible car."

Click! in that sensitized brain, the secret he has pretended to know: her hot pants, her blind passion for MPs, this is what the lawyer fears. That's why she can't be trusted. Doubly so, for this Baker was certainly a friend.

"No, I don't think I know him," says Taub.

"Then what you worry about, *Kaeru,*" she says. He shakes her in the mind's eye, slaps her hard, and says, I worry for Popkin, slut, my *lansman,* my friend.

"No one is worried, Akemi. There's no reason to be, yet. You've already talked to the authorities, have you?"

"*Hai.* Lieutenant see me Friday night. I tell him what I know."

"I see. You told the truth about who stole the car."

For a split second fear pays a visit to that small, pretty face. She sips her drink, wipes her mouth, and shrugs her shoulders. "*Mochiron yo.* Akemi never lie."

But he's caught it, and it thrills him, for while it ought to mean she has already done or contemplates doing a disservice to the truth, he had despaired of making her afraid. Things have been very shaky from the start; but at least, at last, the bitch knows fear. He would love to work that vein, dilate that fear, then free her from it before she can do so (in her awful resilience) on her own.

But she has already done so. All the same, he slaps his billfold on the table. Thousand-yen notes, too big for the wallet, protrude. He rotates it on the table. Akemi gulps her drink and half rises. "Corporal *Kaeru,*" she says, "you make me bored. What do you want?"

His plan, to call it that, is new. It came to him moments before, when he bought her out of the bar. It's far from foolproof. It is, frankly, as much a gesture as a plan. But he feels it to be right: he knows already the warmth and the pain, the enriching agony of sacrifice.

"I wish to make a purchase. This will not be a new experience, you are in the habit of selling service, *deshō?* For fifteen hundred yen, is it not, we could go off and share a delightful, sordid time."

"Out of the question. Tonight you must pay twenty-five hundred."

"That's fine. You know that that is not what I ask of you. Although what I do ask I'm willing to pay well for. I want to be *absolutely certain* you've told the truth about the accident. No, don't speak, listen. I'm ready to give you five thousand, repeat, five thousand yen for this certainty. Now: if you've already told the truth, consider this money a reward, yours to keep with no questions asked; if you've in any way lied—I don't ask you now if you have—you're being paid to undo the damage. Go and see Lieutenant Frick and tell him what really happened. Ring him up, I'll give you his office number. Tell the truth, whatever your personal feelings in the matter. You're not a stupid girl. You know it's wrong to harm an innocent man. Is it a bargain, Akemi?"

He stares into her face, but fails to see that he has hit her where she lives: for the second time in four nights (and the first only dimly remembered—something occurred that angered him and lit up life for her with brief startling clarity) he has indicated order, meaning, guideposts, in this crazy souped-up world. Since the incident, which she looked upon (in its unfolding) as a way to punish the MP for infidelity, she has suffered less from remorse than from a sense of self-betrayal; for at heart she is not really a vindictive soul. She was fuddled by a transient grudge and the rapidity of events—the accident, Helver's offer, the immediate interview with Frick—and now, because of what she said, the child Baker would go to jail for a thousand years. But she'd taken the step. The money, duly delivered Saturday morning, did not matter so much as the bargain itself, and that not so much as laziness. Inertia and honor held her back, not greed, or fear.

And now came this plump instigation to repair the damage, bearing funds. Arrives this divine prig with an obscure cause which sets straight her own. *Voilà!* Child of impulse, she will do it: contact, confer with, unbeguile the Law. She shakes with what for her is rare, silent laughter.

He studies his wallet now. He counts out the fresh bills, one to five. Pushes them toward her, lifts her hand and puts it on the pile. "It's a deal then, Akemi."

From the money she looks doubtfully up at Taub. "Not too goddamn much here, *Kaerusan.* I can remember, these days, when I get more for doing less. But," she says, "you an old friend and . . ." she remembers! "you a Jew. *Dakara sa,* I give cut-rate price to tell the truth."

"Good," Taub said. Immured, immune. "Exactly that. I ask no more. *Au revoir, ma petite.* Take no drugs excessively harmful to the health."

"Stay loose." *Bakayarō,* Akemi said.

VI

Popkin listened to the voices. The outer door was open, revealing the unfloored corridor that ran the length of the house, the crockery and the kerosene stove, the basins of water she drew from the well outside. The two rooms in which they lived were off to the left and higher, cut off from the "kitchen" by sliding doors. These were drawn shut; beneath them, neatly, two pairs of thonged sandals, beyond them the mournful voices. He took off his own shoes. Probably, this was for the best. She knew damn well he was restricted to the post. With a guest, she'd be less likely to press for details. He pulled back the doors. Reiko sat on the mats, propped against the wall. The other girl sat in the only chair. He had seen her before, but he couldn't place her. He avoided Reiko's glance, stepped over her legs and went into the bedroom. From beneath the double bed he pulled out a cardboard carton, from this took a bottle of wine. He carried it to the sitting room and dropped down next to Reiko. "Well," he said. "Home sweet home."

The other one had been crying, but he thought he would overlook this, at least until they were reintroduced. Two tears worked loose just then and ran a jagged course down the sides of her flat, oily nose. He turned to Reiko. "What's wrong with your friend?"

He was shaken to see she was not far from tears herself. "What's going on?"

"What you do? Scape from monkey house?"

"What monkey house? You know I wasn't in no jail."

"You suppose be in jail now."

"Who in hell told you that? Who is this?"

Kazuko snuffled. "I friend your *Tomodachi* Helversan."

"Bob's girl, that's it. We met once over at the service club. What you cryin' for?"

"Why she cry *ka!*" Reiko exploded. "She cry because for two years she have one boy friend, no have nothing from today. She cry because half GIs stupid, other half sonabitch. She cry because she have good boy friend, sergeant, kind. Now Lieutenant Frick take away stripes, send him Korea, maybe Taiwan. You know why? Because *you* steal car. Because you no-good, drunk, selfish, shit. Everything your fault. So I no can cry."

She turned away. Kazuko reached out a hand, pulled it back, ran her sleeve across her eyes. "*Chigau wa, chigau wa.* Not his fault. My boy friend make big mistake. He lawyer, suppose be smart, *ne,* he want to help you, why he trust whore? Whore always make trouble. Akemi go see lieutenant other day tell him everything. She no give back money too. Now you in big trouble, Bobby too. He only want to help you. Now he must go *sayonara* . . . good-by . . ." Sobs choked her off. Popkin took a long drink of wine. Reiko kept her face turned away.

Popkin felt terrible. What was the sense of going AWOL to walk into this? She thought because she had a steady shack and Akemi assed around there was a difference between them. Everybody had a name for everybody else. He took another drink of wine.

"Ah, Akemi's all right. Who in hell knows why she switched her story. It's the stinking Army. . . ."

"Why you no tell me you steal car?" Reiko said. "To take a ride with whore."

Popkin hightailed it to the bedroom and came back with a bottle of wine. The first was half full, but he was looking ahead. "Anyone care for a drink?"

"Why you no tell me, ah?"

"You know goddamn well why. That was the day you went to your old man's grave. I didn't know where in hell you were. I needed somebody to talk to."

To his disgust, Kazuko sobbed harder and buried her face in her hands.

"Trouble with you broads, you grow attached. You call yourselves 'business girls,' but you're too soft. That's why a kid like Akemi does the smart thing. She works in a bar, she stays independent. When a beau gets sent to the big eight she figures this is life, and picks up on somebody else. Now you two will do the same friggin' thing when me and Helver go. But you have to get over it first. You have to bawl awhile. So you think that makes you different from a whore." To shut himself up he went to work on the wine.

Reiko said, "You like Akemi *ka?*"

He tore at the foil of the second bottle.

"You catch Akemi *ka?* I go way one day, Kyoto temple, you make love *panpan* work in bar."

"That ain't true," Popkin said glumly. "We just went for a lousy drive in the car."

"I no believe you. You catch her many times before, *ne*. You answer, you catch Akemi before?"

"Yeah," Popkin said. "Can't a guy have a past?"

"*Kamahen.* You can have past. Because you no have nothing else. You can take Akemi to monkey house." She stood, stormed into the bedroom, and banged shut the doors.

Kazuko looked up. "GIs all time same," she said. "All time do bad thing Japanese girl. Go back home, mess up, go with Japanese whore. GIs all time no good, all time hurt Japanese girl."

Popkin rose. They were even now, they had exchanged their views. "Why don't you go home now. Helver needs you. This might be mine and Reiko's last night together. You ought to respect that. But you come cryin' over here and spillin' the beans. Why don't you be a good kid and buzz off."

The doors squealed apart and Reiko flew into the room. "She my friend, she can stay! She go home when she want, not when you say!"

Kazuko protested in Japanese.

"*Iya,*" Reiko said. "I don't care. He say Japanese girl soft, always fall in love. I no in love. Crazy old man, PFC, drink too much . . . look! He stay here twenty minutes, already finish near two bottles wine. You . . . PFC!"

"I ain't going to stand for that," Popkin said. "Abuse in my own goddamn house. I'm goin' for a walk. Maybe I'll come back, maybe not. You don't seem to give a damn either way." But she was right: he had finished nearly two bottles in record time, and didn't feel a thing. It would hit him at once within the next quarter of an hour, a devastating blow, but there was no help for it now. He stepped down into his shoes, leaving them unlaced, and turned back into the room. Reiko stood in its center, her arms straining toward him, anguish large on her simple face, and terror. Which was how it ought to be. "Send your friend home," Popkin said gently. "I'll be back in ten minutes. Just going to clear my head," and walked outside. He went to the mouth of the alley, waited, then made his way back to the house. He'd wait around until Kazuko left. He stood in the tall grass along the side, peering in at the window. They huddled a foot apart on the straw mats, balled against their grief, canceling grief by canceling themselves. They took up no room, made no sound.

He'd take his walk. This much was certain—he would lose Reiko hard. When he went back to the house he was going back to stay. He'd hole up there until they found him; not do their work for them by running back to the post and waiting with his finger up for Frick's whim to lower the boom. Another AWOL on top of the theft-perjury charge could not hurt him now, if he cared. He should return at once and tell her the news, have her lay in supplies, but better to wait until the other had definitely gone; took her tears, the world she called up he no longer had the stomach for, out into the night; so he staggered along the mesh fence which separated this part of the camp from the Japanese town. Beyond the dispensary the familiar landmark caught his eye, reaching into the drizzle and mist, and he recalled that for the first time since the bargain was struck he had let a Friday pass without depositing his body in the chapel. As he stood there the lights went out, the door swung open, and Taub stepped into the rain. Popkin watched him lock up and walk toward the barracks. "We're all square, Rabbi." Popkin said. "No more house of worship; no more bedcheck worries for me. I don't owe you a miserable thing." Then, suddenly very drunk, he came out onto the main road.

Across and to the left was the football field. It extended by one hundred fifty yards the eastern half of Camp Hara, facing for its length souvenir shops, an off-limits restaurant, two laundries, a dozen limp and tired shacks, the last outpost of the town. The railway tracks ran between the playing field and the houses, alongside the road. Here a ditch contained them; further up they climbed and leveled with the road, and a Japanese security guard stood from nine until six between the main gate and the bus depot regulating traffic as the antiquated trolley clanged a warning and lumbered by. As Popkin waited in the rain and darkness a northbound train shrieked past a crossing somewhere below the camp, came into sight a moment later, left the hollow for the level stretch and sank again as it neared him, its round eye freezing a cone of rain. Then it was past, slowing, clanking to a stop at the small station just past the football field. An Army bus coughed out of the depot and turned south, Kyoto bound. A farmer rolled by behind him with a nightsoil-laden mule, then a GI passed with his girl. Standing there was fairly risky. Soon he'd head back to the house and begin hiding out, whether or not Helver's girl was there. To be recognized now would be the death of his plans. Someone yelled, "Hey you! Buddy!" the voice of disaster, right smack on schedule, and, outraged, he slipped and slid down the grassy slope on his back and behind until he reached level ground. He was unharmed. He'd been startled, tripped on his laces, lost control, but once down he shucked shoulders and hips and helped himself to the bottom of the grade. Out of sight and reach of whoever had called. He lay there, proud of himself, tasting the rain. The wine throbbed in his head, and he closed his eyes. That was much better—not sickening as the week before. I'm holding it better, he thought; but that had been rotgut, not the sweet, familiar wine. The throbbing seemed friendly, sedative, like the sound of a familiar clock. He'd rest there a moment until it was safe to return. He drew a leg to his body, extended the other, threw his arm across his eyes. Vivid pictures raced through his brain. The throbbing softened, ceased. The rain fell harder. Popkin slept.

May your father turn like a roasting pig over eternal flames. Let the host devour your whore-mother's breast at a leisurely clip. Cholera and lesser plagues infect your kin. I pray you should lose your means of livelihood. Old World imprecations in ascending practical order batter the Asiatic's head, for he isn't blind. To get the job he must pass a rigorous eye test, and for a moment, approaching and exiting from opposite gates, they faced each other across the narrow road. To avoid the ghost of misunderstanding he began to trot as well as wave the umbrella, stepped ankle-deep in a puddle, and was wet through in both directions by the rain. What *chutzpah!* He all but shakes his fist at the bus's brown behind as it veers left, yards away, and rumbles toward the town. Almost no one is aboard. Granted there are rules; granted he wasn't at the stop in time; no harm would befall the man for relenting in such weather. Complaining to the Transportation Officer does not really enter his mind, but the driver of even a military vehicle should be able to distinguish when legality is not the higher form of wisdom.

So there he stands. Chagrined? Enraged? As the bus disappears he adjusts to the busless world with the efficient languor of an animal, Out of sight, out of mind. The Japanese driver need not be forgiven who has never sinned. The *densha* will see him through. The *densha* goes by the small, local station every quarter of an hour. If it makes for a longer, less comfortable ride it at the same time launches his plan, the invocation of an atmosphere. Better the bedraggled townsfolk for a beginning, country bundles in the aisles, than neat and chattering Army wives. Moments earlier a train grumbled northward and he hears it echo still, clattering along the lakeside. The sounds do not recede, perhaps they blend with the noises of a nearing Kyoto train. He quickens his step, so as not to miss that too.

"You! Hey buddy!"

The building closest to him is the dispensary, set back a way from the fence. On its porch, out of the weather, stands the man who called. There seems little doubt that he is hailing Taub. The cantor slows.

"You got a match?"

"Yes."

"How about a light?"

"How do you propose I get it to you?"

"Hang on, I'll come over."

He limps through the rain, reaches through the mesh and takes the book from Taub. "Like feeding monkeys," he says. "I just this minute ran out." He cups the match, lights up, exhales. "Hell of a note. Pulled a muscle in that night problem the other week. They said I was too old to go running around in the dark, but I felt I had to do it. Fell into a hole."

"I'll need those back."

"Yeah, here. I asked some guy for a light not two minutes ago and he disappeared. He was standing right there, by the gully. My eyesight must be goin' bad too."

"Thank you."

"Where'd you get that umbrella? I ought to pick up one like it for my wife. Just to give her a hard time. She's a Jap, yet she don't like anything gook. Not even clothes. For a minute there, I thought you was a gook yourself."

"No," Taub says. "The gooks are different from us. I must move on."

To conceal his repugnance. He leaves behind the instant intimacy of the friendless, the empty yearning of the dumb and old. Who are, to return to a favorite topic, the heart's blood of the Army. For only fools remained (below commissioned level) to age gracelessly, or at all, in the self-immolating looking-glass sub-society which has never lost a war. But (in the present instance) redeemed as well as damned by ignorance, married to a Japanese girl. Wonderful shoeless evenings at home, a back rub, make the rest worth while. Life with a war child who denies her dislocated heritage from the safety of the PX while it is all around her, to languish and die in Tulsa or Frankfurt for a piece of *sushi* or the smell of incense or the sight of a Japanese sign. Making dead communion with Italian war brides in Asheville and White Sands because the great white mother saw it that way, American Army wife, imposing her tiny vision by the simple process of majority rules. America, the melting pot. It's suicide and stupid to deny what you are. Particularly if it's etched on your face, but likewise if not—either way they'll bury you in the end. So your suffering is more to the point if you understand why. Acknowledge, admit, *secretly approve*. He knows these anti-Japanese Japanese, as he knows non-Jewish Jews, and they must all reap *bupkas* for their pains. Rejectors of the unrejectable, he has met them in New York, and since. They affect indifference, distaste, or, back to the wall, they bolster with bland egalitarian argument. And they are all, as they should be, sniffed out in the end. For they are the Chosen People. The designation Jew will always be pejorative. There must be an out-group. This is the divine order of things. If lucky enough to be born one, rejoice! Savor the proud martyrdom, hate when required, hold your head high. This is the Old Testament Message, what it means to be a Jew. This is also what it means to be other things, but it is not necessary (even if possible) to work up a kinship with the Underdog. Anti-Semitism transcends. It shatters boundaries. It welds diverse national/ethnic groups. The wife of the old regular on the dispensary porch is in trouble, but she will never know what real suffering means.

The sound builds in volume, the approach of a southbound tram. They crossed somewhere beyond the camp, but he reaches the station in time. A few folk alight, Taub alone boards. He sits toward the front of the first car, close to the standing man who manipulates the complicated levers and bars which control the ancient train. Rows of straw seats face across the aisle. Taub adjusts the inverted umbrella between his legs, and the droplets trickle to the floor, form a pool. He studies the party opposite. It's a school-girl, engrossed in a book, her chin supported on her fist. Rose-cheeked, seventeen, sweet mouth, braided hair. Wearing the black skirt and white blouse which is the student's uniform, and wooden clogs against the rain. She reminds him in some ways of a cousin in New York, the same air of innocence. Immediately he notes the resemblance a warmth engulfs him, suffusions of self-approbation. This is odd (if pleasant), because he has thought this kind of thing, without loving himself, before: has remarked that many Japanese faces call white ones to mind, of types, usually, but often (as now) of individuals, as if in Japan he has stumbled onto a space-time continuum where one found slightly distorted mirror-images of family and friends. That's already struck him—uniformly black-haired and black-eyed, there was enough variety in their features to evoke the heterogeneous world of whites, and more: faces unduplicated outside of Asia, or Japan.

Yet now this warmth grips him. To the current observation accrues an astounding moral: *We are all the same.* This mystical platitude moves him (though it sits uneasy with the ruminations which precede). Despite himself, all unawares, he is, has been, a bastion of brotherhood.

But he senses the glare of the girl's neighbor, a crone. She hates him, he sees sadly, and for the wrong reasons: all this time he has been staring at the girl. He is a conqueror, come to rape the countryside. She doesn't need to read his dog tags, this ancient lady, she'll judge him anyway. For the primal antagonism she, they, can look to their own. They have their *eta*, unmentionable outcast class, persecuted in accord with antique, hallowed laws. The *eta* lives in ghettos, though no longer obliged to do so, but both parties want it that way. The relationship has reached an advanced stage, become, by common consent, a mutual act of mind. The Japanese (as Helver said) do not need the Jews.

But, this being so, neither does he need the Japanese. If Taub, in what he conceives as his essence, is irrelevant to these people, the opposite is likewise true. It is in being *God's eta* that the Jew truly exists: supremely affirmed by being thus divinely denied. Bother the babel of the non-Jewish world. He's been right from the start, right both ways. Nothing of the tortuous dialectic need be disclaimed.

He looks toward the front of the car, at the conductor's back, where something is taking place. The man's head sinks mollusc-like, he yells, makes frantic passes at the levers and dials. The second car lurches into the first and Taub is thrown into the aisle. All is confusion and overturned parcels and a mad sound eclipses the conductor's screams— it is the sound of death and loneliness, and he knows, crouching at the schoolgirl's feet, the train has hit a living thing. Already people crane from windows; conductor and ticketseller lower themselves through doors built for platform level onto the tracks below. Taub looks at the girl's stiff, frightened face; he has the wild impulse to sit beside her and soothe away the sickness he feels welling up on his own. He picks himself from the floor. A hand tugs at his trouser cuff, it is the ticketseller, below, nearly in tears: *"Amerikajin da yo. Orite kuremahen ka?"*

"So it's an American! What can I do!" But he retrieves his umbrella and suffers the man to help him through the door. He descends, pained and dreamy, keeping his face averted from the lantern and the torment. The yell breaks again from the thing on the tracks, not human, he can no longer look away.

The beam of light traps the gaping mouth and the pain-maddened eyes. The body is unharmed (men of both races will say, later, "A lucky man"), but the right foot is crushed and gone beneath the wheels. His fingernails bite deep into his skull, blood runs past his ears. He seems to be waiting; shudders; once more he screams.

On his knees, Taub digs his fists into his cheeks and through his roaring sickness indicts the might-have-been, Why, why did you not let him come to *shul?*

WALLACE MARKFIELD

THE COUNTRY OF THE CRAZY HORSE

AS THE TRAIN BEGAN THE LONG CRAWL UNDER THE
tunnel to Brooklyn I thought again of the crazy horse. It was Saturday
morning, and all the mothers sat before the stoop on bridge chairs, opening tangerines and helping themselves from a big bag of polly seeds,
budging not one inch as the super shot his dirty looks about and
warned of summonses for each and every one who blocked his path to
the cellar. The movie-house was not yet open; my crew and I waited,
waited for the moment to draw near, killing the time with marvelous
deathfalls—the slow, coin-flipping sag of George Raft; the sharp flinch
and spin of the settler as the arrow strikes; the stool pigeon's slow
crumple as they cut him down in the phone booth, behind the bill-
board, atop the church steps.

When all of a sudden the horse came clopping down the street. Heavy
and handsome he was, the kind Buck Jones and Hoot Gibson sat, looking smart enough to pull you out of quicksand or loosen your bonds
with his teeth, and white as a centaur. He bucked and wove through
the traffic, taking little hip-hops up and down the sidewalk, kicking at
the hedges that lined the one- and two-family houses. The cluster of
mothers broke and scattered, then joined together again to form a
circle around us like a wagon train. One, wilder even than the rest,
made a run for her boy's two-wheeler, crying, for no good reason,
"What did he need it for? What, tell me, what?" From an open window someone sloshed a pail of water. We began throwing pebbles and
bottle caps and flipping little cardbord squares with our rubber band
guns, but they fell short. The laundryman turned the corner in his

189

truck and let go on the horn. Seymour, my best friend, who could imitate anything, brought up from deep within his chest the spang of bullets on rocks and trumpeting of wild bull elephants spotting the white hunter. Somehow stung by this, the horse whinnied back. He lowered his head, took delicate little steps to the sidewalk and stopped before the house of Ringleman, the dentist. He reared up, he flared his nostrils and showed his terrible teeth. Then, in a movement that seemed as precise and formal as a dance step, he made a long, low leap. And impaled himself upon the iron fence.

They removed the carcass later, on an open truck, and washed down Ringleman's lawn with a hose. My mother dragged me upstairs, bore me into the bedroom and caught fiercely at the neckband of my shirt. Her face trembled, and she opened and closed her mouth as if there lay in her mind some fearful pronouncement no tongue could utter. I saw the horse heave and rear between us again, his eyes glittering like the future. I stand, awaiting my mother's explanation for all that has passed. But there is only her hand, heavy as brass upon my face, and the cry, "Look at him. Feel him. How perspired he is, how it drips from him!"

Two stops now from my station and I am drenched with sweat again. I move to another seat, fleeing the fan's powerful draft, conscious of how vulnerable I am, of my tendency to colds and swollen glands, of the way I load my stomach with rich and spicy foods. From across the aisle a woman jumps up and, marvelously balancing against the pitching and bucketing, looms over me. She is plump and moon-faced and there is a tenderness in her eyes, as though she would like to stroke me as I sit there. A swift half-turn, a languid shrug, and she allows herself to fall heavily upon the seat next to mine, with a smile that stretches from one end of the world to the other. Her hands begin to flutter nervously, and I move closer to the window, pretending to lose myself in the boring vista of playgrounds and cemeteries and television antennae that spear the last light like crucifixes. She is stooped over, working very hard and furtively at something; once, she lifts her head to smile again, as though there was a secret between us. I watch her like a grim eavesdropper, awaiting the fulfillment of events. She strains, she wriggles, she falls back, spent. Then, gathering all her forces for one compulsive effort, she reaches deep into the straw cushion and draws out a maimed magazine.

"I used to love to read," she says at last, blinking her mad, moist brown eyes.

I nod profoundly and slowly spread my arms, the gesture of one who sees no escape from his miserable existence.

"But now, who has the mind for it? And every day to the hospital, that can knock anybody out. Not that the traveling bothers me. It's the going up and down to change trains. But it's the very least I can do for him. My brother-in-law. Oh, I knew already, even before the operation, when he complained that he can't eat any more, that he lost his appetite. Because that was an eater! Yeah, yeah! I knew already when they finished, I looked at the doctor's face. I didn't have to ask. They opened him up, they took a look, and they sewed him up again. And you know what he got it from? From one thing only. Aggravation."

"Oh yes, oh yes," I chant liturgically. "I can imagine, I can believe it. Aggravation. . . ." Till the age of fourteen I had been certain it was a Yiddish word.

"Since he's sick I don't give a damn for anything. I walk out of the house without even—you should pardon the expression—a girdle on. Though before I complain I should first bite my tongue off. A person has his health, he has everything."

"That's it. To be healthy is the main thing," I echo. Then, thank God, I recognize my station, like the beginning of an old movie, and I hustle for the door.

"Goodbye, good luck," she howls after me. "In whatever you undertake. You're a very, very nice person."

I feel a tickle of nervous excitement as I enter the streets. There's a brand-new community center where my old lot was and a hive of garden apartments whose brick is colored the sickly pink of a rabbit's eye. I stare inside the picture windows, into each living room with its Van Gogh sunflowers, its kidney-shaped coffee tables, its gigantic mohair chairs with their cold unrumpled covers. For a moment the acres of cement under my feet seem to turn into wall-to-wall capeting, and I have a sudden impulse to shout something wild and crazy— *"God is Love!"* or *"Sauve qui peut!"* But I content myself with the idea as Flatbush sprawls vast and arctic and baffling before me, holding only the etherized silence of a museum. Not a gurgle anywhere, not a cheep, not even the yap of a backyard dog. I fondle the reassuring bulk of the candy box under my arm, dreaming of myself as a good son, an accountant, a chiropodist, a professional certainly, one who phones his mother each day from the office, even before his wife. At that moment I hear a cry that sounds as though it rose from a throat clogged by blood and rage. I stand, dumbfounded, till I catch the one terrible word, the speaking of the unspeakable: "Ma!" A yowl, a lunatic roar and then, with rising fervor, "Ma, open the window, Ma!"

I move along, tense and poised as a tightrope walker. Every corner, every garage, every alleyway and clothesline is an announcement of old sins. Here I broke, here I tore, here I mocked, here I raged, here I stole. . . . I near the candy store where I'd once applied my criminal mind to loose cigarettes and comic books, fighting it out with old man Teller over the water-bag I'd hurled into his fountain. "Oh, you killed him," his wife announced when the stroke came to finish him, "you ate him up alive, you and yours." Yet business was business, and she went on selling me my cockemamies, my skate keys and pencil boxes, and when she had to, sent me out to pick up a few pennies calling people down to the phone.

A powerful longing for an egg-cream assails me; I assure myself that it will wash down the nauseous sense of homelessness. With the chilly, menacing air of a movie gunfighter I walk past the little group of shmoozers clumped around the magazine racks and plant my elbows on the fountain. I give my order to the runty owner, making foolish conversation as he works the syrup dispenser. "It's a very strange thing," I say, "but I notice that you just cannot get a decent egg-cream in Manhattan. Why is that? After all, chocolate is chocolate, milk is milk, and seltzer is seltzer."

He puts the drink before me and whispers dramatically, "It's all the syrup. What I use, I have to pay forty cents more on the gallon."

I let out a cunning, portentous "Ah!" Then I drain the glass in two long swigs and finish up with a big fig newton. The mixture turns bitter in my mouth. I wonder if, somehow, I have not been taking in the body and blood of old man Teller.

He wipes his hands on a soiled apron. "A malted," he moans. "They don't know how to make it and they don't want to know. You got to freeze the milk. Otherwise, tastes like *pishachs.*"

"Yes, oh yes, now I see." I nod my head as though I'd just heard the seven proofs for the existence of God. "No wonder! You freeze the milk. Yes!"

I put down a quarter and he flicks the change at me. Swiveling around fiercely, he lets out a bellow at a young wise-guy who blocks the doorway and makes too free with the comic books. "Moron," he yells, in rage and despair, "the whole store should burn with you in it!" He coughs and coughs, choking on a cold lump of grief.

"Kids," I soothe, as I stalk to the door. "Kids."

"Sure," he says, wiping and wiping at the marble counter. "But he's old enough to die."

I quicken my steps for the last two dark blocks, palms perspiring, whistling tonelessly through clenched teeth, like a man getting ready for his bride. Even from the corner I can make out my mother's face; it seems to have the eerie luminosity of one of Chagall's angels. I keep to the shadow, but she spots me anyway, hanging out the window to make the neighborhood ring with her "Sonny!" The nitwit yell shakes me up, as it did in the old days, when it would sour my life on the streets, following me wherever I went to catch me *in flagrante delicto*—with a stolen deposit bottle in my hand or a snotty word on my lips. Methodically, I check myself for failings: Am I wearing a hat against the changing weather? Do I strain my eyes on too many movies? Paying fancy prices at the all-night delicatessens? Ignoring overdue notices from the library? And roughage? Does my system get enough roughage? All clear, and I enter the lobby, where the super has long since given up his mop-work against the track of dogs and baby buggies.

"Welcome, stranger," my mother says. "I'm glad you still remember how to get here."

She moves in for the kiss, lowering her head and placing both hands on my shoulders. I block her deftly with the candy box. She averts her eyes, as though it was a telegram announcing disaster.

"No?" I threaten, making a mock grab. "Then here and now it goes out and down, down, into the incinerator."

"Take it home," she pleads. "Do me a favor and take it home." Her enlarged and plaintive eyes fix on the walls behind me, where my honor cards and graduation pictures hang. "He has a few cents and he must spend them. That's him. Even when he was a child."

"Don't you worry." I laugh a big booming Edward Arnold laugh, indicating I can afford this and much more.

"Sidney!" she summons. "Come! He's here!"

And my father drifts in, bearing the magazine section from last Sunday's *Times*. All his life he's never been able to catch up with the papers. His face is overcast with bafflement and a vague horror; at any moment he seems to expect the raising of my hand against him. Ten weeks ago he got himself a coronary, and he keeps rubbing his left side and nodding at me, as if to say, "Now you're a wise-guy, but wait, only wait a while." He leans over, plucking at my sleeve. "That suit," he snorts in derision. "Where did you pick up the bargain?"

My mother winks and bites her lip. "What's the matter?" she asks, a little shrilly. "It's a nice suit. Honest to God, I think it's very, very nice on him."

"Fine," my father grunts. "You bought it. You like it. Wear it in good health."

"In the *best* of health," my mother murmurs, looking passionately into my eyes. "Now come. You'll go inside, you'll have a bite. I have pot cheese. I have sour cream. I can slice in some vegetables."

So it's been, as long as I remember. You can die before you'll get a piece of meat in my mother's house. Still, for all her Gandhi ways my mother keeps alive a marvelous image of herself as a hotsy-totsy cooker, a wonder-woman with stuffed derma and sweetbreads and Old Country soups.

I mumble something to the effect that I have eaten, that I put away a big meal uptown, a costly meal.

Bitterly, tenderly, she says, "You come visit your mother and you eat on the outside."

"Ah, come on, Ma. Ma, come on." I hang my head and scrape my feet like a movie adolescent.

"I shopped. I prepared. I made a special trip."

"Don't force it." My father turns both palms up in his man-of-peace gesture. "You did your duty. You did the right thing."

"You'll take some home with you."

"I'll take."

"I'll wrap a nice little bundle and you'll enjoy it later."

"I'll enjoy."

We move out of the foyer, my mother pulling ahead and steering a desperate course for the kitchen. "Wait, Ma, wait," I tell her. "Why don't we go and sit in the living room? Come, we'll sit in the living room."

"Hah!" my mother cries in terror and disbelief. She back-tracks fast to cut off the living room door. "It's an icebox in there. I had to shut off the steam, it was turning all the drapes yellow. So help me God."

"Oh no, you don't!" I link arms, imprisoning her frail and fearful flesh and lead her tenderly into the living room's cluttered bleakness. We have not sat together here since the druggist came to claim I'd laid hands on his crazy daughter.

I didn't remember so many flowers. Lilies mostly, though here and there a few fat roses. Wherever I look there is the image of a flower.

On the draperies, on the seat covers, on the lamp shades. Imbedded in plaster wreaths on the wall. Spilling all over my mother's apron and housedress. I begin to get a headache and breathing comes harder, as though they're draining oxygen from the air.

Then we get down to business. My father opens with a "What's new?"

To which I make reply, "What should be new?"

This stumps them. They expect more from me, their prophet and augur, their Hamlet and Tamburlaine. From the end table my Bar Mitzvah picture smirks at me. Hey, hey, he calls, this back-talker, this crafty fatso, where's that family chronicle you began at twelve? The ball of tin foil you were saving? And the instruction book in Judo? Gone now, with the old NRA Blue Eagle, with Dickie Moore, with hard-faced Frankie Darro and Garfield in his blackened T-shirt.

My father unfolds his magazine section; he has decided to readmit the present. My mother, in desperation, talks of aunts and uncles and cousins long forgotten. She permits nothing to rest in peace, she treads upon every grave in the family plot. This one owes her money, that one brought no gift to my father as he lay in his hospital bed. They have used her, they have sucked her and drained her, they have turned her heart into a huge festering sore. It's almost beautiful to watch the way she boils and blazes, a regular Old Testament queen, fire-eyed and calling down curses. She plays the clown too, getting her satire across with deviling malice, fingers pulling and probing as though they were molding effigies. And I begin to see how much I've taken from her. I catch a gesture I used at a party, a gibe I delivered the week before, a whine that enters my voice in cafeteria debates. I feel like an anthology of old sorrows.

Spent, consumed, a clawed hand punishing her breast, my mother says, "Strangers. Sometimes they treat you better than your own."

My father warms to the theme. "She's telling me something new. Strangers. When I was in the hospital they couldn't do enough for me. I'm not exaggerating. The nurse once saw that I couldn't digest the milk they were giving out. She made a special trip to get me a little tea when the kitchen was closed. And they would all talk to me. Do you know that when I left, the social worker came over and shook my hand and gave me a kiss? She told me, 'We're all crazy about you, we love you, but we don't want to see you again, you hear. That's an order.'" He laughs, aroused and deeply pleased. "Which reminds me. Tomorrow, without fail I want to give Mostag a ring. He was the one in the next bed who let me use his electric shaver. That's a prince, a real prince. To look at him, would you believe he's worth close to a quarter of a million?"

" 'To look at him'? What do you mean 'to look at him'?" my mother mimics. "When you would sleep I used to sit and talk to him for an hour at a time and he'd have a big, big steamer basket by the bed with fruits and nuts and candy and he wouldn't once say, 'Here, take a piece.' Did you ever notice, the more they have—"

"Come on, get away!" Violently, my father shakes his paper. "I assure you, if you had helped yourself he would not have begrudged it to you. Men don't think of those things, it's not in their make-up."

"You don't let a person sit like a dummy. I didn't need his piece of candy. Thank God, I can afford to go out and buy a box. But be a sport, at least make the gesture."

"You know a lot! As far as I'm concerned and from the way he acted to me, why he's as decent as they come. Money or no money, you'll find goddamn few people who'll run around when you can't wait for the nurse and empty your you-know-what for you; goddamn few!"

My father's eyes are shining, burning with all his energies, and a queer look comes over his face. It's the look of a small boy shaking hands with a cop or a cowboy star, the look he'd get when he spoke of Debs and Norman Thomas, then F.D.R. and the manager of his local. In an instant he can shed his self, ecstatic with mediocrity. He becomes the one who sits in the back, always in the back of group photographs, the one who holds the umbrella over the principal speaker at a street rally or springs from the heart of a crowd to joggle the assassin's gun. . . . Years ago he broke down and wept scalding tears at the dinner table. And when we begged and pleaded for the reason he ground his teeth and quivered and answered, "You didn't see. You didn't read. Westbrook Pegler. What he had the gall to say about the Roosevelt boys!"

My mother rises. She's spotted the imprint of a finger on a window pane and she chases after it, relentless as Old Dutch cleanser. Then, swaying gently from her heels to her toes, she utters a great wrenching groan. "Tell me," she says, "do you remember Mr. Wasserman?"

I indicate my uncertainty with a limp disparaging hand.

"Ah, you should certainly recall," my mother says, a shallow sweetness invading her tones. "He lived near the Parkway, he used to be here day and night. The one who made your suit for the graduation. Everybody talked about it, they couldn't get over his workmanship."

"A mechanic," my father announces. "A pair of golden hands."

"Last week he called me. I couldn't get off the phone. I had to pretend the bell rang, and excuse myself."

Any moment now I know the shaft will come.

"So—" She draws and holds a long breath and her face pales and swells. "Two days ago. A hemorrhage. Go imagine."

"Never, never," my father cries, taking over. "In a million years, never. He wasn't a man, he was a giant. In the old days, when everybody was stretched out from the heat he'd be working the presser. And then first, late, late at night, he'd run around to pick up, to deliver. Yes, yes, oh yes, he was going to be president of the Society, he had big plans, he was going to build and renovate."

My father hunches forward. His words become thick and hazy, his fingers spread and whiten by their grip on his paper. He works and works to bring his awful feelings forth, but it's no go. Then names come scuttling through his mind. One by one he reels them off, a whole Book of the Dead. Kornfeld and Baumgarten . . . Ellinger and Glick . . . Horwitz and Kaplan . . . Old Man Fine, who chased a daughter out of the house for wearing a sleeveless dress . . . Rosen, scarred long ago by gangster acid . . . they've gone out now, the men my father loved, each and every one of them, who had never been before and would never be again, like brilliant stars at the end of night. And what people they were, what snap, what class and quality they had! Who's to keep the Society's books now, send out post cards for unveilings, throw the first clods of earth, and trim the cluttering weeds from grave beds? Nah! Their children were no children, keeping nothing up, paying no dues, coming to meetings only to eat and make stupid jokes.

"You know," my father says thoughtfully, "they'll send a check for five hundred dollars when I die. Thank God, it won't cost you a penny."

"Poo-poo!" My mother spits with a dry mouth against evil eyes and menaces.

"You think he'll bother to say *Yizkor* once in a while?"

"He'll say, he'll say," my mother assures.

A cold wave of penance moves through the room. I feel suddenly like promising all kinds of things: long visits, phone calls to relations, a greater interest in the fortunes of the family, a donation to the Synagogue. My father leans back against the chair. How bad he looks, I realize, how narrow and gray his face, how thin his hair and flabby his jaws, how cruelly shaven his cheeks.

"It's time, it's time," I announce, like a nervous innkeeper.

They rise with me, my father laying aside his paper finally, my mother commenting on the shortness of my stay, promising fantastic dishes, a veritable love-feast for my return. At the door my father describes a new way of returning to the city, and forces me to wait while he writes down the trains and stations, pointing out that I can save myself an extra fare.

"It's the 'D' train," he bellows, as I flee into the hall. "Make sure!"

"I'll make sure," I promise, waving and clutching the directions like a passport.

I've barely made the corner when I seem to hear my name called and the rush of heavy feet. What, I wonder, is it my old crazy horse again, clopping out of the past? Again, the calling of my name, and my mother catches up, proffering a soiled shopping bag.

"The pot cheese and cream. And a few cans of sardines. I made a nice package."

"Ma, Ma," I say, "For God's sake, Ma."

"What does it hurt? You'll enjoy."

"I'll enjoy." I give her a furry kiss and walk away, faster and faster, the shopping bag bulging against my side like an obscene growth.

POETRY

KARL SHAPIRO

THE SYNAGOGUE

The synagogue dispirits the deep street,
Shadows the face of the pedestrian,
It is the adumbration of the Wall,
The stone survival that laments itself,
Our old entelechy of stubborn God,
Our calendar that marks a separate race.

The swift cathedral palpitates the blood,
The soul moves upward like a wing to meet
The pinnacles of saints. There flocks of thanks
In nooks of holy tracery arrive
And rested take their message in mid-air
Sphere after sphere into the papal heaven.

The altar of the Hebrews is a house,
No relic but a place, Sinai itself,
Not holy ground but factual holiness
Wherein the living god is resident.
Our scrolls are volumes of the thundered law
Sabbath by sabbath wound by hand to read.

He knows Al-Eloah to whom the Arab
Barefooted falls on sands, on table roofs,
In latticed alleys underneath the egg
On wide mosaics, when the crier shrills.

O profitable curse, most sacred rug,
Your book is blindness and your sword is rust.

And *Judenhetze* is the course of time;
We were rebellious, all but Abraham,
And skulked like Jonah, angry at the gourd.
Our days are captives in the minds of kings,
We stand in tens disjointed on the world,
Grieving the ribbon of a coast we hated.

Some choose the ethics of belief beyond
Even particular election. Some
In bland memorial churches modify
The architecture of the state, and heaven
Disfranchised watches, *caput mortuum*,
The human substance eating, voting, smiling.

The Jew has no bedecked magificat
But sits in stricken ashes after death,
Refusing grace; his grave is flowerless,
He gutters in the tallow of his name.
At Rome the multiplying tapers sing
Life endless in the history of art.

And Zion womanless refuses grace
To the first woman as to Magdalene,
But half-remembers Judith or Rahab,
The shrewd good heart of Esther honors still,
And weeps for almost sacred Ruth, but doubts
Either full harlotry or the faultless birth.

Our wine is wine, our bread is harvest bread
That feeds the body and is not the body.
Our blessing is to wine but not the blood
Nor to sangreal the sacred dish. We bless
The whiteness of the dish and bless the water
And are not anthropaphagous to him.

The immanent son then came as one of us
And stood against the ark. We have no prophets,

Our scholars are afraid. There have been friars,
Great healers, poets. The stars were terrible.
At the Sadduccee court he touched our panic;
We were betrayed to sacrifice this man.

We live by virtue of philosophy,
Past love, and have our devious reward.
For faith he gave us land and took the land,
Thinking us exiles of all humankind.
Our name is yet the identity of God
That storms the falling altar of the world.

MURIEL RUKEYSER

FROM *LETTER TO THE FRONT*

To be a Jew in the twentieth century
Is to be offered a gift. If you refuse,
Wishing to be invisible, you choose
Death of the spirit, the stone insanity.
Accepting, take full life. Full agonies:
Your evening deep in labyrinthine blood
Of those who resist, fail, and resist; and God
Reduced to a hostage among hostages.

The gift is torment. Not alone the still
Torture, isolation; or torture of the flesh.
That may come also. But the accepting wish,
The whole and fertile spirit as guarantee
For every human freedom, suffering to be free,
Daring to live for the impossible.

SECOND ELEGY: AGE OF MAGICIANS

A baroque night advances in its clouds,
maps strain loose and are lost, the flash-flood breaks,
the lifting moonflare lights this field a moment,
while death as a skier curves along the snows,

204

death as an acrobat swings year to year,
turns down to us the big face of a nurse.
Roads open black, and the magicians come.

The aim of magicians is inward pleasure.
The prophet lives by faith and not by sight,
Being a visionary, he is divided,
or Cain, forever shaken by his crime.
Magnetic ecstasy, a trance of doom
mean the magician, worshipping a darkness
with gongs and lurid guns, the color of force.
He is again the unity of light.

The Magician has his symbols, brings up his
    children by them:
the march-step, the staircase at night, the long cannon.
The children grow in authority and become
Molitor, Dr. Passavant, powerful Dr. Falcon,
bring their professors, and soon may govern
the zone, the zodiac, the king on his throne.
"Because the age holds its own dangers.
"Because snow comes with lightnings, omens with
    all seasons."
(The Prophet covers his face against the wall,
weeps, fights to think again, to plan to start
the dragon, the ecliptic, and the heart.)

The Magician lifts himself higher than the world.
The Prophets were more casual. They endured,
and in the passive dread of solitude
heard calls, followed veiled, in midnight humility.
They claimed no preference;   they separated
unity from blindness
living from burning
tribute from tribute.

They have gone under, and do they come again?
The index of prophecy is light
and steeped therein
the world with all its signatures visible.

Does this life permit its living to wear strength?
Who gives it, protects it.   It is food.
Who refuses it, it eats in time as food.
It is the world and it eats the world.
Who knows this, knows.   This has been said.

This is the vision in the age of magicians:
it stands at immense barriers, before mountains:
'I came to you in the form of a line of men,
and when you threw down the paper, and when you sat at
     the play,
and when you killed the spider, and when you saw the
     shadow
of the fast plane skim fast over your lover's face.
And when you saw the table of diplomats,
the newsreel of ministers, the paycut slip,
the crushed child's head, clean steel, factories,
the chessmen on the marble of the floor,
each flag a country, each chessman a live man,
one side advancing southward to the pit,
one side advancing northward to the lake,
and when you saw the tree, half bright half burning.
You never inquired into these meanings.
If you had done so, you would have been restored.'

The word is war.
And there is a prediction that you are the avenger.

They cut the people's hands, and their shoulders were left,
they cut their feet off, and their thighs were whole,
they cut them down to the torse, but the voice shouted,
they cut the head off, but the heart rang out.

And in the residential districts, where nothing ever hap-
     pens,
armies of magicians filled the streets,
shouting
Need!   Bread!   Blood!   Death!

And all this is because of you.
And all this is avenged by you.
Your index light, your voice the voice,
your tree half green and half burning,
half dead half bright,
your cairns, your beacons, your tree in green and flames,
unbending smoke in the sky, planes' noise, the darkness,
magic to fight. Much to restore; now know. Now be
Seer son of Sight, Hearer, of Ear, at last.

THE WAY OUT

The night is covered with signs. The body and face of man,
    with signs, and his journeys. Where the rock is split
    and speaks to the water; the flame speaks to the cloud;
    the red splatter, abstraction, on the door
    speaks to the angel and the constellations.
The grains of sand on the sea-floor speak at last to the noon.
And the loud hammering of the land behind
    speaks ringing up the bones of our thighs, the hoofs,
    we hear the hoofs over the seethe of the sea.

All night down the centuries, have heard, music of passage.

Music of one child carried into the desert;
    firstborn forbidden by law of the pyramid.
Drawn through the water with the water-drawn people
    led by the water-drawn man to the smoke mountain.
The voice of the world speaking, the world covered by signs,
    the burning, the loving, the speaking, the opening.
Strong throat of sound from the smoking mountain.
Still flame, the spoken singing of a young child.
The meaning beginning to move, which is the song.

Music of those who have walked out of slavery.

Into that journey where all things speak to all things,
　　refusing to accept the curse, and taking
　　for signs, the signs of all things, the world, the body
　　which is part of the soul, and speaks to the world,
　　all creation being created in one image, creation.
This is not the past walking into the future,
　　the walk is painful, into the present, the dance
　　not visible as dance until much later.
These dancers are discoverers of God.

We knew we had all crossed over when we heard the song.

Out of a life of building lack on lack:
　　the slaves refusing slavery, escaping into faith:
　　an army who came to the ocean: the walkers
　　who walked through the opposites, from I to opened Thou,
　　city and cleave of the sea. Those at flaming Nauvoo,
　　the ice on the great river: the escaping Negroes,
　　swamp and wild city; the shivering children of Paris
　　and the glass black hearses; those on the Long March:
　　all those who together are the frontier, forehead of man.

Where the wilderness enters, the world, the song of the world.

Akiba rescued, secretly, in the coffin
　　by his disciples carried from Jerusalem
　　in blackness journeying to find his journey
　　to whatever he was loving with his life.
The wilderness journey through which we move
　　under the whirlwind truth into the new,
　　the only accurate. A cluster of lights at night:
　　faces before the pillar of fire. A child watching
　　while the sea breaks open. This night. The way in.

Barbarian music, a new song.

Acknowledging opened water, possibility:
　　open like a woman to this meaning.
In a time of building statues of the stars,
　　valuing certain partial ferocious skills

while past us the chill and immense wilderness
spreads its one-color wings until we know
rock, water, flame, cloud, or the floor of the sea,
the world is a sign, a way of speaking. To find.
What shall we find? Energies, rhythms, a journey.

Ways to discover. The song of the way in.

LOT'S WIFE

I have become a gate
To the ruined city, dry,
Indestructible by fire.
A pillar of salt, a white
Salt boundary stone
On the edge of destruction.

A hard lesson to learn,
A swift punishment; and many
Now seek to escape
By looking back: and they
Too become monuments.

Remember me, Lot's wife,
Standing at the furthest
Commark of lust's county.
Unwilling to enjoy,
Unable to escape, I make
Salt the rain of the world.

PHARAOH'S MEDITATION
ON THE EXODUS

The thing is finished now, there is no more
Administration worth attending to,
And I have withdrawn to this inner room
To think, or dream. From the ridiculous
To death itself we have traveled in the space
Of ten days more or less (and my child dead),
But the damp stone may weep, the wall sweat blood
(And he may take his god and go elsewhere),
Since I no longer care? Why did I care?

To come from Midian, and need his brother's help
To turn a rod into a snake—there's no
Magician here who wouldn't be ashamed
To deal in parlor magic; yet his snake
Certainly swallowed theirs, and they were out
That many rods, and had their tempers up
Besides, that they could do what he could do.
So when he turned the water all to blood,
My idiots had to have fresh wells dug out
And turn them bloody too, assisting him
While seeming to compete; if he brought frogs,
And thousands of 'em, each wizard of mine
Must proudly add some six or seven frogs
To the total disaster and say it wasn't hard—
But luckily they stuck at the lice and flies
(Though by then we were past what luck could do).

The thing is finished, and I've had enough.
If the nation break, and the rude tribes
Flood in over the marches of the South;
If the commanders elaborate confusion
Because they have heard nothing; if one whole
Division has been drowned with its equipment—
It is nothing to me, it means nothing,

I will refuse to hear. All the last week
Things were bled white of meaning, and I say,
Enough! and have imposed my solitude
On kingdom and court, so that I may have time,
In this inner room, where I need not endure
Daylight or darkness but am soothed by lamps,
To think, should there be anything left to think.
Alone, in the cool silence of the stone,
Where only my heartbeats happen, and my thoughts
Follow the small flame's wavering against the wall
Until that meaningless motion is my thought,
It may be that the world outside has stopped,
The fountain dried up, and the brickwork broken
Under the insane silence of the sun
Centuries ago, and the whole course of the world
Shifted like sand; and I alone, the brain
In this room the skull of Egypt, am alive.

My first-born son is dead, the first-born sons
Of all Egypt are dead, but that's no matter.
I am astounded, but I do not weep.
How did that power come? Out of the desert?
Out of the empty land of Midian?
May he take his god and go back there
Again, and die there.
                            But he will not die.
I'll be the one to die, and when I do,
When they replace my gut with spices, wrap
My body in the rich cloth, and write me
Immortal on the soul's stone hull I sail
Beneath the world, into some inner room
Like this, where blue Polaris, through a shaft,
Shines coldly on my smile, Egypt and I
Shall triumph. And have I hardened my heart?
I harden it again, for the greatest virtues
Are cut from stone. And on the day I rise
Once more, driving my horses up the East,
Let him and all his people fear the whip
And run to their confusion through the world.

DELMORE SCHWARTZ

ABRAHAM

(To J. M. Kaplan)

I was a mere boy in a stone-cutter's shop
When, early one evening, my raised hand
Was halted and the soundless voice said:
"Depart from your father and your country
And the things to which you are accustomed,
Go now into a country unknown and strange,
I will make of your children a great nation,
Your generations will haunt every generation of
    all the nations,
They will be like the stars at midnight, like the sand
    of the sea."
Then I looked up at the infinite sky,
Star-pointing and silent, and it was then, on that evening,
    that I
Became a man: that evening was my manhood's birthday.

I went then to Egypt, the greatest of nations.
There I encountered the Pharaoh who built the tombs,
Great public buildings, many theaters, and seashore villas:
And my wife's beauty was such that, fearing his power and lust,
I called her my sister, a girl neither for him nor for me.
And soon was fugitive, homeless and almost helpless again.
Living alone with my sister, becoming very rich
In all but children, in herds, in possessions, the herds continually
    and newly

Increased my possessions through sublime prodigies of progeny,
    and
From time to time, in the afternoon's revery
In the late sunlight or the cool of the evening

I called to mind the protracted vanity of the promise
Which had called me forth from my father's house unwillingly
Into the last strangeness of Egypt and the childless desert.
Then Sarah gave me her handmaid, a young girl
That I might at least at last have children by another.
And later, when a great deal else had occurred,
I put away Hagar, with almost unbearable remorse
Because the child was the cause of so much rivalry and jealousy.
At last when all this had passed or when
The promise seemed the puzzle parts of an old dream,
When we were worn out and patient in all things
The stranger came, suave and elegant,
A messenger who renewed the promise, making Sarah
Burst out laughing hysterically!

But the boy was born and grew and I saw
What I had known, I knew what I had seen, for he
Possessed his mother's beauty and his father's humility,
And was not marked and marred by her sour irony and
    my endless anxiety.

Then the angel returned, asking that I surrender
My son as a lamb to show that humility
Still lived in me, and was not altered by old age
    and prosperity.

I said nothing, shocked and passive. Then I said, but to
    myself alone:
"This was to be expected. These promises
Are never unequivocal or unambiguous, in this
As in all things which are desired the most:
I have had great riches and great beauty.
I cannot expect the perfection of every wish
And if I deny the command, who knows what will happen?"

But his life was forgiven and given back to me:
His children and their children are an endless nation:
Dispersed on every coast. And I am not gratified
Nor astonished. It has never been otherwise:
Exiled, wandering, dumbfounded by riches,
Estranged among strangers, dismayed by the infinite sky,
An alien to myself until at last the caste of the last alienation,
The angel of death comes to make the alienated and indestructible
  one a part of his famous and democratic society.

JACOB

All was as it is, before the beginning began, before
We were bared to the cold air, before
Pride. Fullness of bread. Abundance of idleness.
No one has ever told me what now I know:
Love is unjust, justice is loveless.

So, as it was to become, it was, in the black womb's ignorance
Coiled and bound, under the mother's heart.
There in the womb we wrestled, and writhed, hurt
Each other long before each was other and apart,
Before we breathed: who then committed greed,
Impersonation, usurpation? So, in the coming forth,
In the noose and torment of birth, Esau went first,
He was red all over. I followed him, clutching his heel,
And we were named: Esau, the one of the vivid coat,
Jacob, the one who clutches the heel of the one
Who has a vivid coat. The names were true
As the deceptive reality into which we were thrown.
For I did not know what clutching was, nor had I known
Would I have known whose heel I clutched, my brother's or
  my own!

So, the world we entered then and thus was one
In which the second must be second that the first may be first.

The world of precedence, order, other, under and above,
The darkness, sweetness, confusion and unity of love!
How the truth of our names became, as we grew, more true,
Growing like truth. How could it be otherwise? For truth
    abides
Hidden in the future, in the ambush of the marvellous,
Unknown and monstrous, at the very heart of surprise.

The gift was mind. The gift was eminence. The gift
Like every gift, was guilt. The guilt began
In the darkness and dark mystery where all begins.
The mystery of the perpetual invisible fires whence flow
The very beast and woods where—
                        with what happiness!
                        what innocence!—
Esau my brother hunted, centering like the horses of summer,
And sleeping, when he returned, the sleep of winter farms,
Spontaneous and blessed, like energy itself, sleeping or awake.
Until the hour when the angel struck!

So it was: so:
O angel of the unspeakable,
Why must a gift be guilt and hurt the gifted one?
O angel of the unspeakable, power of powers,
Locking my reins, my arms, my heart all night
So that my body was burdened as with the load of all stones
Dost thou remember what, in the darkness, I cried,
During the desperation in which I died
The last death of hope and the little deaths of the heart
Wrestling and writhing between two rivers—on one bank,
Esau, awaiting me, like a river slept—beneath me once more.
"Hast thou not seen," I cried aloud, to the unspeakable,
"Esau my brother: his handsome hunting heart upon a horse?"
How should it seem so strange that I should win,
Since victory was my gift? Unjust, like every gift,
A something neither deserved, nor gained by toil . . .
How else could it be gift and given?
Favor: favored: favorite:
Gold hair: great strength: Esau was very tall,
Possessed by the supple grace of the sea's waves, breaking.

Now Joseph is, as I was: in Egypt's pit,
In that accustomed depth and isolated height
The solitude of eminence, the exiled intelligence,
Which separated me even as it created me:
Estranged and unloved, gifted and detested,
Denied the love of the servants and the dogs.
Joseph a stranger in Egypt may only know
What I have known: my gifts, my victory, my guilt.
For Egypt is a country like a gift.
The gift is loved but not the gifted one.
The coat of many colors is much admired
By everyone, but he who wears the coat
Is not made warm. Why should the gift be the cause of pain,
O thou unspeakable? Must the vivid coat
Of eminence elect the favored favorite
As scapegoat or turncoat, exile or fugitive,
The love of mother and God, and by all others
Shunned in fear or contempt?
                              I knew what it was,
When Joseph became my favorite: knew the sympathy
Of the long experience of the unasked-for-gift:
Knew the nature of love: how many colors
Can a coat have? What should we wish, if
We could choose? What should I desire
—Not to have loved my son, the best of sons?
Rejected the choice of love? Should I have hidden
My love of him? Or should he have concealed the self
I loved, above all others, wearing the coat
Which is customary, the coats his brothers wore?
To how many coats can a color give vividness?
How can the heart know love, and not love once the more?
Love is unjust: justice is loveless.

ALLEN GROSSMAN

THE SANDS OF PARAN

I have questioned them all, Miriam and Aaron
And many who hated him more, of what he saw
Those days and nights of storm. In the plain
Fear compounded deity of desire
And memory, for to a querulous people
To be leaderless is an Egyptian servitude
And they were wanderers in a hard place.
But there,
Beyond the consolation even of shrubbery
Under a sky complicated by light
Some novelty was endured that I would like to know.
My mind is in the wilderness with Moses.

Here beyond Pisgah, where he did not come,
Now Joshua is dead, I cannot think but
Of the sands of Paran. His brother is a priest.
Miriam remembers the leprosy he gave her
For carping at the arrogance of insight
And the woman of Ethiopia in his tent
Who was his wife, and knew him face to face.
They can no longer say where he is buried.

I seek the wilderness again, and light
Falling in flights of arrows; the long
Way round, and the imminence of the mountain where
The plough-share hardly serves as an adequate weapon.

I would recover, not the dream,
But the confrontation, not the nice complement
Of olive and cedar, but the complex face
That talked with Moses there, and spoke on stone.

I am not the remnant, and I lack
The hatred of my people. Yet in some dawn,
Usurping the hierarchy of the birds,
When I have climbed up there to where he stood
I shall in my own voice speak of my need.

THE LAW

Though any physician knows that all I am,
Body and soul, is what he sees before him
With his most ordinary instruments,
It is my deep desire to be wise.
Therefore I sometimes dream about a woman,
Such as you may have met in your own dreams,
A whore but very beautiful, standing undressed
Almost knee-deep in weeds in the garden
Early in the morning. She is a girl,
Younger at least
Than any woman I have ever known;
A Jewess, her hair as dark as night;
And we are of a single race, but she
Is beautiful.

By these marks you will know the woman Wisdom:
She will appear in a familiar place
On a windless morning. Her hair will hide her face.
Her shoulders will be white as the daylight
Disk of the moon.
Her little breasts as she is bending down
Seem like sick dreams of infinite despair
They are so beautiful. Her nipples will be made
Rose pink by some mysterious rouge applied

By a skilled servant.
Her belly will be like a flowery hill,
Her mound a shadowy place of dreams and phantoms,
Where the Chalice, the White Rose, and the Lost Pearl
Lie closed within the soft thin thighs of a girl.

You will awaken with the dignity
Of beauty still upon you, and go forth
Like one who has not long since worshipped.
It will be like some mysterious Sabbath
When the Book was taken from the Ark,
The crown, the breastplate with its wreath of bells,
And all the royalty that hides the Law
Opened and laid aside, and you knew the words,
As a man knows a woman who is raven haired
And odorous.
You will be as infinite as your desire
Knowing the Law is young and beautiful
When you awake one morning in your cold hotel
After a night of vision.

THE SECRET RELIGIONIST

My father loafs and combs
The knots and curls of hunger from his hair.
The sunlight spends itself upon the air.
Woe to the house when the eldest son dreams.
My father has no wares to sell. No price,
Now that the Temple's gone, will buy
Doves for sacrifice.
And dreaming is best done at home at ease;
Dreaming is labor in the fields of peace.
My father's skin is sweet. He does not sow
But reaps continually where strange flowers grow.
His house is ruinous. Who will dower me
To a husband if my father cannot?
He leans against the doorpost in a derby hat.

He will be rich when that day comes again
When angels minister like lovers to a man.
And eldest son must to this father cry.
I am so hungry I shall surely die.
I love a man and he has asked for me.
My father, lay my wedding clothes upon me.
Let me walk white out of my virgin tower,
And carry to my husband one strange flower,
Any lay upon the altar an unblemished dove.
Now that the Temple's gone dreams are his love,
And the red heifer bellows from the cold altar.
Ashes drifting down two thousand years
Darken my hair, and eyes, and all my laughter.

ALLEN GINSBERG

HOWL

(For Carl Solomon)

I

I saw the best minds of my generation destroyed by madness,
 starving hysterical naked,
dragging themselves through the negro streets at dawn looking
 for an angry fix,
angelheaded hipsters burning for the ancient heavenly connection to the starry dynamo in the machinery of night,
who poverty and tatters and hollow-eyed and high sat up
 smoking in the supernatural darkness of cold-water flats
 floating across the tops of cities contemplating jazz,
who bared their brains to Heaven under the El and saw
 Mohammedan angels staggering on tenement roofs illuminated,
who passed through universities with radiant cool eyes hal-
 lucinating Arkansas and Blake-light tragedy among the
 scholars of war,
who were expelled from the academies for crazy & publishing
 obscene odes on the windows of the skull,
who cowered in unshaven rooms in underwear, burning their
 money in wastebaskets and listening to the Terror
 through the wall,
who got busted in their pubic beards returning through
 Laredo with a belt of marijuana for New York,

who ate fire in paint hotels or drank turpentine in Paradise
    Alley, death, or purgatoried their torsos night after night
with dreams, with drugs, with walking nightmares, alcohol
    and cock and endless balls,
incomparable blind streets of shuddering cloud and lightning
    in the mind leaping toward poles of Canada & Paterson,
    illuminating all the motionless world of Time between,
Peyote solidities of halls, backyard green tree cemetery dawns,
    wine drunkenness over the rooftops, store-front boroughs
    of teahead joyride neon blinking traffic light, sun and
    moon and tree vibrations in the roaring winter dusks of
    Brooklyn, ashcan rantings and kind king light of mind,
who chained themselves to subways for the endless ride from
    Battery to holy Bronx on benzedrine until the noise of
    wheels and children brought them down shuddering
    mouth-wracked and battered bleak of brain all drained
    of brilliance in the drear light of Zoo,
who sank all night in submarine light of Bickford's floated
    out and sat through the stale beer afternoon in deso-
    late Fugazzi's, listening to the crack of doom on the
    hydrogen jukebox,
who talked continuously seventy hours from park to pad to
    bar to Bellevue to museum to the Brooklyn Bridge,
a lost battalion of platonic conversationalists jumping down
    the stoops off fire escapes off windowsills off Empire State
    out of the moon,
yacketayakking screaming vomiting whispering facts and
    memories and anecdotes and eyeball kicks and shocks of
    hospitals and jails and wars,
whole intellects disgorged in total recall for seven days and
    nights with brilliant eyes, meat for the Synagogue cast
    on the pavement,
who vanished into nowhere Zen New Jersey leaving a trail
    of ambiguous picture postcards of Atlantic City Hall,
suffering Eastern sweats and Tangerian bone-grindings and
    migraines of China under junk-withdrawal in Newark's
    bleak furnished room,
who wandered around and around at midnight in the railroad
    yard wondering where to go, and went, leaving no broken
    hearts,

who lit cigarettes in boxcars boxcars boxcars racketing through snow toward lonesome farms in grandfather night,

who studied Plotinus Poe St. John of the Cross telepathy and bop kaballa because the cosmos instinctively vibrated at their feet in Kansas,

who loned it through the streets of Idaho seeking visionary indian angels who were visionary indian angels,

who thought they were only mad when Baltimore gleamed in supernatural ecstasy,

who jumped in limousines with the Chinaman of Oklahoma on the impulse of winter midnight streetlight small-town rain,

who lounged hungry and lonesome through Houston seeking jazz or sex or soup, and followed the brilliant Spaniard to converse about America and Eternity, a hopeless task, and so took ship to Africa,

who disappeared into the volcanoes of Mexico leaving behind nothing but the shadow of dungarees and the lava and ash of poetry scattered in fireplace Chicago,

who reappeared on the West Coast investigating the F.B.I. in beards and shorts with big pacifist eyes sexy in their dark skin passing out incomprehensible leaflets,

who burned cigarette holes in their arms protesting the narcotic tobacco haze of Capitalism,

who distributed Supercommunist pamphlets in Union Square weeping and undressing while the sirens of Los Alamos wailed them down, and wailed down Wall, and the Staten Island ferry also wailed,

who broke down crying in white gymnasiums naked and trembling before the machinery of other skeletons,

who bit detectives in the neck and shrieked with delight in policecars for committing no crime but their own wild cooking pederasty and intoxication,

who howled on their knees in the subway and were dragged off the roof waving genitals and manuscripts,

who let themselves be . . . . . . in the . . . by saintly motorcyclists, and screamed with joy,

who blew and were blown by those human seraphim, the sailors, caresses of Atlantic and Caribbean love,

who balled in the morning in the evenings in rosegardens and

the grass of public parks and cemeteries scattering their
semen freely to whomever come who may,

who hiccupped endlessly trying to giggle but wound up with
a sob behind a partition in a Turkish Bath when the
blonde & naked angel came to pierce them with a sword,

who lost their loveboys to the three old shrews of fate the one
eyed shrew of the heterosexual dollar the one eyed shrew
that winks out of the womb and the one eyed shrew that
does nothing but sit on her ass and snip the intellectual
golden threads of the craftsman's loom,

who copulated ecstatic and insatiate with a bottle of beer a
sweetheart a package of cigarettes a candle and fell off
the bed, and continued along the floor and down the hall
and ended fainting on the wall with a vision of ultimate
c . . . and come eluding the last gyzym of consciousness,

who sweetened the snatches of a million girls trembling in the
sunset, and were red eyed in the morning but prepared
to sweeten the snatch of the sunrise, flashing buttocks
under barns and naked in the lake,

who went out whoring through Colorado in myriad stolen
night-cars, N.C., secret hero of these poems, cocksman
and Adonis of Denver—joy to the memory of his in-
numerable lays of girls in empty lots & diner backyards,
moviehouses, rickety rows on mountaintops in caves or
with gaunt waitresses in familiar roadside lonely petticoat
upliftings & especially secret gas-station solipisisms of
johns, & hometown alleys too,

who faded out in vast sordid movies, were shifted in dreams,
woke on a sudden Manhattan, and picked themselves up
out of basements hungover with heartless Tokay and
horrors of Third Avenue iron dreams & stumbled to un-
employment offices,

who walked all night with their shoes full of blood on the
snowbank docks waiting for a door in the East River to
open to a room full of steamheat and opium,

who created great suicidal dramas on the apartment cliffbanks
of the Hudson under the wartime blue floodlight of the
moon & their heads shall be crowned with laurel in
oblivion,

who ate the lamb stew of the imagination or digested the crab
at the muddy bottom of the rivers of Bowery,

who wept at the romance of the streets with their pushcarts full of onions and bad music,

who sat in boxes breathing in the darkness under the bridge, and rose up to build harpsichords in their lofts,

who coughed on the sixth floor of Harlem crowned with flame under the tubercular sky surrounded by orange crates of theology,

who scribbled all night rocking and rolling over lofty incantations which in the yellow morning were stanzas of gibberish,

who cooked rotten animals lung heart feet tail borsht & tortillas dreaming of the pure vegetable kingdom,

who plunged themselves under meat trucks looking for an egg,

who threw their watches off the roof to cast their ballot for Eternity outside of Time, & alarm clocks fell on their heads every day for the next decade,

who cut their wrists three times successively unsuccessfully, gave up and were forced to open antique stores where they thought they were growing old and cried,

who were burned alive in their innocent flannel suits on Madison Avenue amid blasts of leaden verse & the tanked-up clatter of the iron regiments of fashion & the nitroglycerine shrieks of the fairies of advertising & the mustard gas of sinister intelligent editors, or were run down by the drunken taxicabs of Absolute Reality,

who jumped off the Brooklyn Bridge this actually happened and walked away unknown and forgotten into the ghostly daze of Chinatown soup alleyways & firetrucks, not even one free beer,

who sang out of their windows in despair, fell out of the subway window, jumped in the filthy Passaic, leaped on negroes, cried all over the street, danced on broken wineglasses barefoot smashed phonograph records of nostalgic European 1930's German jazz finished the whiskey and threw up groaning into the bloody toilet, moans in their ears and the blast of colossal steamwhistles,

who barreled down the highways of the past journeying to each other's hotrod-Golgotha jail-solitude watch or Birmingham jazz incarnation,

who drove crosscountry seventytwo hours to find out if I had

a vision or you had a vision or he had a vision to find out
Eternity,

who journeyed to Denver, who died in Denver, who came
back to Denver & waited in vain, who watched over
Denver & brooded & loned in Denver and finally went
away to find out the Time, & now Denver is lonesome for
her heroes,

who fell on their knees in hopeless cathedrals praying for each
other's salvation and light and breasts, until the soul
illuminated its hair for a second,

who crashed through their minds in jail waiting for impossible
criminals with golden heads and the charm of reality in
their hearts who sang sweet blues to Alcatraz,

who retired to Mexico to culivate a habit, or Rocky Mount to
tender Buddha or Tangiers to boys or Southern Pacific to
the black locomotive or Harvard to Narcissus to Wood-
lawn to the daisychain or grave,

who demanded sanity trials accusing the radio of hypnotism &
were left with their insanity & their hands & a hung jury,

who threw potato salad at CCNY lecturers on Dadaism and
subsequently presented themselves on the granite steps
of the madhouse with shaven heads and harlequin speech
of suicide, demanding instantaneous lobotomy,

and who were given instead the concrete void of insulin
metrasol electricity hydrotherapy psychotherapy occupational therapy pingpong & amnesia,

who in humorless protest overturned only one symbolic pingpong table, resting briefly in catatonia,

returning years later truly bald except for a wig of blood, and
tears and fingers, to the visible madman doom of the
wards of the madtowns of the East,

Pilgrim State's Rockland's and Greystone's foetid halls,
bickering with the echoes of the soul, rocking and rolling
in the midnight solitude-bench dolmen-realms of love,
dream of life a nightmare, bodies turned to stone as
heavy as the moon,

with mother finally * * * * * *, and the last fantastic book
flung out of the tenement window, and the last door
closed at 4 AM and the last telephone slammed at the wall
in reply and the last furnished room emptied down to the

last piece of mental furniture, a yellow paper rose twisted
on a wire hanger in the closet, and even that imaginary,
nothing but a hopeful little bit of hallucination—
ah, Carl, while you are not safe I am not safe, and now you're
really in the total animal soup of time—
and who therefore ran through the icy streets obsessed with
a sudden flash of the alchemy of the use of the ellipse
the catalog the meter & the vibrating plane,
who dreamt and made incarnate gaps in Time & Space through
images juxtaposed, and trapped the archangel of the soul
between 2 visual images and joined the elemental verbs
and set the noun and dash of consciousness together
jumping with sensation of Pater Omnipotens Aeterna
Deus
to recreate the syntax and measure of poor human prose and
stand before you speechless and intelligent and shaking
with shame, rejected yet confessing out the soul to con-
form to the rhythm of thought in his naked and endless
head,
the madman bum and angel beat in Time, unknown, yet
putting down here what might be left to say in time
come after death,
and rose reincarnate in the ghostly clothes of jazz in the
goldhorn shadow of the band and blew the suffering of
America's naked mind for love into an eli eli lamma
lamma sabacthani saxophone cry that shivered the cities
down to the last radio
with the absolute heart of the poem of life butchered out of
their own bodies good to eat a thousand years.

II

What sphinx of cement and aluminum bashed open their
skulls and ate up their brains and imagination?
Moloch! Solitude! Filth! Ugliness! Ashcans and unobtainable
dollars! Children screaming under the stairways! Boys
sobbing in armies! Old men weeping in the parks!
Moloch! Moloch! Nightmare of Moloch! Moloch the loveless!
Mental Moloch! Moloch the heavy judger of men!
Moloch the incomprehensible prison! Moloch the crossbone

soulless jailhouse and Congress of sorrows! Moloch whose buildings are judgment! Moloch the vast stone of war! Moloch the stunned governments!

Moloch whose mind is pure machinery! Moloch whose blood is running money! Moloch whose fingers are ten armies! Moloch whose breast is a cannibal dynamo! Moloch whose ear is a smoking tomb!

Moloch whose eyes are a thousand blind windows! Moloch whose skyscrapers stand in the long streets like endless Jehovahs! Moloch whose factories dream and croak in the fog! Moloch whose smokestacks and antennae crown the cities!

Moloch whose love is endless oil and stone! Moloch whose soul is electricity and banks! Moloch whose poverty is the specter of genius! Moloch whose fate is a cloud of sexless hydrogen! Moloch whose name is the Mind!

Moloch in whom I sit lonely! Moloch in whom I dream Angels! Crazy in Moloch! C . . . sucker in Moloch! Lacklove and manless in Moloch!

Moloch who entered my soul early! Moloch in whom I am a consciousness without a body! Moloch who frightened me out of my natural ecstasy! Moloch whom I abandon! Wake up in Moloch! Light streaming out of the sky!

Moloch! Moloch! Robot apartments! invisible suburbs! skeleton treasuries! blind capitals! demonic industries! spectral nations! invincible madhouses! granite cocks! monstrous bombs!

They broke their backs lifting Moloch to Heaven! Pavements, trees, radios, tons! lifting the city to Heaven which exists and is everywhere about us!

Visions! omens! hallucinations! miracles! ecstasies! gone down the American river!

Dreams! adorations! illuminations! religions! the whole boatload of sensitive bullshit!

Breakthroughs! over the river! flips and crucifixions! gone down the flood! Highs! Epiphanies! Despairs! Ten years' animal screams and suicides! Minds! New loves! Mad generations! down on the rocks of Time!

Real holy laughter in the river! They saw it all! the wild eyes!

the holy yells! They bade farewell! They jumped off the
roof! to solitude! waving! carrying flowers! Down to the
river! into the street!

III

Carl Solomon! I'm with you in Rockland
    where you're madder than I am
I'm with you in Rockland
    where you must feel very strange
I'm with you in Rockland
    where you imitate the shade of my mother
I'm with you in Rockland
    where you've murdered your twelve secretaries
I'm with you in Rockland
    where you laugh at this invisible humor
I'm with you in Rockland
    where we are great writers on the same dreadful type-
    writer
I'm with you in Rockland
    where your condition has become serious and is reported
    on the radio
I'm with you in Rockland
    where the faculties of the skull no longer admit the worms
    of the senses
I'm with you in Rockland
    where you drink tea of the breasts of the spinsters of Utica
I'm with you in Rockland
    where you pun on the bodies of your nurses the harpies of
    the Bronx
I'm with you in Rockland
    where you scream in a straightjacket that you're losing the
    game of the actual pingpong of the abyss
I'm with you in Rockland
    where you bang on the catatonic piano the soul is in-
    nocent and immortal it should never die ungodly in an
    armed madhouse
I'm with you in Rockland
    where fifty more shocks will never return your soul to its
    body again from its pilgrimage to a cross in the void

I'm with you in Rockland
> where you accuse your doctors of insanity and plot the
> Hebrew socialist revolution against the fascist national
> Golgotha

I'm with you in Rockland
> where you will split the heavens of Long Island and
> resurrect your living human Jesus from the superhuman
> tomb

I'm with you in Rockland
> where there are twentyfive-thousand mad comrades all to-
> gether singing the final stanzas of the Internationale

I'm with you in Rockland
> where we hug and kiss the United States under our
> bedsheets   the United States that coughs all night and
> won't let us sleep

I'm with you in Rockland
> where we wake up electrified out of the coma by our
> own souls' airplanes roaring over the roof they've come to
> drop angelic bombs the hospital illuminates itself
> imaginary walls collapse   O skinny legions run outside
> O starry-spangled shock of mercy the eternal war is here
> O victory forget your underwear we're free

I'm with you in Rockland
> in my dreams you walk dripping from a sea-journey on
> the highway across America in tears to the door of my
> cottage in the Western night

HYAM PLUTZIK

PORTRAIT

Notice with what careful nonchalance
He tries to be a Jew casually,
To ignore the monster, the mountain—
A few thousand years of history.

Of course he personally remembers nothing,
And the world has forgotten the older objections—
The new ones not being socially acceptable:
Hangdogs, hiding in the privies and alleys of the mind.

It is agreed
That he of all men has gained the right to his soul
(Though like the others he no longer believes in one).
He lives in his own house under his oak.
He stands by his car, shod in decently-grained leather.
He is smiling. His hair is peacefully in place.
His suit is carefully pressed; his cravat harmonious.

Whose father, it is whispered, stubbornly cried old clothes
    and bric-a-brac,
He of all men might yet be master of self, all self-possession,
Were it not (how gauche and incredible!) for the one illfitting
    garment—
The historical oversight in the antique wardrobe—
The shirt, the borrowed shirt,
The Greek shirt.

Notice how even when at ease he is somehow anxious,
Like a horse who whiffs smoke somewhere nearby faintly.
Notice with what nonchalance,
The magazine in his hand and the casual cigarette to his lips,
He wears a shirt by Nessus.

✷✷✷

THE PRIEST EKRANATH

I who am sanctified—
Having lain with the holy harlots of Askelon
On the roof of the great temple under her visage
Who graces with splendor the night in the god-filled sky:
Mother, rich-wombed mistress, whose thighs are forever
Rising and falling like the dies in the roadstead of Gath,
To strike with fear the arid and impotent damned
And assure the fruit of field and man and animal
With Adonis and her chosen, fortunate priests—
Must tell you of these barbarians from the mountains,
From the anarchic hills come to destroy us,
Recent siftings out of the east and south.

They call her the White One or the White Lady
But do not worship her nor any mother-goddess.

I have seen them on the high days in Askelon
When the harlots dance naked through the gala streets
For the joy of Adonis and the blessed thirst of the loins
Turn away angry, cursing these holy bodies,
Crying, "Let them be stoned and their evil wombs ripped up."
They hate delight. They have but a lone god
And he is their enemy. I met a certain one:
Sly as a jackal yet arrogant as a lion,
Rough-bearded, out of the desert, desperate
With his private phantoms, his eyes like an animal's
(Fearful, and darting here and there, yet ready
To spring and rend), his hair and garments filthy

With the rot of caves, his skin flayed red by scorpions.
Though his nights are writhings of fire, he will not clasp
The salvation of sweet flesh, but for sustenance
Communes with this impossible imageless demon,
Stuff of a barren race, who has tainted him
With a sickness I cannot fathom, an evil spirit
Like the guilt which dogs a murderer. So always
He looks behind him, before, and within himself,
And the voice he hears becomes this maniacal thundering
On our sunlit streets and before our gleaming temples.

What I saw in the eyes of this vagrant (one of a tribe
Cultureless, without iron, art, or altar)
Was the whole world made somber, and man lonely
In a proud empty heaven like a hell,
Estranged from the field and the beast and his own body
And kin to the mothering earth only in death.
I cannot break this knot, but I know he thought—
And I thought too in the wizardry of that moment—
Our sunwashed cities despicable and meaningless,
Our splendid artistic productions abominable,
Our majestic pantheon foul as a kennel,
The harbor jostling with keen ships and mariners
From the farthest ocean, trivial as a sigh.
And joy unimportant too. The dignity of sorrow
Was the only blessing under the cloud of his god.

I say these are faces of stone no years can weather.
They scheme to take your ease. Listen, you nations:
They will lure you from your spontaneous ecstasies
And positive possessions, and with themselves,
Carry you forth on arduous pilgrimages
Whose only triumph can be a bitter knowledge
Out of the suffering they make our worth.
They see the desert in the growing leaf:
That is their sickness. The sky will be darker then;
The White Lady of splendid thighs and bosom
Without a seedsman or a harvester,
A pallid virgin; and the lands beneath
Dark with this god and people. I who am wise

Through the sacred harlots' embraces know the syllables
(Ah, they are powerful and barbarous!)
Of the secret incantation that gives them strength.
Hear how they thunder! Listen: *Issachar*
Levi simon reuben judah dan
Zebulun asher naphtali menassah ephraim.

DAVID IGNATOW

NOAH

He must wade out to a high point
and build an ark of the trees,
take two of each kind of happiness.
And send out
a pigeon that shall not return,
after the bubbling shriek of the drowned:
it shall land upon a rock.
God of his crying shall have made the flood subside.
He shall emerge
upon the earth, brown for grief
of its dead, and know no better
than before, save there is a promise
to cling to when the floods arise.

SAMSON

Did I love God for myself alone
or for my enemies' sake also
that I might not despair of God's goodness?
With the jawbone of an ass
I had killed contemptuously.
I loved Delilah and I would teach her

His love that she might go and speak
to them in earnest and she did speak
and I pulled the pillars down
one by one in bitter surprise
that goodness could give my enemy
triumph.

AND I STAND

Behind my enemy stands God,
watching how near I come
to killing, to making
my own world and time,
and then ask His love.
And I stand and gaze
past my enemy at Him.

IRVING FELDMAN

FROM THE WANDERING JEW

THE GATES OF GAZA

I sidelong in this obscene world going,
Under battery of filth, bawdry of elements,
Perjurious day forsworn and grieving
At night's bar, all loud and absurd,
Absurd and foul, in this butchery
Of flesh, carnival of fur, I
Running, and on my back the Gates
Of Gaza from the world's muck pulled
Like a rotten tooth—to be carried where?

Never to rest, never to sink down at road's end,
Knowing the journey over, the thing done;
Never to reach settled city, never come home,
By every road moving from that;
Never to rest, accounting this taint of
The soul's honor, debasement of its gold;
Never to sleep, never to know long rhythms
Of earth, the water slowly moving, a light.

O Jerusalem, where shall I build thee? What hill
Is high enough? what earth so rich? what people
Good? Where shall I set down the Gates?
Having no city but this heart of weed and cloud,
Trampled and foraged by herd of folly,
By brutal bodies' violent milling there.

Ridden by goodness I go,
God, in the damp mist descending,
Running at my ankles like a dog.
Why for the pure task these tools of dirt?
This abstracted heart, this fever, this world?

THE FACE OF GOD

Upon the altar of the kitchen stove,
Enameled white and shining with the cares
Of hands that giving graced with love
Three meals a day for thirty years—

There at Friday dusk it crouched beside
The week-end's pit, the mount of Sabbath:
A tumbler-candle dimly hissed and sighed,
Too sweet to judge, too nice for wrath.

All night long the wax ran down
—Crying dead to whom we burnt that rod.
They in the ghostly tallow lay to drown
The bent body of the dying god

Who lit a platter-clock that ticked our sleep.
Its even hands dipped in the dark streaming
And up and down carried us in its sweep.
Chests rose and fell like empires dreaming.

And now I wander accused by that Sinai
In a glass, by muteness of our closet wish,
By a God humble, tiny, and good. And I choke
  with pathos of a clean dish.

THE WAILING WALL

O God, in my exile and affliction, hear me!
From my enemies, save me! Scourge, burn, hash,
Make their inner rot grow badges on their flesh!
Why did You tempt me with goodness? why do You crease
With pain? why this suffering that won't cease?

Here am I stupidly living in sackcloth and ash.
Why was I born just a year before the Crash?
Why'd my father lose his lots and his cash
And go jobless till his gentle lack of courage
Was endemic? Then why'd I grow in this image?
How can I be a hero if I'm not half-a-fake
Like my cousins Joe and Jake?
To be Chosen—that means having only one part.
But if I'm Elect, why all this fat around my heart?

Why was I born in Brooklyn in the lower middle-classes?
Is that a hero's place? Was Moses freckled! Samson wear glasses!
Why me? Haven't You had FDR and Cecil de Mille?
(Pardon me, O Lord, if I question Your will,
But wouldn't Seymour or Sherman have done as well?)
Why do You tell me to build when I want to destroy?
Can't a Jew get that job, is it only for a goy?
Can't a Jew be bad and mean, why sad and nice?
Do You think it's better to have ulcers than a vice?
Why, when I damn others, must I look for my own guilt?
If the evil aren't all bad, the good all good, can't I cry, Tilt!
Couldn't You come as an angel, not a pebble in my shoe?
When I crashed Katz's car did he have to sue?
And then in court, why didn't You put in Your Word?
Don't I know what Sisyphus doesn't, that only pain's absurd?
Then why don't You teach me to strike and not to complain?
Why do You let me suffer if it's not to suffer better again?
Isn't my hardship bitter? my pain pain?
Why did You send that toadying bureaucrat against me?
And that spiteful sage and that selfish landlady?
Why, if You love me, didn't You strike them down?
Bend closer, My God, I can complain till all the stars drown.

HARVEY SHAPIRO

DEATH OF A GRANDMOTHER

Let me borrow her corpse a little.
Over that clown in finest linen,
Over that white-dressed dummy, pretty girl,
(Dressed for a party! the daughters cried)
Let me speak a line.

The dead lie in a ditch of fear,
In an earth wound, in an old mouth
That has sucked them there.
My grandmother drank tea, and wailed
As if the Wailing Wall kissed her head
Beside the kitchen window;
While the flaking, green-boxed radio
Retailed in Yiddish song
And heartache all day long.
Or laughter found her,
The sly, sexual humor of the grave.

Yet after her years of dragging leg,
Of yellowed sight,
She still found pain enough
To polish off the final hours with a shriek.
To what sweet kingdom do the old Jews go?
Now mourned by her radio and bed,
She wishes me health and children,
Who am her inheritor.

I sing her a song of praise.
She meddled with my childhood
Like a witch, and I can meet her
Curse for curse in that slum heaven where we go
When this American dream is spent—
To give her a crust of bread, a little love.

THE BOOK

Violent in its blood, the dark book
Hangs like a tree of night upon the sky.
It batters history, that genesis,
Word that whelped a world up,
While priest and king and all
Raged at the syntax they were swaddled by.

And this is law, or so is said
Within the darkening synagogue
By old men, honored in their beards
By the unsealed, heroic sounds.
Celebration without end, the dark book
Whispers to the wind,
Wind cradles the destructive globe.

Outside, the night is far away.
Space is empty. One might touch,
If the necessary power were given,
All with human eloquence.
What hangs upon the tree is man.
With his blood the book is written.

NONFICTION

PHILIP RAHV

INTRODUCTION TO
DISCOVERY OF EUROPE

THIS ANTHOLOGY OPENS WITH A LETTER WRITTEN
from London in 1772 and closes with an excerpt from a book published
in 1939, a few months before the outbreak of World War II. These
dates are not arbitrary. Prior to the period of the Revolutionary War,
Americans were colonials who perhaps felt themseves more at home in
the Old World than in the New. It is a fact, for example, that Americans visting England in the first half of the eighteenth century did not
regard themselves as foreigners or outsiders. The record of their stay
there reveals almost no signs of estrangement on their part. In general
it may be said that their national self-awareness was then far too undeveloped to have produced any special attitudes toward the 'old countries' which are interesting in more than a strictly historical sense.

But if the literature of our European experience before the seventeen-seventies is so meager as not to tempt the anthologist, the literature
of the most recent years is so rich and various that he must of necessity
refuse the hazard of it. The material accumulated since 1939 is at once
so abundant and so close to us as scarcely to permit the test of critical
selection and arrangement; and since it is as yet impossible to view the
experience it documents from any sort of clear perspective, it seems
futile to load this book with accounts of it. Actually this latest phase of
our trans-Atlantic involvement is by no means ended. Though it has
already brought about a decisive change in the relationship between
the two hemispheres, the measure and significance of that change are
still in doubt.

The interest of the American experience of Europe is to be sought primarily in the expressions of the American character it brings to light. Hence in selecting the contents of this book I have proceeded more with an eye to the subject of the experience than to its object. American descriptions of Old-World scenes are often engrossing in their own right, but what is really of value in them is the attitude of the given author, his subjective response, the turns and twists of his imagination when forced to cope with the challenge of the great European world. For that world has served the native imagination both as myth and reality, and to the challenge it offered Americans have reacted with sharp differences among themselves—differences involving their deepest commitments to their country and sense of participation in the national fate. Thus Europe becomes one of the poles of American culture, the other pole being that most indigenous of indigenous places—the frontier; and, like Europe, the frontier too is no less myth than reality. Many phenomena of the national life—the national literature, for instance—are hardly to be understood unless approached in terms of this polar orientation of the American mind.

T. G. Appleton once said that Europe means so much to the Yankee because "it is the home of his protoplasm, of the long succession of forces which make him what he is." That statement was made many decades ago, but the feeling behind it has persisted. According to the young American poet, Delmore Schwartz, Europe is "the greatest thing in North America"—an observation one-sided yet essentially true. For completion it needs to be supplemented by a further truth: that Europe is also the most rejected thing in North America. It represents the past, and the past is a threat to those who escaped from it in their own selves or through the lucky venture of their forbears. Mr. Ferner Nuhn, a student of our native pieties, has remarked that the 'true' American, the "true child of the Western star," spurned the past "as a bucket of ashes, and generally his instinct was right. The past was a peasant shawl, a bit of faded lace, an old wives' tale, a younger son's portion, a broken chain." In a book entitled *The Wind Blew from the East*, written in criticism of such Americans as Henry Adams, Henry James, and T. S. Eliot, who went back to the past for a point of orientation, Mr. Nuhn has analyzed the "two-way pull" or the East-versus-West argument in our culture. On the one hand there is "the message of the East Wind," the message of money, ease and grace, piety, status; and on the other hand there is the West, standing for work, profanity, action, and democratic color. But even Mr. Nuhn, who is entirely a devotee of the Western star, finds a kind of enchantment—"a witchery of the time and place dimensions"—in the pilgrimage of Americans like Henry Adams and Henry James. This enchantment is, however, an organic part of our imaginative experience, and to assign it a purely literary function, as Mr. Nuhn tends to do, is in a way to exclude it. The trouble with Mr. Nuhn's neat historical scheme is that it oversimplifies the relation between Europe and America. It is a relation of combined attraction and repulsion, and perhaps those Americans who have felt the attraction are in their way just as "true" to the national ethos as those who have felt nothing but the repulsion.

To say that the message of the East Wind has been exclusively a message of money, ease and grace, piety and status, is to put an exceedingly narrow interpretation upon it. It means that one identifies Europe wholly with the feudal and aristocratic past, with the power of its ruling classes rather than with the vitality of its art and thought, its revolutionary traditions, and the constant revivification of its culture through revolt and experiment. It is plain that there is no single formula that could possibly do justice to the complexity of "Europe" as an idea in the American mind. What is Europe to the immigrant population of this country? It is the realm of ignorance, poverty, and political oppression. But as a cultural entity Europe has also stood for spontaneity, sensibility, poetry, intellectual freedom, and moral idealism: values which not a few of our artists and thinkers have championed by appealing to the greater traditions of the Old World. Randolph Bourne's letters from Paris, reprinted in this volume, beautifully illustrate the tonic effect of the European scene on a young American idealist. Bourne was of course attracted by the ease and grace of European society; but it is not necessarily true that ease and grace are compatible only with money, piety, and status.

It has often been observed that the relation between America and Europe becomes coherent and meaningful in moral terms when defined as a relation between innocence and experience. The American novel, in so far as it has dealt with the so-called "international" theme, fully confirms this idea. Whatever may be the case at the present time, it is certainly true that historically Europe has stood—to Henry James no less than to the expatriates of the nineteen-twenties—for the fullness and richness of personal experience as against a puritanical abstention from the rewards of life for the sake of practical gains, such as the accumulation of wealth and the good opinion of one's neighbors. Paradoxically enough, to Europeans the practical conduct of life seems to have nothing in common with innocence, for in their tradition practicality is more often associated with cynicism than with a clear conscience. The American novelist, however, has been much too close to his material to adopt this exacerbated European view, and in his presentation of native types he has shown that innocence and devotion to practical ends are by no means incompatible. In the American novel the 'innocent abroad' appears in a dual rôle. His actions take on a positive meaning when he goes forth to battle the old evils of history encountered on "Europe's lighted and decorated stage"; but in another mood this same 'innocent abroad' ceases to be a crusader and becomes a philistine, shallow, complacent, and vulgarly insensitive to the splendor and glory of the past.

There is no doing away with the fascination of the past. It is something one has missed and therefore longs to recapture, to make real again. Thus we get the long procession of American pilgrims beating a retreat in time by crossing the Atlantic in search of the relics of the past. Washington Irving was among the first of our writers to turn this quest to a major literary purpose. There is a passage in the introductory chapter to *The Sketch-Book,* describing the mood in which Irving embarked on his first trip abroad in 1815, which precisely because of its dated rhetoric carries us directly back to the inspiration of those early pilgrimages. "Europe held forth the charms of storied and poetical associations. There were to be seen the masterpieces of art, the refinements of highly cultivated society, the quaint peculiarities of ancient and local custom. My native country was full of youthful promise: Europe was rich in the accumulated treasures of age. . . . I longed to wonder over the scenes of renowned achievement—to tread, as it were, in the footsteps of antiquity—to loiter about the ruined castle—to meditate on the falling tower—to escape, in short, from the commonplace realities of the present, and lose myself among the shadowy grandeurs of the past."

That is exactly the feeling which Henry James embodied in his early *nouvelle, The Passionate Pilgrim.* The pilgrim in this case is an American who, repelled by the raw taste of life in his own country, journeys to England to present his claims to an old and rich estate of which he is presumably the lost heir. What strikes us above all in this archetypal Jamesian hero is the ambiguity of his attempt to re-attach himself to the old soil—an ambiguity the source of which is nothing less than doubt of his true historical identity. Now a doubt of that sort is at once creative and inhibitive. If it lifts the individual out of his national mold, thus weakening his capacity for simple adaptation, it on the other hand intensifies and refines his powers of memory and appreciation, his consciousness of origins, of the intermixture of past and present, and of the values gained as well as those irretrievably lost in the process of constructing a new civilization. The voice that Henry James heard in Venice and other Old-World cities—a strong voice "full of history and humanity and waking perpetual echoes"—put to him the question that he incessantly asked himself: Which is more real, the past or the present, Europe or America? It is along these lines that one may perhaps best explain why the appeal of this novelist, who found his theme in the far-flung entanglements of the American character, is resisted to this day by so many of his countrymen. The secret of that resistance may well be the desire to simplify the notion of the American character, to conceive of it as all of a piece, rooted in the Western soil and owing no allegiance of sympathy or pathos to its "old home." For despite all bluster the newly created national ego is at bottom uncertain of its identity; hence the compensatory self-assertion and inability to tolerate even the suspicion of divided loyalties. No wonder, then, that it is writers like Whitman and Mark Twain who achieved the most popular interpretations of the national ethos. For their work is nothing if not a wholehearted response to the demand for unity, simplification, and the unequivocal avowal of national identity.

In the phantasy of the lost heir that haunts some of the earlier American books there is, after all, something disquieting for the security of the New-World ego. Particularly susceptible to this phantasy is a certain type of nineteenth-century American who comes to "Mother England" with the intention of re-discovering the original sources of his personality and culture. (Characteristic of his state of mind is the following notation I found in a forgotten old journal of travel-impressions. The author is the Reverend Orville Dewey, who set out on a tour of Europe in June, 1833. This is what he wrote on the day he landed in England: "If I were approaching the coast of Kamtschatka or New Holland, it would be a different thing; it would be comparatively a commonplace occurrence; but here is the birthplace of my language, of my mind's nurture—the world where my thoughts have lived, my fatherland—and yet strange and mysterious, as if it were the land of some pre-existent being!") And Henry James was not the only American storyteller who converted the figure of the lost heir into the hero of a trans-Atlantic romance. Hawthorne, for instance, dealt unsparingly with the realities of English life in *Our Old Home,* but in his unfinished novel *Dr. Grimshawe's Secret* he yielded to the singularly American nostalgia for all things English. As a child the hero of this novel used to imagine 'the true heir wandering all this while in America, and leaving a long track of bloody footsteps behind him; until the period when, his sins being expiated . . . he should turn back upon his steps and return to his old native home.' In time this hero realizes his wish and goes to England, whither he was drawn, we are told, 'by feelings which every educated and impressible American feels, in a degree scarcely conceived by the English themselves. And being there . . . he began to feel the deep yearning which a sensitive American—his mind full of English thoughts, his imagination of English poetry, his heart of English character and sentiment—cannot fail to be influenced by—the yearning of the blood within his veins for that from which it had been estranged; the half-fanciful regret that he should ever have been separated from these woods, these fields, these natural features of scenery, to which his nature was moulded, from the men who are still so like himself, from these habits of life and thought which . . . he still perceives to have remained in some mysterious way latent in the depths of his character.'

It is in such authentic expressions of nostalgia for the mother-country that one discovers the source of that Anglophile sentiment of which the patrician class of New England has been accused time and again. And the accusers are not all outsiders. Henry Adams found it possible to write in *The Education* that 'the true Bostonian always knelt in self-abasement before the majesty of English standards; far from concealing it as a weakness, he was proud of it as his strength.' That is but another way of saying that the Anglophile sentiment is impure because through social diffusion it becomes mixed with aspirations to worldly status and aristocratic exclusiveness. And by the law of recoil it turns into its opposite—into Anglophobia—the farther West it travels and the more it is exposed to plebeian pressures of the larger American scene. Our dual attitude toward England thoroughly confirms Mr. Nuhn's thesis of a two-way pull in our culture. All aspects of the national life are affected by it, including our foreign policy. It is impossible to understand the debates that preceded our entrance into both world wars without taking into account the contradictory American attitude toward England—an attitude which in periods of peace and equilibrium seems to be divorced from political action, but which in periods of international crisis is inevitably transformed into a stark political force.

But of course the attachment to "Mother England" is in itself only a very close and concrete version of the attachment to the Old World generally. This was felt by many Americans of the nineteenth century, such as Charles Francis Adams, who is reported by his son Henry to have been of the opinion that Americans should stay away from Europe because it unfitted them for life in their own country. American literature exhibits this notion in a thousand and one ways. In *The Rise of Silas Lapham* Howells, for instance, makes an ironic use of this notion in the scene where the elder Mr. Corey expatiates on the perils of the European contagion. "I am always saying that the Bostonian ought never to leave Boston," he remarks. "Then he knows—and then only—that there can be no standards but ours. But we are constantly going away, and coming back with our convictions shaken to their foundations. One man goes to England, and returns with the conception of a grander social life; another comes home from Germany with the notion of a more searching intellectual activity; a fellow just back from Paris has the aburdest ideas of art and literature. . . . It ought to be stopped. . . . The Bostonian who leaves Boston ought to be condemned to perpetual exile." Yet this desire to exclude European influences is contradicted in the American character by an equally deep desire to accept the challenge of Europe and to utilize the experience of it for self-advancement and self-improvement. To go to Europe is for an American not at all the same thing as going to Asia or to Africa. His background and quality are tested in Europe as they are tested nowhere else; going to Europe thus becomes a cognitive act, an act of re-discovering and re-possessing one's heritage. And this valuation is not peculiar to the intellectuals alone. In *A Story Teller's Story* Sherwood Anderson recalls that when he was a boy in Ohio going to Europe meant "something tremendous. . . . It was of infinitely more importance than, let us say, getting married. Such and such a one had been to Europe three times. He was consulted upon all occasions, and was allowed to sit on the platform at political meetings. . . ." And when Anderson made his way as a writer and came to New York, he felt that perhaps he had not gone far enough. He no longer had the naïve faith in Europe that he observed in his childhood, but he felt that "something pulled." In New York he found it difficult to understand the "realities of feelings, of hungers," and he asked himself whether he might not learn more by going to the source of "all this vast river of mixed bloods, mixed traditions, mixed passions and impulses?"

But what happens to the American when he goes back, when he reaches the source of his own mixed blood and traditions? Nearly a hundred years ago Margaret Fuller listed the Americans in Europe under three headings: the servile, the conceited, and the thinking Americans. The latter, she added, can only become more American, despite their awareness that "our position toward Europe as to literature and the arts is still that of a colony." Emerson was one of the Americans who went to Europe to learn "what is the uppermost which social man has yet done," and he came home with the conviction that "we are playing the game with immense advantage." Many of his compatriots, however, were not concerned with the ultimate results of the game. They wanted to be certain that their country was already superior to the "old countries," and in the absence of proofs they gave free rein to their imagination. Thus Abigail Adams, the wife of the first Ambassador of the United States to the Court of St. James's and our second President, wrote to her sister from London in 1786: "Do you know that European birds have not half the melody of ours? Nor is their fruit half so sweet, nor their flowers half so fragrant, nor their manners half so pure, nor their people half so virtuous; but keep this to yourself, or I shall be thought more than half deficient in understanding and taste. . . ."

In later years, when the citizens of the Republic were no longer quite so uncertain of its future, it was no longer necessary for them to react with such literal declarations of superiority. For many decades their chief purpose in coming to Europe was to collect "the spoils of culture," to assimilate the higher standards of European art and learning so as to apply them in the development of their own culture. The period of expatriation, of exile from home, did not properly begin till after the Civil War, when the enormous expansion of industry and the definitive triumph of the businessman led to the estrangement of the artist from his society. But even in that period expatriation was only one side of the American experience in Europe, and by no means the most important side. World War II has put an end both to the theory and practice of expatriation, for in a Europe shaken loose from its old foundations and chaotically moving toward a new and unknown future, there is plainly no room for Americans seeking to recapture the past or to discover a secure basis for the creative life.

Much has been said and written on both sides of the Atlantic about the contradiction between the Old World and the New. If there is such a contradiction, it surely cannot be resolved either by Americanizing Europe or by Europeanizing America. The resolution lies not in the submission of one hemisphere to another, but in the attainment of a higher level for Western civilization, in the use of all its resources to achieve a new unity of loyalties and values, and of political and economic institutions. In the past it was possible to claim that America is no more than an outpost of Western civilization and that only in Europe is its essence preserved intact. But these old claims and assumptions are no longer valid. Our share in that civilization now fully equals that of the Europeans, and to make good its promise we must be ready to assume the responsibilities that go with an equal partnership.

ALFRED KAZIN

❧❧❧

THE KITCHEN

IN BROWNSVILLE TENEMENTS THE KITCHEN IS AL-
ways the largest room and the center of the household. As a child I
felt that we lived in a kitchen to which four other rooms were annexed.
My mother, a "home" dressmaker, had her workshop in the kitchen.
She told me once that she had begun dressmaking in Poland at
thirteen; as far back as I can remember, she was always making dresses
for the local women. She had an innate sense of design, a quick eye
for all the subtleties in the latest fashions, even when she despised
them, and great boldness. For three or four dollars she would study
the fashion magazines with a customer, go with the customer to the
remnants store on Belmont Avenue to pick out the material, argue the
owner down—all remnants stores, for some reason, were supposed to
be shady, as if the owners dealt in stolen goods—and then for days
would patiently fit and baste and sew and fit again. Our apartment was
always full of women in their housedresses sitting around the kitchen
table waiting for a fitting. My little bedroom next to the kitchen was
the fitting room. The sewing machine, an old nut-brown Singer with
golden scrolls painted along the black arm and engraved along the
two tiers of little drawers massed with needles and thread on each side
of the treadle, stood next to the window and the great coal-black stove
which up to my last year in college was our main source of heat. By
December the two outer bedrooms were closed off, and used to chill
bottles of milk and cream, cold borscht and jellied calves' feet.

The kitchen held our lives together. My mother worked in it all day
long, we ate in it almost all meals except the Passover *seder*, I did my
254

homework and first writing at the kitchen table, and in winter I often had a bed made up for me on three kitchen chairs near the stove. On the wall just over the table hung a long horizontal mirror that sloped to a ship's prow at each end and was lined in cherry wood. It took up the whole wall, and drew every object in the kitchen to itself. The walls were a fiercely stippled whitewash, so often rewhitened by my father in slack seasons that the paint looked as if it had been squeezed and cracked into the walls. A large electric bulb hung down the center of the kitchen at the end of a chain that had been hooked into the ceiling; the old gas ring and key still jutted out of the wall like antlers. In the corner next to the toilet was the sink at which we washed, and the square tub in which my mother did our clothes. Above it, tacked to the shelf on which were pleasantly ranged square, blue-bordered white sugar and spice jars, hung calendars from the Public National Bank on Pitkin Avenue and the Minsker Progressive Branch of the Workman's Circle; receipts for the payment of insurance premiums, and household bills on a spindle; two little boxes engraved with Hebrew letters. One of these was for the poor, the other to buy back the Land of Israel. Each spring a bearded little man would suddenly appear in our kitchen, salute us with a hurried Hebrew blessing, empty the boxes (sometimes with a sidelong look of disdain if they were not full), hurriedly bless us again for remembering our less fortunate Jewish brothers and sisters, and so take his departure until the next spring, after vainly trying to persuade my mother to take still another box. We did occasionally remember to drop coins in the boxes, but this was usually only on the dreaded morning of "mid-terms" and final examinations, because my mother thought it would bring me luck. She was extremely superstitious, but embarrassed about it, and always laughed at herself whenever, on the morning of an examination, she counseled me to leave the house on my right foot. "I know it's silly," her smile seemed to say, "but what harm can it do? It may calm God down."

The kitchen gave a special character to our lives; my mother's character. All my memories of that kitchen are dominated by the nearness of my mother sitting all day long at her sewing machine, by the clacking of the treadle against the linoleum floor, by the patient twist of her right shoulder as she automatically pushed at the wheel with one hand or lifted the foot to free the needle where it had got stuck in a thick piece of material. The kitchen was her life. Year by year, as I began to take in her fantastic capacity for labor and her anxious zeal,

I realized it was ourselves she kept stitched together. I can never remember a time when she was not working. She worked because the law of her life was work, work and anxiety; she worked because she would have found life meaningless without work. She read almost no English; she could read the Yiddish paper, but never felt she had time to. We were always talking of a time when I would teach her how to read, but somehow there was never time. When I awoke in the morning she was already at her machine, or in the great morning crowd of housewives at the grocery getting fresh rolls for breakfast. When I returned from school she was at her machine, or conferring over *McCall's* with some neighborhood woman who had come in pointing hopefully to an illustration—"Mrs. Kazin! Mrs. Kazin! Make me a dress like it shows here in the picture!" When my father came home from work she had somehow mysteriously interrupted herself to make supper for us, and the dishes cleared and washed, was back at her machine. When I went to bed at night, often she was still there, pounding away at the treadle, hunched over the wheel, her hands steering a piece of gauze under the needle with a finesse that always contrasted sharply with her swollen hands and broken nails. Her left hand had been pierced through when as a girl she had worked in the infamous Triangle Shirtwaist Factory on the East Side. A needle had gone straight through the palm, severing a large vein. They had sewn it up for her so clumsily that a tuft of flesh always lay folded over the palm.

The kitchen was the great machine that set our lives running; it whirred down a little only on Saturdays and holy days. From my mother's kitchen I gained my first picture of life as a white, overheated, starkly lit workshop redolent with Jewish cooking, crowded with women in housedresses, strewn with fashion magazines, patterns, dress material, spools of thread—and at whose center, so lashed to her machine that bolts of energy seemed to dance out of her hands and feet as she worked, my mother stamped the treadle hard against the floor, hard, hard, and silently, grimly at war, beat out the first rhythm of the world for me.

Every sound from the street roared and trembled at our windows—a mother feeding her child on the doorstep, the screech of the trolley cars on Rockaway Avenue, the eternal smash of a handball against the wall of our house, the clatter of *"der Italyéner"*'s cart packed with watermelons, the sing-song of the old-clothes men walking Chester Street, the cries *"Árbes! Árbes! Kinder! Kinder! Heyse gute árbes!"* All day long people streamed into our apartment as a matter of course—

"customers," upstairs neighbors, downstairs neighbors, women who would stop in for a half-hour's talk, salesmen, relatives, insurance agents. Usually they came in without ringing the bell—everyone knew my mother was always at home. I would hear the front door opening, the wind whistling through our front hall, and then some familiar face would appear in our kitchen with the same bland, matter-of-fact inquiring look: no need to stand on ceremony: my mother and her kitchen were available to everyone all day long.

At night the kitchen contracted around the blaze of light on the cloth, the patterns, the ironing board where the iron had burned a black border around the tear in the muslin cover; the finished dresses looked so frilly as they jostled on their wire hangers after all the work my mother had put into them. And then I would get that strangely ominous smell of tension from the dress fabrics and the burn in the cover of the ironing board—as if each piece of cloth and paper crushed with light under the naked bulb might suddenly go up in flames. Whenever I pass some small tailoring shop still lit up at night and see the owner hunched over his steam press; whenever in some poorer neighborhood of the city I see through a window some small crowded kitchen naked under the harsh light glittering in the ceiling, I still smell that fiery breath, that warning of imminent fire. I was always holding my breath. What I must have felt most about ourselves, I see now, was that we ourselves were like kindling—that all the hard-pressed pieces of ourselves and all the hard-used objects in that kitchen were like so many slivers of wood that might go up in flames if we came too near the white-blazing filaments in that naked bulb. Our tension itself was fire, we ourselves were forever burning—to live, to get down the foreboding in our souls, to make good.

Twice a year, on the anniversaries of her parents' deaths, my mother placed on top of the ice-box an ordinary kitchen glass packed with wax, the *yortsayt*, and lit the candle in it. Sitting at the kitchen table over my homework, I would look across the threshold to that mourning-glass, and sense that for my mother the distance from our kitchen to *der heym*, from life to death, was only a flame's length away. Poor as we were, it was not poverty that drove my mother so hard; it was loneliness—some endless bitter brooding over all those left behind, dead or dying or soon to die; a loneliness locked up in her kitchen that dwelt every day on the hazardousness of life and the nearness of death, but still kept struggling in the lock, trying to get us through by endless labor.

With us, life started up again only on the last shore. There seemed to be no middle ground between despair and the fury of our ambition. Whenever my mother spoke of her hopes for us, it was with such unbelievingness that the likes of us would ever come to anything, such abashed hope and readiness for pain, that I finally came to see in the flame burning on top of the ice-box death itself burning away the bones of poor Jews, burning out in us everything but courage, the blind resolution to live. In the light of that mourning-candle, there were ranged around me how many dead and dying—how many eras of pain, of exile, of dispersion, of cringing before the powers of this world!

It was always at dusk that my mother's loneliness came home most to me. Painfully alert to every shift in the light at her window, she would suddenly confess her fatigue by removing her pince-nez, and then wearily pushing aside the great mound of fabrics on her machine, would stare at the street as if to warm herself in the last of the sun. "How sad it is!" I once heard her say. "It grips me! It grips me!" Twilight was the bottommost part of the day, the chilliest and loneliest time for her. Always so near to her moods, I knew she was fighting some deep inner dread, struggling against the returning tide of dark- ness along the streets that invariably assailed her heart with the same foreboding—Where? Where now? Where is the day taking us now?

Yet one good look at the street would revive her. I see her now, perched against the windowsill, with her face against the glass, her eyes almost asleep in enjoyment, just as she starts up with the guilty cry—"What foolishness is this in me!"—and goes to the stove to prepare supper for us: a moment, only a moment, watching the evening crowd of women gathering at the grocery for fresh bread and milk. But between my mother's pent-up face at the window and the winter sun dying in the fabrics—"Alfred, see how beautiful!"—she has drawn for me one single line of sentience.

ISAAC ROSENFELD

AMERICA,
LAND OF THE SAD MILLIONAIRE

I HAD LONG AVOIDED "THE RISE OF DAVID LEVINSKY" because I imagined it was a badly-written account of immigrants and sweatshops in a genre which—though this novel had practically established it—was intolerably stale by now. It is nothing of the kind. To be sure, it is a genre piece, and excellence of diction and sentence structure are not among its strong points; but it is one of the best fictional studies of Jewish character available in English, and at the same time an intimate and sophisticated account of American business culture, and it ought to be celebrated as such.

The story is a simple one and fundamentally Jewish in conception, as it consists of an extended commentary on a single text, somewhat in the manner of Talmud. This text is presented in the opening paragraph:

Sometimes, when I think of my past . . . the metamorphosis I have gone through strikes me as nothing short of a miracle. I was born and reared in the lowest depths of poverty and I arrived in America—in 1885—with four cents in my pocket. I am now worth more than two million dollars and recognized as one of the two or three leading men in the cloak-and-suit trade in the United States. *And yet . . . my inner identity . . . impresses me as being precisely the same as it was thirty or forty years ago. My present station, power, the amount of worldly happiness at my command, and the rest of it, seem to be devoid of significance.*

I have set in italics what I take to be the key sentences. These express Levinsky's uniquely Jewish character, as they refer to the poor days

259

of his childhood and early youth ("my inner identity") when, supported by his mother, he devoted himself to the study of the Jewish Law. Nothing in a man's life could be more purely Jewish, and his constant longing, through all his later years, for the conditions of his past confirms him in an unchanging spirit. But the remarkable thing about this theme, as the late Abraham Cahan developed it, is that it is, at the same time, an exemplary treatment of one of the dominant myths of American capitalism—that the millionaire finds nothing but emptiness at the top of the heap. It is not by accident that Cahan, for forty years and until his death the editor of the *Jewish Daily Forward*, and identified all his life with Jewish affairs and the Yiddish language, wrote this novel in English (it has only recently been translated into Yiddish). He was writing an American novel par excellence in the very center of the Jewish genre.

It seems to me that certain conclusions about the relation between Jewish and American character should be implicit in the fact that so singularly Jewish a theme can so readily be assimilated to an American one. I am not suggesting that Jewish and American character are identical, for the Levinsky who arrived in New York with four cents in his pocket was as unlike an American as anyone could possibly be: but there is a complementary relation between the two which, so far as I know, no other novel has brought out so clearly.

David Levinsky was born in the Russian town of Antomir in 1865. His father died when David was three, and he lived with his mother in one corner of a basement room that was occupied by three other families. "The bulk of the population [of Antomir]," writes Cahan, "lived on less than . . . twenty-five cents . . . a day, and that was difficult to earn. A hunk of rye bread and a bit of herring or cheese constituted a meal. [With] a quarter of a copeck (an eighth of a cent) . . . one purchased a few crumbs of pot cheese or some boiled water for tea. . . . Children had to nag their mothers for a piece of bread." But Levinsky's mother, who "peddled pea mush [and did] odds and ends of jobs," was kind to him and indulgent, "because God has punished you hard enough as it is, poor orphan mine."

At the usual early age, Levinsky was sent to *cheder*, where he was made to feel very keenly the disadvantages of poverty, as his teachers risked nothing in punishing a poor boy. His mother would intervene for him (this impulse was to prove fatal) and fought with many a *melamed* for laying hands on her David. In spite of the humiliations and hardships, she maintained him in *cheder,* and after his Bar Mitzvah sent him to Yeshiva (Talmudic seminary) at an even greater sacrifice, as it meant he would not be in a position to relieve her distress by learning a trade. She was determined that he devote his life to God, and he showed great aptitude for holy study. He soon distinguished himself as a student, but his sexual instincts began to distract his mind. His contacts with women, as was the case with all Yeshiva students, were extremely limited. It was considered "an offense to good Judaism" for a pious man to seek feminine company, attend dances, dress in worldly fashion, or in any other way to behave as a "Gentile." Naturally, these restraints only multiplied Levinsky's temptations. He would do penance, undergo a period of religious exaltation, and again fall into sin (in his mind).

The next great event in his life was the death of his mother. Levinsky, in earlocks and black caftan, was attacked by Gentile boys on his way from the Yeshiva. When he came home bruised and bleeding, his mother, against his entreaties and those of their friends and neighbors, ran to the Gentile quarter to avenge him. This was the last time he saw her alive. She was brought back with a broken head.

It is a credit to Cahan's economy as a writer and to his grasp of character that at this point, in the sixty-odd pages which I have summarized, he has already drawn so convincing a picture of Levinsky, including all essential details, that Levinsky's subsequent adventures in the old country and America, his further encounters with poverty and with women, the rest of his intellectual development, and his ultimate transformation into a millionaire, have all been fully prepared. I will therefore cut off the exposition and attempt some generalizations which may serve the understanding of the whole of Levinsky's character and perhaps help explain how the old-world Yeshiva student is essentially an American in ethos.

Levinsky's character was formed by hunger. The individual experiences of his life—poverty, squalor, orphanage, years of religious study and sexual restraint, the self-sacrificing love of his mother and her violent death—all these experiences contain, as their common element, a core of permanent dissatisfaction. This dissatisfaction expresses itself in two ways: first, as a yearning for fulfilment, where it operates to win for him all the goods and values he has been deprived of—wealth, dignity, a "father principle" as well as substitute for his father (as shown in his passionate attachment to Reb Sender, with whom he studied at the Yeshiva), the pleasures of intellectual liberty that attend his break with Orthodoxy, the pleasures of sex, and unrestrained access to the society of women, though he goes among them mainly to find a substitute for his mother. (These are the positive "Americanizing" tendencies of his discontent.) At the same time, dissatisfaction has become an organic habit, a form which determines his apprehension of experience in general, and actually directs the flow of experience his way, so that he is not merely the result of what has happened to him, but on the contrary, the events in his life are predetermined, in large measure, by what he has already become. In the second sense, dissatisfaction is unending; instead of providing the urge to overcome privation, it returns every fulfilment, by a way no matter how roundabout, to the original tension, so that no satisfaction is possible.

Thus Levinsky is a man who cannot feel at home with his desires. Because hunger is strong in him, he must always strive to relieve it; but precisely because it is strong, it has to be preserved. It owes its strength to the fact that for so many years everything that influenced Levinsky most deeply—say, piety and mother love—was inseparable from it. For hunger, in this broader, rather metaphysical sense of the term that I have been using, is not only the state of tension out of which the desires for relief and betterment spring; precisely because the desires are formed under its sign, they become assimilated to it, and convert it into the prime source of all value, so that the man, in his pursuit of whatever he considers pleasurable and good, seeks to return to his yearning as much as he does to escape it.

Levinsky's entire behavior is characterized by this duality. In love, he is drawn to women he cannot have. They are either hopelessly above his rank in wealth, sophistication, and culture, or married and faithful mother-surrogates, or simply not interested. The women who do find him attractive fail to move him. He goes to prostitutes, one frustration feeding the other.

His accumulation of wealth, which he wins through preseverance, ingenuity, and luck, is also of this pattern—it, too, represents a loss, a virtual impoverishment. Before he turned to business enterprise, Levinsky had entertained serious academic ambitions. Though he had broken away from Orthodoxy, shaved his beard, adopted American dress, and gone to night school to learn English, he had retained his Talmudic intellectuality and love of scholarship. He took a job in the garment industry only as a means of sending himself through college. The event to which he attributes his becoming a businessman fell on a day when he was having his lunch in the factory. A bottle of milk slipped out of his hands as he was trying to open it and spilled on some silks. His employer, Jeff Manheimer, who witnessed the accident, broadly made fun of his clumsiness and called him a lobster. The humiliation festered, and that very day Levinsky decided to steal the boss's designer and go into business for himself. This is the reason he gives, but it is a rationalization. He would never have entered business and gone on to wealth had it not been necessary to sacrifice something—in this case his desire for learning. And when he obtains great wealth, it makes a circle, joining the pattern of his love life by condemning him to loneliness, as he suspects all women who smile on him want only his money.

So with everything. All things in Levinsky's life are divided, alienated from themselves, and simplicity is impossible. But no matter how many transformations it undergoes, his hunger remains constant. He longs for his wretched boyhood (which appeals to him "as a sick child does to its mother") from which, were he able to re-enter it, he would again be driven in an endless yearning after yearning.

Now this is a profoundly Jewish trait, our whole history is marked by this twist. The significant thing about the structure I have been describing is that it is not confined to single personalities like Levinsky, but is exactly repeated on an impersonal and much larger scale in Jewish history, religion, culture—wherever our tradition and its spirit find expression. Consider *Galut*, the Diaspora, through the centuries in which it has dominated Jewish life: the theme of the Return, of yearning for Eretz Israel, to which are linked Cabala and Messianism, modes of prayer and worship as well as modern political and social movements, so that the whole becomes a compendium of Jewish activity *per se*—the yearning for Israel runs through the Diaspora in no simple sense, as of a fixed desire for a fixed object. It is a reflexive desire, turning on itself and becoming its own object. This is the meaning of the passage: "If I forget Thee O Jerusalem. . . ." The yearning is itself Jerusalem, as in the words ". . . if I prefer not Jerusalem above my chief joy," and it is to this yearning that the good Jew remains faithful. Otherwise, why the proscription of temporizing in *Galut*, of making any compromise with desire, no matter how small, even down to the obdurate and seemingly ridiculous prohibition of shaving the beard? The hunger must be preserved at all cost. This theme is taken up and elaborated all through Yiddish literature, receiving its ultimate ironic sanctification in the work of Sholom Aleichem, where squalor, suffering, and persecution become the "blessings of poverty," signs and stigmata of the condition of being Chosen, "for which the whole world envies us." The character of David Levinsky, therefore, does not stand alone, nor does he come, with his four cents, unattended to the American shore. He drags the whole past after him, being himself the Diaspora Man.

But what is so American about this? Nothing directly, especially if I am right in calling Levinsky the essential Jewish type of the Dispersion. And yet in the character of the American businessman and in the surrounding culture that his figure dominates, there is also such a twist, a similar play on striving and fulfilment. We worship success; all the same it is on process and origin that we place the emphasis of gratification, seldom on the attainment as such. The value of the successful man's career lies in "rags to riches," it is defined in our saying, "He worked himself up." Of those who are born to wealth we say, "Poor little rich boy." Now this, I am aware, is folklore, and there is a great deal of irony in it, too. Nevertheless, our favorite representation of the rich is of a class that doesn't know what to do with its money. It has brought them no real accretion of happiness, and the process of accumulation, on which the emphasis falls, is manifestly a self-destructive one, as it never can be stopped in time: the successful man faces the futility of retirement. He, too, loves to dream about his boyhood in an unreal *askesis,* having for the most part been ashamed of the ascetic impulse (poverty, we protest too much, is no disgrace) which he has concealed under a conspicuous acquisition; and yet he is not enough a materialist to enjoy his goods as they come to him and welcome the spiritual consolations that worldly pleasures bestow. "Money isn't everything," he will say, making more, and he says this to preserve an air of disconsolateness, as though virtue were impossible without a sour face. He does all this for show, but unconsciously his affectations hit upon the truth. All his life he is at loose ends, and expert only in ennui, which Tolstoy defined as the desire for desire, cousin to Levinsky's yearning. And even if none of this is true, and there is (as I strongly suspect) a direct gratification in wealth as such, it is still significant that most of us profess it to be true, clinging to a protective disenchantment.

Whatever the case with our much disputed and still, I suppose, amorphous American character, Levinsky, the Diaspora Man, had relatively little to overcome (speaking inwardly) to grow into the typical American of fortune. Only the environment was alien to him, but its inner loneliness was anticipated in his own, for one loneliness is much like another; and the very fact that the American environment was alien, and would remain so, to his Jewishness, enabled him to make good in it on his own peculiar terms—to satisfy everything but hunger. To be sure, his is only a single career, a single example of the Jew as American, but it draws our attention to the considerable structural congruity that must underlie the character and culture of the two peoples. And if Levinsky's career is understood in its essentially Jewish aspect, it may explain why the Jews, as an immigrant group, were among the first to achieve a virtually flawless Americanization.

I have purposely refrained from treating David Levinsky as a fictional character and have spoken of the novel as though it were the actual memoir of an American Jew, in tribute to Cahan's power of characterization. Such immediacy of revelation is the novel's strongest quality, and Levinsky is made to talk about himself not only with an authentic accent, but with a motive in disclosure verging on something sly—precisely as such a man would talk. This well-known and widely-respected businessman tells the truth about himself, his love affairs, his efforts to outsmart the unions, the way other men tell lies—to see if he can get away with it! But as fiction, Cahan's writing lacks continuity: his transitions from subject to subject tend to be abrupt, with a perseveration in the linking of sex and economics. Thus when he describes Levinsky's broken engagement (the cause was his falling in love with another woman), Cahan devotes less than twenty lines to the scene, and opens his very next paragraph (after a line space, but this may have been the typographer's doing) with the words, "Our rush season had passed. . . ." Often the trains of thought collide within the single paragraph, business plowing into everything else. True, Levinsky's mind would work this way, and the habit would also serve him the purpose of saying, "I may not be doing so well with the girls—but think of the money I'm making." (Though business is meaningless to Levinsky, one of the most touching insights of the novel is provided by Cahan's showing how he succumbs to a businessman's vulgarity of tone and manner, and berates himself for the weakness.) Yet it is not always possible to distinguish character from author, and this failure in detachment, the consequence of an imperfectly developed ear for nuances in language, becomes noticeable and sometimes quite confusing when there is no lucky congruity to justify it, as in the matter of the abrupt transitions from pleasure to business.

But these flaws, as I have already indicated, are of minor account. So much so, that I wonder what the critical reception and, no doubt, misunderstanding, of *The Rise of David Levinsky* must have been, that is should languish in the status of an "undiscovered" book, a standard footnote or paragraph in surveys of American Jewish literature, and not be known for the remarkable novel it is.

SHLOMO KATZ

MY FATHER WAS A HERO

MY FATHER WAS ALWAYS AN OLD MAN. MY EARLIEST
recollections of him go back almost forty years, and even then his long
beard was streaked with gray. Now his beard is entirely white. He
is impersonal and remote, and as I sit before him, his mild gaze
seems to imply forgiveness. Though my conscience is fairly clear,
I submit to his forgiveness. Who isn't guilty before his father?

He is an old man and his mind often wanders. He begins with the
time-honored prologue: "Well, it's this way. . . ." But he gets no
farther. I try to draw him on, to reestablish the thread of his thought.
The gentleness in his eyes changes into a faraway look that reaches
across distances over which I cannot follow. Then he seems to return
for a moment, he recognizes me, and asks: "When are you leaving
town?"

"In a few days," I say.

"And where are you going?" He is a very old man and his memory
sometimes fails him. He no longer remembers that I live in New York.

If it wasn't for his age, and that he is so forgiving of me, I might
suspect him of irony. There was a time when the question "Where are
you going?" was in place. Each time I left I went off in another
direction. But he would only shake his head and say, "Well, go in
good health and succeed." Now that I have ceased running off at a
different tangent each journey, he no longer remembers where I came
to rest.

So every day I tell him anew that I am going back to New York.

He nods assent, but doesn't seem to care. New York is only a name to him. At this point the conversation ends, to be repeated in almost identical words the following day, and the one after that, until I depart a week or so later.

I sit across the table from him trying to sum him up, and I am suddenly struck with the thought that he has been a hero all his life. How is it that I had never seen him in this light? And yet it is quite obvious.

There was that incident only a few years ago, for instance, when he was already in his late seventies. Who would have expected him to act as he did? Yet when it happened it only seemed to be a nice, slightly amusing occurrence.

The neighborhood in which my parents live was once almost exclusively Jewish but was long since abandoned by nearly all except a handful of the aged Jews who no longer move with the stream. In their place, there moved in some Negroes, some poor white people, and many Mexicans. The character of the neighborhood changed. Where formerly there was one bar, there are now half a dozen. The streets that had resounded to the sound of Yiddish now ring with Spanish. Outside the bars Mexican boys and young men pass the time and argue volubly. The remaining Jews in the neighborhood utter the name "Mexican" with overtones of suspicion and apprehension. What the Mexican residents say I do not know, but the expressions one can frequently see on the faces of the young men in front of the bars at the sight of some bearded old Jew reveal an uncomprehendingness that seems ready to leap to hostility. One of the half-unused synagogues is now wedged between a bar and a wooden frame house that has been transformed into a Catholic church.

"Well, it happened this way," Father told me when I came on my annual visit that year. "It was afternoon and I was going to the synagogue for *mincha* and *ma'ariv.*"

"I was going," he said, but now I recalled that his walk was then already an aged shuffle.

"And on the corner there was a bunch of Mexican fellows, outside the saloon. One of them knocked my hat off. Well, you know, I am a *kohen* and *kohanim* are short-tempered. Without thinking I grabbed this guy by the shirt and pushed him. He didn't expect it and fell. All the other Mexican fellows laughed at him and clapped their hands. 'That's good, old man,' they said, 'good work.' And ever since they haven't bothered me again. I go by there twice every day. Sometimes, when they see me, they laugh and say, 'Good, old man, good work.' But I never again had any trouble with them."

When he first told me about this incident I also laughed; but later, mulling over this matter, there came to my mind two other incidents involving Father that took place long ago in faraway Ukraine during the turbulent times after the First World War.

There was the first pogrom in town—in itself not an unusual event at that time and in that place. As I think back to it I try to reconstruct the mood and the "flavor" of the two days during which the pogrom lasted. It was a warm and cloudy-gray early summer morning when Mother woke me up and without any prologue announced: "Get up, there is a pogrom in town." I leaped out of bed and dressed quickly, suddenly aware of a strange and sharp new sense of being that was not altogether without a pleasant tang. There was an atmosphere of haste in the house, though nothing was being done. Everyone walked about tense, ready to leap, but the time to run had not come yet.

Thus no doubt a flock of chickens in their coop might feel when the housewife announces in the evening that she is going to have one of them killed for dinner the following day. The chase hasn't begun yet. There is no telling which one will be caught. There may still be a last-minute reprieve if the menu is changed. Meantime each chicken feels trapped and nervous and tense—and also chosen.

All of us behaved this way, fearful yet somehow elected, all except Father. He remained calm.

The doors were still open to the summer morning. Outside, Jews nervously congregated in bunches, rehashing the various rumors. Individuals drifted from one group to another in search of the ultimate rumor that would satisfy them. Without any apparent reason, sudden panic would seize the people in the street and they would flee into the houses and quickly lock the doors, only to emerge again a few minutes later. Outside, it is true, one was not in hiding, but neither was one trapped there. And somehow, intuitively, all knew that "it" had not yet begun, that minutes, perhaps hours, would pass before "it" started.

The terror hung heavy in the sultry air. Peasants from neighboring villages slowly drove into town in their horse- and ox-drawn carts, though it was not a market day. They scowled and occasionally some muttered something indistinct but hostile. Then other wagons, drawn by horses, began arriving. These carried Jewish fugitives from other towns. They chattered hysterically to the clusters of people that instantaneously formed about them. Then there arose the problem of their housing. By noon we had more than a dozen refugees in our house.

By noon "it" began. Somebody came running down the street; and somebody else screamed that "it" had begun, and in a split second the street was deserted and all doors were locked and all window shades drawn. A last frightened man dashed by shouting something incoherent about what went on downtown, and then the street was silent.

There were about twenty people in the three-room house and in the attic, and all were silent. Occasionally someone would whisper a terrified, "Did you hear?" as a muffled cry was heard from afar. Someone would move a window shade a fraction of an inch to peek outside. The street was empty as during a curfew.

Hours passed before the street began coming to life again, in a different way. Peasants who had come early in the morning were now returning to their villages, their wagons loaded with loot. Many of them were drunk and sang at the top of their voices plaintive, drawn-out Ukrainian tunes. Inside the house as many as could crowded near the windows to catch a glimpse of the loot and to learn from it what had happened. A bolt of cloth on a wagon, a few yards of it trailing in the dust, told about the looted dry-goods store and aroused concern for its owner. Pots and pans strung on a rope told the story of the hardware store. Men's and women's clothes had their own stories, though it was impossible to tell to whom they had belonged. A light-colored dress dangling from the side of a wagon was stained with what might have been blood, but it was impossible to know definitely. Small Ukrainian boys appeared in the street shrieking gaily and playing with all kinds of trophies of the looting. Then darkness descended.

Among the twenty in the house there were enough for a *minyan* and the evening prayers were whispered in unison. Then bread was doled out—cooking was avoided lest the smoke from the chimney attract attention to the house—and the terror of the night descended. From the distance came the sound of screams and the glow of fires.

Early the next day a new problem arose. There was no running water in the house. Water was brought daily in buckets from a well some blocks away and stored in a barrel. The twenty had consumed whatever water there was in the house. By noon thirst began to assert itself.

It was then that Father acted. Without saying a word he took the two buckets and went out by the rear door. We watched his progress. Groups of peasants were once again roaming the street, some sober, others drunk. We saw Father nodding a greeting to them and going on his way. Then he was stopped. He was still in sight but too far away for us to hear what was being said. He put the buckets on the ground. The peasants were saying something, then one of them pulled a long knife from the legging of his boot. The knife was passed around and examined. The group seemed to be going through some terrifying mummery.

Mother stood near the window wringing her hands. All others who could had their eyes glued to the narrow strip of window glass between the shade and the frame. Animation was suspended.

Then we saw some of the peasants roar with laughter. One of them slapped Father on the back, and they left him. Steadily he went to the well and returned some minutes later. Three times he repeated the trip, till the barrel was full, then he put down the buckets without saying a word.

The second incident which I remembered took place at about the same time in the same place as the first. This one, too, involved a pogrom, but this time we were in hiding with a family of Gentile friends. In the course of the hasty exodus from home the family treasures, which had been packed in a sack in anticipation of the event, had been left behind. Some hours after we reached our refuge, when things seemed to have quieted down somewhat, Father went to retrieve the "valuables" accumulated in the course of a lifetime. He did not fare so well this time. He returned a while later carrying the sack, but his mouth was bleeding and he had lost two teeth on this mission. He joined us in our allotted alien corner in a stranger's house and sat down quietly.

Since there is so little we can say to each other, especially now that his memory is faulty and his articulation difficult, I become restive after a while, despite my filial intentions. Yet I am determined not to go away before the two hours I assign daily to my parents have elapsed. Rescue appears from an unexpected quarter. Some friends whom I had promised to meet later at my hotel room come to pick me up. They exchange a few words of greeting with my parents and, before we notice it, we are in the midst of an argument on a painful current issue. Who was right during the Congressional investigations of un-

American activities? Those who named their former colleagues, or the ones who refused to answer questions about the activities of former friends? The discussion becomes heated. Someone tosses out the word "informers." This puts things in a different emotional light. Nobody wants to condone "informing," yet how define it under present conditions?

Even as the argument rages I remember what my father did about it. This incident also dates far back, to the time before I was born. I was a child of eight when he told me about it. I then attended *cheder* and already knew that while it was no crime to complain to Mother if a sister had taken something I considered my own, it was an unforgivable crime to report to the *rebbe* anything done by another pupil. That was informing and there was no more base and villainous creature on earth than a *mooser*—an informer. The only type of informer among adults I then knew of—the only kind then possible—was a person who reported someone to the authorities, or, more correctly, a Jew who reported another Jew to the Gentile authorities.

"Well," my father began, "there was this Yossel and he was an informer. Regularly he carried tales to the *Ispravnik*. Jews trembled before him. If anyone did a bit of business without a license, or tried to dodge the draft, Yossel always knew about it and informed. People begged him and argued with him, bribes were offered to him, but it didn't help. A committee once went to him. 'Why do you want to harm your fellow Jews?' they asked him. 'Have you no decency? Have you no regard for anyone? Does it hurt you if poor people try to earn bread for their children?' But Yossel only laughed. That was the sort of man he was. He knew he had the authorities on his side. Just a mean and vicious man. Then he pulled a particularly bad one. The man he informed on had a big family and simply couldn't make ends meet. So he began selling whisky without a license to the peasants on market days. He didn't have a regular place, just went around with the bottle from one to the other, selling it by the drink. And Yossel informed on him. He was caught and fined, but he couldn't pay it so he had to go to jail for three months and his family almost starved.

"I couldn't stand it any longer. There was another man in town who felt the way I did. He moved away some years ago. So the two of us decided something had to be done. We tried to get others to help us, but everybody was afraid of Yossel on account of his pull with the authorities. They even begged us to leave him alone so as not to cause more trouble than there was already.

"The following Saturday, just as they took the Torah out of the Ark, the other man and I went up to the platform and banged on table three times. *Ikuv hakriah* it is called, and when anyone in the congregation has very important public business, he does this and they have to wait with the reading of the Torah till the matter is settled. 'We want to make an example of an informer,' we announced and the two of us went up to Yossel. Let me tell you, he was scared. He turned white. He didn't know what we were going to do to him. Maybe he thought we would kill him. As we came up he begged us. 'Don't do anything. I promise. I will never inform again. Don't do anything here, before the entire congregation. I will give you anything you like. I will do anything you say.'

"But we were mad. That last bit of informing could not be forgiven. So we took his arms and marched him around the platform three times, shouting 'Thus shall be done to an informer!' I said we marched him around. I should say we dragged him. He was so pale and weak he couldn't stand on his feet. And, you know," Father concluded his story, "it worked. He never informed again and a short time later he left town and we got rid of the informer."

That was long, long ago. Now Father looks at us as we argue back and forth. He does not follow the argument, partly because he doesn't know enough English and partly because the thread of his thought snaps frequently.

In the midst of the argument I wonder: If he were younger, would he know that answer? Of course, it was so much simpler in those days. The authorities were black; the victims white and pure. In our case the issue is more involved. But the fact remains: he knew what was right and what was wrong. He not only knew, he also acted on his convictions.

Father had little formal education. Yet he had the answers to many perplexing questions that befuddled much younger people. I often wondered about some of his particularly apt replies, whether he had heard them from others or had made them up himself. Eventually I concluded that they were his own, otherwise he would have given appropriate credit. In his studies of the Talmud he had learned many times how Rabbi X, quoting Rabbi Y in the name of Rabbi Z, said. . . . It became an ingrained habit to shun claiming others' wisdom as one's own.

We, the "younger generation," were in rebellion against nearly everything that he and his generation of Jews had stood for. His generation engaged in petty business, the enlightened part of the younger generation were all Zionists, singing the glories of work on the land in Palestine, or socialists, dedicated to the eradication of all business. His generation implicitly believed in the efficacy—or at least the urgent desirability—of prayer. The younger generation sneered at the mechanical recitation of prayers, frequently performed without comprehending the meaning of the words recited.

Father was not much impressed by this criticism. Most of the time he simply ignored it and would not be provoked into argument. But there was one instance when he took up the cudgels on behalf of the practices of his generation.

The particular discussion concerned the recitation of prayers. The "younger generation" felt on solid ground and indulged in some particularly biting sarcasm. How much true religious feeling could one pour into the repetition of sounds without knowing their meaning?

But Father was not impressed. He listened patiently, and when all the fire and thunder had been exhausted, he began his answer in his usually mild manner.

"Why don't you understand?" he said. "Consider it this way. A father has a child of a year, let us say. The child still can't talk. It only babbles meaningless sounds. Yet when the father returns home at the end of the day's work and the child hurries toward him on all fours, babbling its incomprehensible sounds, and it raises its little arms to be picked up, the father beams with pleasure and is convinced that his is a wonderfully bright child and that its babbling is the greatest wisdom ever uttered.

"It is the same when Jews go to the synagogue," he continued. "It is true that many of them don't understand the meaning of what they recite and they mumble their prayers mechanically. But God looks down and sees his children hurrying to his house of prayer. He listens to the sounds they make there and he beams at them with delight. 'What wonderful children I have!' he exclaims. And the prayers are thus perhaps more effective than they would be if everyone understood each word he recited."

There was no answering this line of argument. There were a few weak attempts at rejoinder; there were some defensive remarks about obscurantism, mysticism. But they lacked conviction.

In late middle age, and later in mounting old age, far from the time and place in which he was brought up and where he belonged, he began to retreat inward. He drifted into the private chambers of his mind where all was clear and where he could commune with his Father, the One who would always understand and appreciate and forgive. He walked about, a strange figure resurrected from a past that extended much further back than his actual age. With a slight change of garb he would have been in place on the ancient plains of the Negev where Jacob's sons pastured their sheep. Yet he passed along the icy streets of St. Paul, by now a walking principle more than a contemporary man.

Because of sickness in the family I was visiting St. Paul. It was midwinter and the temperature hovered around zero. It was Saturday. I came to take him to the hospital where Mother lay sick. Visiting hours were from two to three in the afternoon and from six to seven in the evening. Though the hospital was miles away and the streets were slick with ice, he would not even consider my suggestion to take a streetcar. He did not say "no"; he merely looked at me as if I had said something entirely incomprehensible. We started out at half past twelve. We reached the hospital a quarter after two and stayed with Mother for the remaining three-quarters of an hour. Then he took a seat in the waiting room to spend the next three hours there. I was impatient and went to a cafeteria nearby. When I returned it was after four and dusk was rapidly setting in. The waiting room was quickly filling with visitors to other wards where visiting began after five.

The waiting room had the depressed hush of such places. People whispered to each other, though there was no need for it. Occasionally the silence was rent by the harsh voice over the intercom calling some doctor and everyone involuntarily winced as though it necessarily meant an emergency. Through the thickening gloom outside the windows the bare branches of the trees swayed disconsolately. We in the waiting room felt at the edge of crying, as an abandoned child might cry to be taken home.

The waiting visitors were Swedes, Norwegians, Irish, Germans. Now and then a furtive glance would be directed toward the patriarchal, white-bearded old man, questioning, uncomprehending glances.

Then Father got up and slowly went to the corner facing east. Completely oblivious of the presence of any other people he began reciting his afternoon prayers in an inaudible voice. Only his body gently swayed back and forth. A hush fell on the waiting room. Everyone looked at him. What was the old man doing in the corner? They were mystified, slightly fearful of the thing they did not understand, and also vaguely reverent. There was something about the rocking figure in the rapidly darkening corner that transcended the waiting room, the rasping voice on the intercom, the pain in the wards above. Had they heard his voice they would not have understood the Hebrew words. And if they had understood the words they would have been still more mystified. There seemed to be no obvious point in intoning: "And to Jerusalem thy city return in compassion . . ." on a cold winter afternoon in the waiting room of a hospital. But he was probably not considering the meaning of the words either. The old man was again a child speaking to his Father without caring what he said.

Some of the visitors looked at me, as if expecting an explanation. I did not volunteer any.

Later, when we were about to leave the hospital to return home, I saw Father fumbling under the corner of the mattress on which Mother lay. It was a frightening gesture as his fingers searched the end of the bedstead. Then I saw him remove a dime from somewhere beneath the frame that held the spring. He explained the matter to me. "When I go to visit Mother on Friday it is still light and I can carry money, so I take along an extra dime and hide it under the spring. Then I walk home. On Saturday, as you saw, I walk to the hospital in the afternoon but when it is time to return it is already dark and after the Sabbath, so I have my carfare here and can take a streetcar back."

I sit across the table from him. The glasses of tea before us are getting cold. I want to establish some sort of communication with him and find it difficult. He is so far away. I am reconciled. Perhaps true communication between human beings is impossible at any time.

This not very profound reflection brings to my mind a little story Father told me when I was a child. He liked to tell me stories, some of them above my head and others of a kind that modern educators would disapprove of for a child under ten.

He told me about the *lamed vov,* the thirty-six secret saints who live in each generation, and for the sake of whose merits the world remains in existence. They never reveal their true identity to anyone. They are only known to each other. In order not to attract attention, the thirty-six generally engage in some such lowly trade as tailors, shoemakers, or itinerant peddlers; they perform their saintly and sometimes incomprehensible deeds in secret, and then they vanish from the scene.

It happened in the time of Nicholas I, Father told me. At that time small Jewish boys were kidnapped in the streets and farmed out to Russian peasants far away from their homes. When they reached their teens they were taken into the Russian army where they had to serve for twenty-five years. If after all this time they survived and remained Jews—for they were cruelly beaten all the time and in other ways driven to become converted to Christianity—they were free to return home. Those who did return seldom found their parents still living. Grief generally had carried them off.

When a Jewish boy was thus kidnapped he was often held in town for a few days until the authorities could get together a party of boys to be sent away. During this time it was sometimes possible to ransom the child by substituting another recruit.

My story, Father went on, concerns such a kidnapped boy, nine years old, who was snatched in the street and confined to jail. His parents came to the prison and wept bitterly outside the walls every day. They tried to bribe the guards to let the boy escape but did not succeed. But there lived in that town a *lamed vovnik,* one of the secret thirty-six saints. He could not bear to see the mother's tears, so he volunteered as a recruit to go in the place of the young boy.

He was sent far away to a remote Russian city where there was a fortress. Because he was a grown man they put him in the army right away. He lived on bread and water alone so as not to eat anything that was not kosher.

Often they assigned him to sentry duty. It was then a custom in the Russian army that on dark nights the sentries called to each other every few minutes to make sure that all were awake, because they could not see each other. One sentry would cry out *"Sloo-oo-oo-shay"* ("Hear"), and the one next to him would answer the same call, and so it would go around the wall of the fortress till it completed the circle and they knew that all was well and none of the guards was asleep. But whenever the guard next to the *lamed vovnik* cried out *"Sloo-oo-oo-shay,"* he would mournfully respond, *"Shechinta begaluta vai"* ("The *Shechinah* is in exile, woe").

From a distance it sounded like the regular sentry call.

IRVING HOWE

INTRODUCTION TO
YIDDISH LITERATURE

MODERN YIDDISH LITERATURE FOCUSES UPON THE
shtetl during its last tremor of self-awareness, the historical moment
when it is still coherent and self-contained but already under fierce
assault from the outer world. Between language and milieu there is a
curious, ambivalent relationship: the one seems to batten on the other.
Yiddish reaches its climax of expressive power as the world it portrays
begins to come apart.

The Yiddish of Mendele and Sholom Aleichem is a remarkably fluid
and intimate language. Perhaps because it is a language forged in opposition to the most powerful groups within the Jewish community,
perhaps because it is the voice of the folk rising organically from the
life of the folk, Yiddish is breezy in tone, richly idiomatic in flavor, free
in its literary possibilities. This very freedom, of course, is also a severe
burden: many a Yiddish writer suffers from the absence of inherited
modes and forms.

When the first major Yiddish writers appeared toward the end of
the nineteenth century, the language did not impose upon them any
stylized patterns of expression—which allowed them verbal spontaneity
and improvisation but also forced them to create, as it were, the very
standards of usage from which they were already deviating. At its peak,
however, Yiddish was neither a folk voice nor a sophisticated "literary"
language. It was open at both sides, still responsive to the voice of the
folk yet beginning to model itself on literary patterns of the West. The
most valuable writing in Yiddish appears at the moment when the two
opposing forces, the folk voice and the self-consciously literary, achieve

278

an exquisite, if almost always precarious, balance. To strike an extreme comparison which is not meant to suggest an equation of value between the two literatures: Yiddish found itself for a moment in the position of creative youthfulness that English enjoyed during the Elizabethan Age.

It is almost inevitable that in speaking of Yiddish literature one should refer to an inner dialectic, a tension of counterposed elements: the traditional past and the immediate experience, the religious structure and the secular infiltration, the folk voice and the modern literary accent. But even Yiddish literature itself can be seen and, by its most important critics, has been seen as part of a similar dialectic. The pioneering Yiddish critic Baal Machshoves, and in our own time Samuel Niger, repeatedly employ the formula, "two languages and one literature." Such a view of the relationship between Yiddish and Hebrew is partly motivated, no doubt, by a desire to preserve the historic continuity of the Jewish tradition, and partly by the fact that any empirical study of the formation of Yiddish literature must constantly take into account the Hebrew base and the Hebrew component. "Bilingualism," writes Niger, "became among us an accepted fact, a tradition. . . . "The essence of the Jewish experience," he continues, "was reflected in this partnership between Hebrew and Yiddish," a partnership that is indissoluble no matter who would wish to dissolve it. And when he turns to the late nineteenth century Niger finds a great deal of evidence to support his theory. Mendele, the first major Yiddish writer, began by composing in Hebrew and only later, in 1863, did he turn to Yiddish. During the last decade of his life Mendele translated back into Hebrew the works he had written in Yiddish—with the result that his position as a pioneer in modern Yiddish literature is matched by an equivalent position in modern Hebrew literature. Among recent writers there are numerous examples of a similar bilingualism: the great Hebrew poet Chaim Bialik wrote Yiddish verse; the distinguished Hebrew poet Zalman Schneour has written stories and novels in Yiddish. Nor are these to be taken merely as instances of creative virtuosity. The cultural kinship between the two literatures is so profound that almost any well-educated serious writer in the one literature must be affected by and concerned with the other. Ultimately both literatures draw from and give expression to the same ethos.

But not entirely the same ethos. The theory of "two languages and one literature" is indispensable to an understanding of Yiddish literature; it helps to clarify, for example, how the presence of Hebrew in the background enables Yiddish literature to avoid the painful fate of those literatures of small countries which either become stalled in provinciality or fall into a slavish imitation of the latest vogue from Paris. Yet a too rigorous application of the theory might soon blur those elements and modes that are unique to the Yiddish. For there *is* something qualitatively unique to the whole cultural aura of Yiddish, something in its characteristic gestures and tones that is summoned by the word *Yiddishkeit*. One way of making this point, perhaps, is to note that Yiddish literature releases a profound yearning for a return not to the supremacy of Hebrew but to those conditions of life that would make possible the supremacy of Hebrew—that is, a yearning for the end of the dispersion and a reintegration of Jewish life. But during most of the span of Yiddish literature this is a hope impossible to realize; and it is the recognition of its impossibility that gives rise to that distinctive Yiddish note which cannot and should not be assimilated into Hebrew, or any other, culture.

Somewhat along the same lines, the Yiddish critic B. Rivkin has advanced the theory that Yiddish literature, more through necessity than choice, came to serve as a substitute for a "would-be territory," thereby taking over the functions of a nation that did not yet exist. This meant that many of the communal needs which for other peoples were met by the nation had somehow to be satisfied by Yiddish literature. In the historical interim during which the hold of religion had begun to decline and the idea of nationality had not yet reached its full power, Yiddish literature became a central means of collective expression for the East European Jews, fulfilling some of the functions of both religion and the idea of nationality. In the absence of a free and coherent national life it had to provide the materials for a sense of national identity; and even as, in honesty, it reported the realities of the *shtetl* and the Pale, it had also to nurture and exalt their collective aspirations. From many points of view, of course, this was an impossible task for any literature, let alone one as frail and youthful as the Yiddish; yet something of the moral seriousness—though little of the metaphysical boldness—that we admire in the nineteenth-century Russian novel is also to be found in Yiddish literature precisely because the Yiddish writers thought of their work in supra-literary terms. One could not say of Yiddish literature, as the critic Chernyshevsky has said of the Russian, that it "constitutes the sum total of our intellectual life"; but one can say that the Yiddish writers came before their audience, as did the Russian writers of the nineteenth century, with an instinctive conviction that their purpose was something other than merely to entertain and amuse. The achievements of Russian literature are obviously greater than those of the Yiddish, but both share the assumption that the one subject truly worthy of a serious writer is the problem of collective destiny, the fate of a people.

Among the East European Jews the taste for imaginative literature did not come easily or quickly. They had to struggle for it, and struggle, most of all, against themselves. "It was natural," writes B. Rivkin, "for Jews to ask, 'Why literature?' After all, literature was a late development among Jews. The world around them had a well-established literature with its own forms. But here was a people living in an unnatural environment, without its own territorial and governmental organs, without its own self-sustaining social and economic structure. . . . The pioneer of Yiddish literature was, therefore, confronted with the difficult, almost impossible task of justifying literature to the people, and with the not much easier task of creating something equivalent to a natural environment. The first task was fulfilled by Mendele, the second by Sholom Aleichem."*

Literature had to be *justified*, it had to be assigned a moral sanction —which is not to say that the Yiddish pioneers, either the writers or the critics, meant that it had to be moralistic. But what, they seemed to be asking themselves, is the distinct use and end of Yiddish literature? How does it take its place in the larger Jewish tradition? The answer they implicitly gave was that Yiddish literature should focus upon one particular experience, the life of dispersion; that it should release, as only imaginative writing can, the deepest impulses of that life and thereby provide a means of both conscrating and transcending the *shtetl*. Yiddish literature, like any other, has always had its schools, groups, and cliques, but there is hardly a Yiddish writer of any significance whose work is not imbued with this fundamental urge to portray Jewish life with the most uncompromising realism and yet to transcend the terms of the portrayal. How could it be otherwise? Simply to survive, simply to face the next morning, Yiddish literature had to cling to the theme of historical idealism. Beyond hope and despair lies the desperate *idea* of hope, and this is what sustained Yiddish writing.

A literature that, even as it is still reeling from the pain of birth, must assume the formidable task of preserving the national sense of identity and adapting it to the unfamiliar modes of the modern world—

---

* B. Rivkin, *Die Grunt-Tendentsen fun Yiddisher Literatur in America*.

such a literature will inevitably turn to language as the only available unifying principle. In another time and under different circumstances language might simply be seen as the familiar, accepted vehicle of cultural realization; but here it becomes, so to speak, the very substance and issue of culture, the living repository of the past and future. The effort to create a Yiddish literature meant the effort to affirm a linguistic patriotism: both are expressions of the urge to national dignity, which became so passionate in the Jewish world of the late nineteeth and early twentieth centuries.

At that time there sprang up the literary and linguistic movement called Yiddishism. Peretz was one of its major spokesmen and Dr. Chaim Zhitlovsky its most ardent defender. How astonishing it now seems—a movement designed to "defend" a language spoken by millions of people, the very people to whom the writers addressed themselves with such assurance and warmth; a movement that felt obliged to justify the existence of a flourishing culture at a time when it needed not apologetics but air, space, and time.

Yet, from another point of view, the Yiddishist movement is entirely understandable. The Yiddish writer felt only too keenly his problem of being part of a national-religious tradition that went back into the depths of history, while he wrote in a language that had barely been touched by modern literary forms and within a culture that had barely acknowledged the idea of non-religious expression. As a result he could not help being self-conscious in his relation to the language; he could not help proclaiming its virtues while cursing its limitations. A writer in French or English, whether conservative or radical in matters of style and diction, took his language for granted: it was *there;* he did not think to question its historical stability or expressive capacities. But for the Yiddish writer of a half-century ago things were very different. Writing for an audience hardly prepared to apply sophisticated standards but only too ready to scrutinize his every word and thought, he had to find everything out for himself. He had to discover, if he could, why Yiddish seemed to lend itself so naturally to intimate speech and to resist so stubbornly more formal address; why it collaborated with the lyric poet so willingly and with the epic so grudgingly; why it took to the picaresque narrative of a Cervantes but not to the psychological webbing of a Henry James; why it frequently reached the loving empathy of a Turgenev but so seldom the metaphysical rhetoric of a Melville. Just as the Yiddish writer had the task of reweaving the fabric of national consciousness, so he had to improvise, to conquer and create, his own language.

Most of the time, this meant an utterly loving, fiercely defensive attitude toward Yiddish. But sometimes it led to the kind of comparison the early Yiddish poet Simon Frug made between the language and the assorted scraps of bread in a beggar's sack—or to his even more bitter remark that Yiddish was a patchwork so curious that it would prevent the Jews from entering heaven: the angel at the gate wouldn't understand it. In his long poem "Monish," Peretz wrote with a blend of affection, irony, and exasperation:

> Differently my song would ring
> If for gentiles I would sing.
> Not in Yiddish, in "Jargon,"
> That has no proper sound or tone.
> It has no words for sex-appeal
> And for such things as lovers feel.
> Yiddish has but quips and flashes,
> Words that fall on us like lashes,
> Words that stab like poisoned spears,
> And laughter that is full of fears,
> And there is a touch of gall,
> Of bitterness about it all.
>
> (*Translation by Joseph Leftwich*)

Once Yiddish literature is seen as the not quite prepared inheritor of national-cultural tasks, it becomes easier to speculate on those of its qualities that often puzzle readers who have not know it from birth.

The fascination with individual character, with the endlessly minute exposure of motives and manners, which pervades twentieth-century Western literature, is only occasionally present, and that during the more recent decades, in Yiddish fiction. The reader of this book may well be struck by a good many representative figures: the student tortured by a conflict between belief and secular desire; the Jewish householder trembling on the edge of poverty yet proud in his independence; the Jewish child wavering between gaiety and sadness; the ignoramus or sainted fool who proves holier than the men ordained to holiness. Such figures stay in the mind, they have the endurance of archetypes, but they are not, in any sense familiar to most Western readers, "individualized" characters; and if the stock notions of criticism are applied, these stories will be difficult to make out.

In reading Yiddish fiction one seldom has the desire to remember more about the characters than their stark, generalized traits. Anyone reading Lamed Shapiro's "Smoke" is likely to remember the Jewish merchant who is at the center of the story; but who will care to know that his name is Menasha? For even so modern a writer as Shapiro, who breaks from many of the traditions of "classical" Yiddish literature, still sees his characters more in their aspect of typicality than as uniquely demarcated individuals.

Not even Sholom Aleichem's Tevye the Dairyman, one of the great figures of modern literature, can be said to be thoroughly individualized; he is seen in the round, in his social relations, in his accustomed gestures, in his inimitable speech, and above all in his typical situations; but not in his inner reflections, not in those moments of exposed consciousness or dream life when he has no defense against the observing eye. For, in the nature of things, a character in Yiddish literature must always have a defense. It is hardly an accident that Tevye tells his stories *to* Sholom Aleichem; he consciously organizes, he provides comment, he lends perspective—and so dominant a speaker is not a convenient choice, at least in literature, for a display of depth psychology. The Yiddish story is sometimes a monologue, more often a dialogue, very seldom a plunge into private rumination. The major Yiddish writer, at least those who began publishing before World War I, are largely untouched by that passion for fret-work psychology which makes modern writing a thing of marvelous refinement but also tends to dissolve behavior into a stream of perceptual notation.

In this respect Sholom Aleichem and Peretz are more like Kafka than any of the three are like most modern writers. The Yiddish masters are largely unconcerned with the psychology of individual difference; Kafka consciously puts it aside. Whether Kafka was greatly influenced by the Yiddish tradition remains an unsettled question, though the similarities between his stories and some of the Hasidic tales are remarkable. But he is akin to the Yiddish writers in that he deals not with psychological arithmetic, the numbers of individual configuration, but with the algebra of situation and emotion. That is why you cannot find in Kafka, as you cannot find in Peretz, those delicately modeled and infinitely subtle character studies we associate with James and Proust. What matters most to the Yiddish writers is the context, the contour, the choreography of social behavior: in short, collective destiny. And even when an occasional writer—like Jonah Rosenfeld in his harrowing story "Competitors"—deliberately employs modern psychological insights, he takes hold of them in their generalized form, he does not try to embody them in private deviations.

This point holds more strongly for the Yiddish story than the Yiddish novel, if only because the story as a genre cannot achieve the detailed scrutiny of character that is possible to the novel. But that can hardly be the whole explanation; something else, something related to the inner qualitles of Yiddish culture, must also be involved.

A culture that has gained inner security or has even begun to decline a little, a culture that has bitten eagerly into the apple of power and success, is likely to indulge itself in the luxury of individual self-examination. Introspection, spiritual testing, self-doubt—these familiar elements of Western life are tied to that sense of estrangement and aloneness, that sense of the self as an insupportable burden, which everyone in an industrial civilization seems to feel to one extent or another. In the literature that appears at such a time the probing of individual differences and nuances in behavior will be far advanced.

Suppose, however, that you are living in a society that, whatever its weaknesses and faults, is still coherent inernally but is constantly threatened from without. Such a society, particularly when its ethos rests upon the assumption that God has granted it a unique destiny, will inevitably aspire toward cultural expressions of a collective type. In this society the individual will not be disdained but neither will he be exalted; he will be seen rather as the agent and embodiment of the community, who must be prevented, if he shows any such inclinations, from tumbling into the pits of Western egotism. It follows that in the literature of such a society the central concern will be not with individual specification but with the unifying patterns of conduct.

Just as the appetite for "individualized" characterization, so chronic among modern readers, cannot be satisfied by Yiddish literature, so will those critics who think of prose fiction mainly in terms of an interplay of social manners be somewhat perplexed by Yiddish literature. The gradations of social manners revealed in a Jane Austen novel depend upon the existence of an ordered world that has had time to settle, ripen, and develop freely; a world that has become sufficiently relaxed to allow its tendencies toward diversification of manners to reach their bloom. But this could never be the case with the world of the East European Jews. Even their pathetic little snobberies, even the cruel vanities of their caste system, were enacted within a sharply compressed area. There wasn't the social space—nor even, by the way, the geographical space—that would make possible a full display of contrasting manners within such a world. In a few later Yiddish writers like

Lamed Shapiro one does find the idea of manners as index to morality and belief, particularly in his story "Eating Days"; but this remains the exception rather than becomes the rule.

Moreover, the social differences among the East European Jews, considerable as these soon became, were never so deep as the social differences between themselves and the outer world. To be a Jew was the determining condition of one's life, far more so than one's wealth or poverty, learning or ignorance. The wealthy Jew of the *shtetl* was far better off than the poor one, but they lived within a few houses of each other, often on the same muddy street, and they trembled equally before the drunken or inflamed peasant. Even in the cities the social range between Jew and non-Jew was almost always greater than the range between wealthy and poor Jew. Clearly, this was not a climate in which fine discriminations of manners could flourish.

But a more fundamental fact needs to be stressed. The notion that a man's appearance reflects, in some mysteriously strategic way, the qualities of his soul—a notion that pervades American writing and in the work of such writers as John O'Hara has become an obsession—never took deep hold in Yiddish literature. Nor in the Russian either. Tolstoi believed that a man's destiny is not a function of his social role; Dostoevski believed that the elder Karamazov, wretched buffoon that he was, could rise to salvation; and the Yiddish writers also knew that in essential human experiences not the play of manners but the direct, fearful encounter of moral assumptions was fundamental. The approach to prose fiction in terms of social manners is clearly valuable, but there are kinds of literature with which it cannot cope. A Jewish belief has it that the world is sustained by thirty-six secret and entirely inconspicuous saints; in Peretz's story "Devotion without End," one of these secret thirty-six suddenly appears, an artisan who has gone unhonored and unnoticed. What can a study of social manners tell us about a saint whose saintliness derives from a secret covenant?

A similar hypothesis may help explain why Yiddish literature, particularly the prose, is so poor in formal experimentation. (By contrast, recent Yiddish poetry has been sensitive to modernist techniques in Western poetry—often with striking results.) A literature so heavily weighted with national tasks is not likely to know the freedom—the possibility for play, in both senses of the word—that is needed for literary experiment. Most of the innovations of twentieth-century literature result from a feeling among major writers that various inherited styles, manners, or genres have become "exhausted"—exactly what "exhausted" means here we shall not try to say—and that radical shifts in literary strategy are necessary if imaginative writing is not to stagnate. At least until recently, the Yiddish writers have found themselves in quite another situation. Among them there was not time enough for a style or genre to become "exhausted"; they were still at the stage of trying to press urgent materials and themes into whatever style or genre seemed to be at hand. The literary curve that ends with avant-garde writing had just begun for them. Nothing could yet seem used up, few things had even been tried; the problem was rather that their material was frequently too immediate to be pacified into the forms they could usefully control.

Yiddish writing is preoccupied, above all, with themes; life is still beating urgently at the doors of art. "The writer was struggling with his themes," begins a story by David Pinski, a Yiddish writer who spent a lifetime struggling with his themes; and this opening sentence might well be the epigraph of all Yiddish literature. For the Yiddish writers did not work in a culture sufficiently at ease to encourage the kind of art that abandons any effort directly to reflect or reform the world in which it appears. The sense of aesthetic distance, the aristocratic savoring of isolation, which make for an intense concern with formal literary problems, were not available to the Yiddish writer. From birth, so to speak, he was an "engaged" writer: in that sense he was indeed chosen. Art for art's sake, whether as a serious commitment or a shallow slogan, finds little nourishment in the soil of Yiddish literature, even though an occasional attempt is made to transplant it there. But then, how could any theory of pure aestheticism take hold in a culture beset by the primary questions of existence and survival?

If the unique circumstances of Yiddish literature imposed certain disabilities and burdens, the advantages gained from its position of historical precariousness now seem far greater. For whatever its limitations of scope and form, Yiddish literature is endowed with a moral poise, a security of values that is very rare in any age.

We live in a time when the literature most likely to be valued by serious people is intense, recalcitrant, and extreme; when the novel is periodically combed for images of catastrophe; and the possibilities of life seem available only through ultimates, prophecies, and final judgments. Formally we accord Dostoevski and Tolstoi equal honor, but in our hearts we feel closer to Dostoevski; his seems the true voice of crisis, and we know ourselves to be creatures of crisis. None of this is said by way of depreciation, for we too join in this response and believe it to be necessary or at least inevitable to our time.

Yet it would be good if we could also celebrate another kind of literature: the kind that does not confront at every moment the harsh finalities of experience, or strip each act to its bare motive, or flood us with anguish over the irrevocability of death. In such writers as Turgenev, Chekhov, Silone, and Sholom Aleichem there is a readiness —never purchased at the price of complacence—to value those milder virtues which can cause only impatience in many modern minds. These writers—let us call them the writers of sweetness—do not assume evil to be the last word about man, and they seem to add: Even if it is the last word, there are others to be declared before we reach it. They do not condescend to the ordinary, or scorn the domestic affections, or suppose heroism to be incompatible with humbleness.

Sweetness is a quality our age suspects. Not many of us are sweet or care to be; and those few who are seem almost ashamed of their gift. "Sweetness and light" now seems a phrase of faint ridicule, calling to mind a genteel academicism. But when Matthew Arnold used the phrase—and we might remember that Jonathan Swift used it before him—he was hardly seeking a warrant for complacence; he knew that the quality of sweetness need not exclude the most stringent realism.

Everything we know about Yiddish literature strengthens our confidence in these remarks. Here is a literature that explored poverty as few others have, that studied the misery of this life as intensely as the French have studied the politics of sex. But while we do not wish to suggest that Yiddish literature has been without its voices of desperation and violence—anyone who reads the stories of Jonah Rosenfeld, Zalman Schneour, and even, in part, Peretz will find plenty of both —we are repeatedly struck by the tone of love, that final register of moral poise, with which such masters as Sholom Aleichem and Peretz faced the grimmest facts about Jewish life.

Why should this be so? Not, we would suggest, because of any special virtues in Jewish life or character; not even because of the distinctive religious cast of the *shtetl*. When Mendele wrote his tribute to the compressibility of the Jewish stomach, and Sholom Aleichem had his Tevye declare, "I was, with God's help, a poor man," these writers were expressing an ethos that reflects a unique historical condition. The East European Jews could be as greedy as anyone else, and as unscrupulous in their pursuit of a livelihood; but they were cut off from the world at an all too visible point; they knew that the fleshpots, tempting as they might be, were not for them. Who in the shtetl world was not finally a *luftmensch,* a trader who dealt in air, exchanging nothing for nothing and living off the profits? This precarious position made the ironic shrug a symbolic national gesture; it made the feeling of fraternity with the poor a foundation for Peretz's earlier realistic stories and Sholom Aleichem's marvelous flights into surrealism.

Because of its own limitations, the world of the East European Jews made impossible the power-hunger, the pretensions to aristocracy, the whole mirage of false values that have blighted Western intellectual life. *The virtue of powerlessness, the power of helplessness, the company of the dispossessed, the sanctity of the insulted and the injured*—these, finally, are the great themes of Yiddish literature.

Nor does the sentiment of humaneness have anything in common with the populist rhetoric and sentimentalty we have come to know in American literature; no one could have been more caustic than Mendele and Peretz in their attacks on their own world. What it signified was that, in the end, the best Yiddish writers knew to whom their sympathies were pledged, and never doubted for a moment that they stood as perhaps the last spokesmen of a tradition the outer world would not tolerate. They wrote from a firm sense of identificaton, an identification that was simultaneously inheritance and choice; and this was the source of their moral security.

None of this has anything to do with *shtetl*-nostalgia. Nor is it uniquely Jewish: the sense of fraternity with the poor is as fine in Silone as in Sholom Aleichem. It is only that the Jews—with God's help—have had more occasion than most peoples to look into the matter.

Before he died Sholom Aleichem wrote: "Bury me among the poor, that my grave may shine on theirs and their graves on mine." He did not speak for himself alone.

A culture that has been able to resist the temptations of worldly power—or has been blocked at the threshold of those temptations— will naturally favor an image of heroism very different from the one we know in Western literature. Few Yiddish novels or stories contain heroes who satisfy the Aristotelian formula. The rhythm of *hybris* and the climb from *hybris* into humility is not really organic to Yiddish literature, though conspicuous examples of it can, of course, be found. Most Yiddish writers, especially those in the generation of Sholom

Aleichem and Peretz, place a far greater stress upon the theme of anti-heroism.* Rejecting the whole ethos of historical aggrandizement as it has come to us from the Greek drama and been colored by the era of Christian expansion, the Yiddish writers express through the theme of anti-heroism their admiration for those who do not exert their social will but live and endure in silence, as well as their contempt for what the outer world takes to be greatness but which they often feel is no more than an appetite for blood. Sholom Aleichem's Tevye the Dairyman is the embodiment of the anti-heroic Jewish hero whose sheer power of survival and comment makes the gesture of traditional heroism seem rather absurd. Peretz too is fascinated by the problem of heroism, but, beng more "modern" than Sholom Aleichem, he ends with a more ambivalent feeling. In a number of his stories the victim is seen as the sanctified agent of moral purity, but in his later work Peretz turns upon this theme with a bitter impatience, as if to say that Jewish heroism has degenerated into weak passivity.

Among the writers of the generation that follows Sholom Aleichem and Peretz there is a deliberate effort to revive the tradition of Jewish heroism (see the dramatic little story by Sholem Asch called "Sanctification of the Name"). These writers, particularly Asch and Joseph Opatoshu, reject the pacific tenor of "classical" Yiddish writing; they seek to inspire their readers with a militant, almost warlike readiness to struggle in behalf of Jewish survival; they feel that, in part at least, the world must be met with the ways of the world.

But in the main the tradition of anti-heroism continues to dominate Yiddish writing. *Dos kleine menschele*, the little man, appears again and again at the center of Yiddish fiction: it is he, long-suffering,

* Perhaps this throws some light on two problems with regard to Yiddish literature, one technical and the other historical.

A good many Yiddish stories deliberately avoid the traditional ending of a dramatic climax. Why? Surely the Chekhov influence cannot be the only reason. Might there not be a connection between this narrative strategy and the theme of anti-heroism—with the absence of climax a kind of rhythmic equivalent to the refusal of heroism?

The prevalence of this theme may also help explain why Zionists have been tempted to look with impatience upon Yiddish literature. In the nature of their effort, the Zionists desired to retrieve—or improvise—an image of Jewish heroism; and in doing so they could not help finding large portions of Yiddish literature an impediment. The fact that Yiddish literature had to assume the burden of sustaining a national sense of identity did not thereby make it amenable to the needs of a national ideology. Having for so long been exposed to the condition of powerlessness, Yiddish culture could not quickly accustom itself to the climate of power.

persistent, lovingly ironic, whom the Yiddish writers celebrate; it is the poor but proud householder trying to maintain his status in the Jewish world even as he grows poorer and poorer who appeals to their imagination far more than might an Aeneas or an Ahab. Anyone, they seem to say, can learn to conquer the world, but only a Tevye or a literary descendant of Tevye can learn to live in it. The ordinary humble man becomes an almost legendary archetype in Abraham Reisen's little sketches, the very fragmentariness of whose form reveals the essence of their *Weltanschauung*.

From this central figure of Yiddish literature—one might call him the Representative Man of the *shtetl*—there emerges a number of significant variations and offshoots. One extreme variation is the wise or sainted fool who has often given up the householder's struggle for dignity and thereby acquired the wry perspective of the man on the outside. Another is the ecstatic wanderer, hopeless in this world because so profoundly committed to the other—as in I. J. Singer's novel *Yoshe Kalb* (in English, *The Sinner*).

The wise or sainted fool—to note a few of his appearances in this book—is seen full-face in I. Bashevis Singer's "Gimpel the Fool," where he acquires, with the piling up of his foolishness, a halo of comic sadness, and where, in the end, his foolish innocence triumphs over the wisdom of the world. Gimpel is the literary grandson of Peretz's Bontsha Schweig, whose intolerable humbleness makes even the angels in heaven feel guilty and embarrassed—though Bontsha, while an epitome of the type, is also meant as a harsh thrust against it. The wise or sainted fool also appears, somewhat muted, in Joseph Opatoshu's little story "May the Temple Be Restored," where his ignorance becomes the thread from which a devotion purer than his rabbi's is woven. And a more somber, less easily recognizable version of the type may be found in Moishe Kulbak's "Muni the Bird Dealer," where he barely speaks at all but ends with a gesture of depair that is terrible beyond the power of words.

Hand in hand with the anti-heroic Jewish hero, and more at the center of things than the sainted fool, goes the Jewish child, precocious, ingenious, deprived, yet infinitely loved. The completely carefree story about the adventurous boy, so favored in English, is virtually absent from the Yiddish, if only because that kind of boy could seldom survive in Jewish life. In the Yiddish story the child almost always carries a social burden heavier than we in America are accustomed to believe appropriate for children. Oppressed by this thought, Sholom Aleichem writes in his autobiography: ". . . this is not meant for you, Jewish children! Yellow sunflowers, sweet-smelling grass, fresh air, fragrant earth, the clear sun—forgive me, these are not meant for you. . . ." This note of deprivation winds through almost all Yiddish children's stories. Too young, far too young, they become *kleine menschelach*, little men—pale and bent scholars who do not see the sun, premature wage-earners scurrying for a peice of bread.

Yet they seem to bear these burdens, at least in the literature, with spirit and even joy. For in Yiddish literature the family is generally shown as a still cohesive unit; fathers may be strict, mothers tearful, brothers oppressive, but love breaks through and beneath the barriers of ritual. If there are few carefree children in Yiddish literature, there are few unloved and brutalized children. A story like Henry James's "The Turn of the Screw" would have puzzled Jewish readers who had been brought up on Abraham Reisen's tender sketches of childhood or Sholom Aleichem's loving stories about Mottel the cantor's son. They would have had difficulty in grasping the moral assumptions behind James's story. How, one can hear them asking, does a father leave his children in the hands of strangers to begin with? The many works in English, from Dickens to Graham Greene, about children hated and exploited do not find an equivalent in Yiddish. There children may have it very hard, but never from coldness. For whatever the deficiencies of Yiddish culture, the power of love remains: for the child, the poor, the weak, for the insulted and injured everywhere. It is the power at the heart of the Yiddish tradition.

Throughout this essay we have spoken repeatedly about the role of tradition in Yiddish literature. In America the idea of tradition has become an icon of literary criticism, and "traditional," though properly a neutral term, now serves for implicit praise. But if by traditional we mean not merely a writer's sense of continuity with the writers who have preceded him but also his sense of being part of a living culture and intimately related to an active audience, then it is in Yiddish literature—far more so than in modern English or American literature —that tradition has been a sustaining force. A writer like Sholom Aleichem could assume that his readers knew not only the world he described but every nuance that could be wrung from his plays of language; he had no need for depth psychology or a minute analysis of character, for his readers lived next door, as it were, to the people who lived in his books. He could count, above all, on one of the main resources of tradition: the powers of implicit communication among members of a coherent group. And he could assume that most of his readers knew that his stories, while immensely entertaining, were far from mere entertainments; that they understood because he felt no need to explain.

The Waste Land is far more recondite than any of Sholom Aleichem's stories, but the footnotes T. S. Eliot felt obliged to append suggest that he was writing in a society where tradition had been disrupted, where tradition had become a problem, *a subject for discussion.* By contrast, the coherence of Sholom Aleichem's stories indicates how much he could demand from his readers. Imagine Sholom Aleichem appending footnotes that explained to his readers how, for comic purposes, he had mangled Biblical and Talmudic texts! He had no need to foreshorten plots or seek fresh devices by which to avoid boring his audience; he was as sure of his readers as of his materials; and how many Western writers have been able to enjoy such advantages?

But it is in the work of another writer that one can most fully see the sustaining power of tradition. A reader coming to Yiddish literature from a distance may wonder at the very high estimate its critics place on the fragile little sketches of Abraham Reisen. In the hundreds of stories he wrote—without dramatic accent or visible plot line, they sometimes read like muted prose lyrics—Reisen has provided one of the truest and fullest portraits that we have of Jewish life in Eastern Europe. His sketches depend so heavily on the tacit cooperation of the audience, they assume so deep a sharing of values and knowledge, that to the unfamiliar reader they may sometimes seem more like literary clues than literary embodiments. Concerned not with events but with situations and predicaments, Reisen writes in a manner that reminds one of those stage designers who, by manipulating a few sticks of wood, create the illusion that a bare stage is really Lear's palace. And this is possible not merely because Reisen is a skilled writer— though it would be a mistake to underestimate the quality of feeling and perception beneath his mildly ironic surfaces—but because he is in complete rapport with his audience. (Some of his poems have almost become folk songs and are often sung by people who would be astonished to learn that they were composed by a twentieth-century poet.) The result is a kind of literary shorthand, a flash of communication achieved through a few phrases, a faint touch of color, a shrug or two—and the Yiddish reader understands and responds. We are not saying that Reisen is the best or the most exciting Yiddish story-writer; we are merely saying that he is in the mainstream of the Yiddish tradition, and that any reader who would savor the particular quality of *Yiddishkeit* will find it embodied with complete purity in his work.

Almost any story in this book could illustrate the living impact of tradition in Yiddish literature, but here we would mention a few examples of how that impact may be apprehended as a literary value. Jonah Rosenfeld's "The Sick Goose," which portrays an old man's dying night, seems at first glance to be a story that could come out of any literature. A closer reading suggests, however, that its swaying prose rhythms are distinctly Yiddish, recalling the rhythms of religious discourse. Thus, in drawing a chiaroscuro of death that might pertain to any old man, the author has endowed it with a unique cultural quality by using rhythms specific to Yiddish life. In Jacob Glatstein's "The Return," the author, while describing his visit to a Jewish family in Poland, brings his account to an end by mentioning, rather casually, that all through the visit he was not wearing a hat but that none of his friends brought this to his attention. The literary appropriateness of this ending rests upon the ritual significance of the Jewish male's wearing a hat; given this awareness, one quickly senses the implicit power of the story's ending. And in Isaiah Spiegel's "A Ghetto Dog" the climax is reached when an old woman, preparing to let herself and her dog be slaughtered by the Nazis, winds his leash around her arm in the way phylacteries are wound by pious men. This bit of symbolic action, which to the Yiddish reader bears the profoundest and most affecting associations, becomes the dramatic center of the story: the traditional symbol is the literary climax.

At this point, however, a qualification needs to be made. In America, at the present moment, most uses of the term "traditional" tend to suggest political and moral conservatism, a wish to return to some earlier and presumably better state of things. In the Yiddish context, however, tradition is almost always bound up with moral and social rebelliousness, for the mere existence of Yiddish literature is itself a rebellion against the assumptions of Jewish orthodoxy. Had the Yiddish writer remained entirely rooted in the orthodox community, he would never have turned to imaginative composition at all. Once he began to write in Yiddish, he implicitly acknowledged that his main desire was to communicate with man as well as God. The mere act of using the untamed secular "jargon" meant a worldly temptation, and it hardly mattered that some of the Yiddish writers were personally devout. Inevitably a good many of the early Yiddish writers came from the yeshivas, where they had been subjected to the long exhausting grind of rabbinical study, and now, in reaction, turned not to the gentile world but to the painful effort to understand their own world in purely human terms. The spokesmen for orthodoxy warned that once Jewish youth began to write stories and verses in Yiddish they would feel a desire to emulate the themes and forms of the West—and they were right enough in a way. What they failed to understand was that the choice had already been made. Slowly, gradually, the Yiddish writers began to disengage themselves from their social-religious community, to acquire a sense of group idenitity, to read the works of Western writers and find in them models of craft and skill they could find nowhere else. The sudden growth of a formal Yiddish literature in the late nineteenth century was a symptom that the Enlightenment was finally establishing itself in the world of the East European Jews.

This rebelliousness was quickened by more immediate, ideological stimulants. Both Zionism and Socialism offered visions of the good life, or at least a better life; both made it seem legitimate to compare the condition of the Jews with the condition of other peoples, a comparison that radically undercut the earlier assumptions of the Jewish milieu; and both brought with them the Western traits of restlessness, self-scrutiny, impatience. Once the Yiddish writer liberated himself from the hold of religious orthodoxy, he could no longer blink the appalling misery and degradation of life in *this* world by keeping his head in the clouds of Messianic expectation. He still loved his folk, and perhaps in his growing loneliness he loved it more than ever; but in his judgment of its condition he could not help applying, almost unwittingly, the standards of the West. That is why the introduction of naturalism into Yiddish literature came as an elemental revolution, a harsh and violent gesture repudiating the tradition of *edelkeit* (refinement, delicacy), from which had stemmed the writings of Mendele, Sholom Aleichem, and, to a lesser extent, Peretz.

Yet the possibilities for revolt were severely limited. The Yiddish writer could not cut himself off from the people: there was no place else to go. He could not find shelter in a bohemia or solace himself with dreams of "the happy few." His world lacked the range to permit him to live apart from or "above" the folk. One cannot imagine in the Yiddish literary life of three or four decades ago a figure like Stefan George, proclaiming an aristocracy of the word, or even like T. S.

Eliot, launching a desperate raid upon an alien tradition. Here and there a Yiddish writer may have tried to adopt an aristocratic or aesthete's pose, but the only result was that he made himself seem pitiable. The Yiddish writer had to remain in intimate relation with the folk even if it turned its back upon him; he had to engage it in a dialogue even if the only answer was his echo.* But during the "classical" period of Yiddish literature and for some time afterward there was a remarkably close tie between author and audience; and the literature that came out of that moment was a literature of affection and intimacy, affection even in complaint and intimacy even in despair.

There is no better way to discover the inner qualities of a literature than to translate from it. Among American Jews who retain vague memories of Yiddish as the tongue of their parents, there has arisen a legend that Yiddish is untranslatable. Such people always ask, with an air of suppressed triumph, how do you translate this or the other idiom? That is no problem at all: most Yiddish idioms, like most French or American idioms, are untranslatable and the translator is under no obligation to try the impossible; he need only hunt for vivid equivalents.

The truth is that all translation involves losses, and the job of the translator is to measure one loss against another: literal meaning against English idiom, original flavor against economy in the new version. But the idea that Yiddish is somehow uniquely untranslatable may very well arise from a hidden sentimental desire to keep it so, to preserve it as a soft sweet haze of memory.

Some of the difficulties in translating Yiddish are "technical," similar to difficulties in translating from any other language. By the standards of modern English, for example, many Yiddish writers have

---

* The briefest notice of the tie between Yiddish writers and their audience should include a word about the Yiddish theater as a force bringing the two more closely together. Beginning with the wandering troupes of Eastern Europe, and particularly Rumania, the Yiddish theater quickly became a popular institution, in fact, the major cultural outlet for the Jewish masses. Not only did professional playwrights like Abraham Goldfaden and Jacob Gordin write for it, but many Yiddish poets and novelists were tempted by the mass audiences it could provide in such centers as Warsaw and New York. To be sure, the Yiddish theater was often sentimental, crude, and melodramatic, but at its occasional best it released an enormous creative and emotional energy. And so long as it flourished, the slow insidious process of alienation between writer and audience, which had already begun in the career of Peretz, could never quite reach its painful finish.

only the haziest notion of syntax and punctuation. The translator must therefore try to break up what seem to be endlessly winding sentences; yet if he does so he runs the risk of losing the reflective or dialectical qualities of the original Yiddish. Similarly, parts of speech enjoy a fluidity in Yiddish that is almost impossible to render in English. In one story that the editors translated, a goose is described as having *beryed* herself toward a food pail. The word *berye* is a noun referring to a super-efficient, even fanatical housewife—its origin is Hebrew, but that is a complication we shall let pass. The author, by twisting *berye* into a verb that describes the busy movements of a goose, has brought to the sentence an aura of suggestiveness that may be said to give the natural environment a distinctive Jewish shade. The best equivalent we could find was "bustle," but it was hardly very brilliant.

In Yiddish, too, there is a frequent use of the "reflexive" voice, about halfway between the active and the passive, which gives a strangely animated effect: the background of the story seems to dance about while the characters stand still. There is no satisfactory equivalent in English. And then there is the problem of diminutives, which barely exist in English but are numerous and rich in Yiddish, where they suggest the compression, intimacy, and vulnerability of East European Jewish life.

One problem in translating from Yiddish, however, *is* unique. Maurice Samuel has discussed the way Hebrew phrases form a sacred canopy over the profane action of Yiddish writing and sometimes become twisted into a backdrop of complex irony. "The fusion of the secular and sacred in Yiddish," he writes, "makes possible a charming transition from the jocular to the solemn and back again. Well-worn quotations from sacred texts mingle easily with colloquialisms, and dignified passages jostle popular interjections without taking or giving offense. There is about it all a suggestion of an oriental bazaar." But if one translates into a language that does not have these two levels of meaning and suggestion, that cannot make a complex point simply by repeating a phrase, first on a sacred and then on a profane level, clearly there will be a serious loss in translation. Such losses occur most of all when translating the work of the "classical" writers, in whose use of Yiddish the Hebrew component, with all its national and nostalgic reverberations, is very strong.

This linguistic problem reflects another and still more serious problem—and here it is surely correct to say that translating from the Yiddish is more difficult than from, say, the French. In translating from

French a certain community between French and English culture can safely be assumed, while in translating from Yiddish it is necessary not only to present a rough facsimile of a verbal sequence, but somehow to summon a world that exists beneath the words. Inevitably, though at great risk, the translator becomes a tacit social historian.

One of the most trying experiences of the translator is the story that reads splendidly in the original Yiddish but that in English seems to have turned pallid. Aside from the limitations of any translator, this kind of disappointment may be put down to certain peculiarities of pace and tone in Yiddish literature.

We Americans are accustomed to the well-made story, the efficient narrative that achieves a hard, precise climax by grouping words into a pyramid of impressions. This kind of "art" story is written by only a few Yiddish writers, generally the later ones. The bulk of Yiddish fiction veers toward one or another extreme: toward an accumulation of sensuous impression or of winding oral narrative, which would seem highly wasteful to most American and English writers; or toward the bare little story in which characters are merely glimpsed, conflict is hardly present, and nothing seems to be happening. What is crucial, for both translator and reader, is that both kinds of Yiddish stories move far more slowly than the usual American story; they reflect a society in which time has not yet become an obsession; they are often monologues or conversations as much as they are narratives, and if the Yiddish writer like Sholom Aleichem wants to stop at a by-way for a chat, why not?

With this problem of pace goes the problem of tone. In the thin, bare, eventless little story favored by so many Yiddish writers, what matters most is the *nigun,* the undercurrent of melody or the humming undertone, which becomes the ultimate carrier of meaning. In such stories one is aware, above all, of the rhythm of a voice, sometimes the voice of the speaker in the story and sometimes the voice of the author himself. Everything depends, in translating such a story, upon hitting the proper key at the very beginning and not deviating from it, not allowing any fancy variations or flourishes. It is problem in literary discipline; the translator must strictly subordinate himself to the material. And that is hard.

One final problem in reading or translating Yiddish literature needs to be mentioned, the vexing problem of sentimentality.

Sentimentality is defined by Cleanth Brooks and Robert Penn Warren as an effort to evoke an "emotional response in excess of the occasion." John Crowe Ransom, in a somewhat different approach, relates sentimentality to "certain inferior performances" in art: "The artist has the right sentiment for the object, but articulates the object no better than a man who has merely the sentiment. Unable to communicate the precise object, he would communicate at least his feeling for it, or his election of it as an object, and he is right in assuming that feelings are contagious among spontaneous persons. So he points reverently to it, and indicates the state of his own affections, and leaves us to explore the object mostly for ourselves."

Both statements are helpful, and the difference between them is probably due to their being focused on slightly different problems. The Brooks-Warren definition seems to emphasize the idea that an author *exploits,* with some degree of deliberateness, those emotions in his audience he knows to be all too readily available. The Ransom definition stresses sentimentality as the familiar outcome of an honest or respectable failure.

Both views are pertinent to a discussion of Yiddish literature. The Brooks-Warren approach recommends itself particularly to an age of mass culture in which the responses of an audience are played upon with scientific malice; the Ransom approach points to the high cost of artistic effort at any time. As it happens, however, the sentimentality that exploits the emotions of a vunerable audience is relatively infrequent in Yiddish literature (it can be found to a far greater extent in the Yiddish theater), if only because the blight of mass culture, which is the blight of an industrialized society, did not attack the Yiddish world until rather late, and then with little of the virulence it spent upon American or English literature. Yiddish writing, to be sure, had its servant-girl novels and still has its tear-jerking newspaper serials; but it is relatively easy to segregate such trash from serious work in a way that becomes increasingly harder to do in American literature. Far more prevalent in Yiddish literature is the kind of sentimentality described by Ransom, the kind that results from indicating an object with "reverent pointing" instead of embodying it imaginatively.

Now a reader who has been raised exclusively upon "modern" twentieth-century literature—let us assume such a deprived unfortunate exists only as a useful straw man—may well find a large amount of sentimentality in Yiddish literature. He is not likely, however, to do more than declare his gesture of dismissal, secure in the knowledge that once a piece of writing has been called sentimental nothing more need be said. But no easy gesture, whether of acceptance or rejection, will quite do. There *is* a considerable streak of sentimentality in Yiddish culture—it is a major deficiency; and one or two stories in this book can be seen as sentimental even by Yiddish standards. More important, however, is that area of Yiddish writing which may seem sentimental to readers who approach it with alien expectations but which is not at all sentimental when seen in the context of Yiddish.

For how can we tell when a piece of writing is sentimental and when it is not? Any definition assumes a set of common emotional and perhaps philosophical attitudes at the base of a given culture. Suppose, however, what is indeed the case: that the attitudes governing one culture are very different from those of another. Suppose that what seems, for one culture, "an emotion in excess of the occasion" is not at all so for another culture. Suppose what may seem, for one culture, a sufficient evocation or a delicate embodiment will for another be merely a "reverent pointing." And suppose that in Yiddish culture there is a greater emotional permissibility, a greater readiness to welcome tears or laughter, than in American culture. The desperate reliance upon blandness and composure, the cult of understatement, the assumption that it is good to feel but bad to show one's feelings—these attitudes, familiar enough to us, are quite alien to the Yiddish ethos. Perhaps this means that the Yiddish is more primitive. Perhaps it means that the Yiddish is healthier.

We must remember that the vocabulary of literary criticism rests largely upon such unexplored assumptions of value; that such notions as "sentimentality" are not eternal constants but are radically shaped by the context of the culture in which they are used. Cultures which have learned to enjoy the taste of worldly dominance and success, which have been able to acquire a sheen of assurance and elegance, will naturally tend to favor different criteria for establishing the margin of permissible emotionality than those which live in the aura of suffering and martyrdom, concerned not with the style of this world but the promise of the next.

A mature literary taste will be open to both varieties of expression; will welcome the possibility of responding to new standards of feelings; will be more than cautious in assuming that a judgment of preference is necessary or easily made.

NORMAN PODHORETZ

ψψψ

JEWISH CULTURE
AND THE INTELLECTUALS

THE PUBLICATION OF A TREASURY OF YIDDISH STORIES
seems to me an event of peculiar signficance in American Jewish life.
This is no mere hodgepodge collection thrown together to provide a
suitable gift for Chanukah or Bar Mitzvah, nor is it the usual work of
mawkish Jewish apologetics. The book is edited by Irving Howe and
Eliezer Greenberg, handsomely published by the Viking Press, and
illustrated by Ben Shahn. Among the translators, not only do such
familiar figures in Anglo-Jewish journalism as Maurice Samuel, Meyer
Levin, and Ludwig Lewisohn appear, but we also find Saul Bellow,
Alfred Kazin, Isaac Rosenfeld, and, again, Irving Howe. These latter
are all writers who have no professional connection with Judaism and
whose work most frequently appears in literary reviews and little
magazines. As for the editors, Eliezer Greenberg is himself a Yiddish
writer of repute and editor of a Yiddish quarterly, while Mr. Howe,
author of books on Sherwood Anderson and Faulkner, is known mainly
for his work on American literature and politics. Ben Shahn, the
illustrator, finally, is a distinguished American painter.

Mr. Howe and Mr. Greenberg have collaborated to produce a long,
informative, painstaking, and sometimes brilliant introduction, which
manages in seventy closely printed pages to supply a sketch of the history of Yiddish literature, a description of this literature in terms of the
shtetl culture from which it grew, and generally to account for
qualities of the literature which might puzzle an unwary American
reader. Anyone who is in the least familiar with critical writing in
English about Yiddish or Hebrew literature will find this introduction

almost as fascinating as the stories themselves, and certainly more unusual. For one thing, the editors have no ax to grind. They simply wish to recommend Yiddish literature to an audience of discriminating readers. They are very—almost overly—careful to make no "extravagant claims" for the work they introduce. While their caution quite rightly does not drive them to shrink from calling Sholom Aleichem's Tevye one of "the great figures of modern literature," they assure us that Yiddish literature as a whole is of the second rank, and that it contains no Shakespeares, no Tolstoys. When they make the inevitable comparison between 19th-century Yiddish and Elizabethan English, they hasten to add that no comparison is intended between the quality of the works written in the two languages. This temperateness is wholly commendable.

Having made the necessary concessions and qualifications, however, Mr. Howe and Mr. Greenberg feel free to draw on a broad field of general comparisons and references. Certainly Sholom Aleichem, Mendele, and Peretz have never been discussed in such grand, such mostly Gentile company: Kierkegaard, James, Brecht, Kafka, Silone, Turgenev, Jane Austen, Dickens, Dostoevsky, Tolstoy, Gogol, Chekhov, Gorki, Melville, Rilke, Whitman, T. S. Eliot—these are only a few of the writers mentioned in the introduction. Some of the critics quoted (along with Jewish authorities like Niger, Buber, and Heschel) are Cleanth Brooks, John Crowe Ransom, Robert Penn Warren, Isaac Rosenfeld, and Clement Greenberg.

It should be clear by now that what we have here is Yiddish literature presented under the auspices, so to speak, of the topmost intellectual fraternity. The critics have investigated it and declared it kosher. It is as though the worlds represented by Eliezer Greenberg and Irving Howe, after carrying on a dilatory flirtation for several years, have finally joined hands to acknowledge their kinship. The university and the yeshiva, the big city and the *shtetl,* have come together to explore one another's wisdom, and they find it comfortably possible to speak the same language—English.

I said that the publication of the *Treasury* was a significant event in American Jewish life. But this volume is no isolated phenomenon. Within the last few years we have seen Mark Zborowski turning the methods of cultural anthropology on the *shtetl* with striking results. An increasing number of serious writers have dealt with Jews and Jewish experience as one of the *données* of the American scene (Rosen-

feld, Malamud, Fiedler, Bellow, Kazin, and Swados, to mention a few).
Lionel Trilling has discovered rabbinic overtones in Wordsworth.
There is, of course, *Commentary*, which from its inception has sought
to fuse an interest in the important intellectual currents of the day
with an equally intelligent concern for specifically Jewish issues.
Nor is this development confined to Jews alone. *Partisan Review* has
printed stories by Bashevis Singer and others, imparting to these Yiddish works the same air of avante-garde distinction that surrounds
the latest literary find from France or Germany. Columbia University
instituted a department of Yiddish language and literature several
years ago. Edmund Wilson has been learning Hebrew, and has
recently spoken (in the *New Yorker*) of the contemporary Hebrew
novelist, Agnon, as a great writer comparable to Kafka.

To interpret the significance of this phenomenon is beyond my
powers. I would only say that, whatever else it indicates, the new
interest seems to betoken a healthier relationship between American
Jewish intellectuals and their Jewish experience than prevailed twenty
or thirty years ago. But perhaps I may be permitted an autobiographical
digression to suggest the qualifications I feel must be introduced into
that observation.

While a student at Columbia, I also attended the Seminary College
of Jewish Studies, which might be described as the undergraduate liberal
arts division of the Jewish Theological Seminary. Naturally, the
Seminary took up a good deal of my time. We spent two evenings a
week and the whole of Sunday afternoon in classes, and, of course,
there were assignments to prepare. I am not sure what drove me to take
this additional burden on myself, but whatever my motives may have
been, they were unusual. Unlike me, most of my classmates were
either preparing for the rabbinate or planning to become Hebrew-
school teachers, and almost all of them considered their work at the
Seminary more important than their work at college. Many of them
were observant Jews, while those who had secular leanings were
frequently passionate Zionists training themselves for life in Israel. I
was neither religious nor much of a Zionist, so I probably seemed an
anomaly at the Seminary, but the fitness of my being there was never
questioned. Within my circle of friends at Columbia, however, I was
under a continual assault to justify my presence at the Seminary. My
friends were grim and earnest young intellectuals, and most of them
were Jewish. We considered ourselves the direct heirs and propagators

of Western civilization, and we felt chosen to study, teach, and possibly contribute to it. It was a glorious mission, demanding a discipline of mind and spirit as arduous in its way as a monastic calling. But no one felt the glory of this vocation more keenly than we did, and we gave to it a devotion so vigorous and loving that I think we even frightened some of our teachers, who were no mean devotees themselves.

We were not stodgy academics. Though our main interest lay in literature, we scorned the scholarly journals like *PMLA*. On the other hand, we read the literary magazines religiously, in particular *Partisan Review* and *Kenyon Review*. Moreover, we thought of ourselves not as Americans or Jews, but as novitiates of the Republic of Letters, a world of whose concrete, physical existence we had less doubt than about the existence of the Midwest. Our Republic included everyone who had ever been instrumental in shaping Western civilization. Herodotus and St. Augustine, D. H. Lawrence and Yeats were all equally distinguished members of the community which we aspired to join. And we conceived of this community in space rather than in time. Despite the fact that we sat at the feet of Lionel Trilling, our sense of history was underdeveloped. Like Mortimer Adler—a Columbia graduate who never grew out of the idea—we saw a "great conversation" going on everlastingly between authors remote from one another in time, space, interest, and intention. We saw them all sitting around a great conference table, discussing the same problems, and always lining up on the same sides. It was the unity of culture, not the differences, that appealed most to our imagination.

But Judaism had virtually no representatives in this parliament of culture. Except for the Old Testament (which was honored both as great poetry and as the "Hebraic" constituent of Western civilization), the Jews did not exist for us. If my friends heard of the Cabbala, it was because Pico della Mirandola had been interested in it, and because it bore some relation to Yeats's occultism. Nothing disgusted my friends so much as the idea that because a man happened to be Jewish it was incumbent upon him to study Jewish culture. This was not "anti-Semitism" (at least not consciously), any more than their conviction that the American novel was inferior to the French, English, or Russian novel could be called anti-Americanism. I think their condescension toward all things Jewish was strikingly similar to their (and my) condescension toward all things American. And it is no accident that the discovery of Jewishness has coincided with the discovery of America for many Jewish intellectuals. The frenetic enthusiasm with which Whitman has been taken up lately may be part of the same process that accounts for the new piety toward Sholom Aleichem. But I should like to say more about that later.

In trying to justify myself against the charges of sentimentality or conformism made by my friends, but feeling in my heart that they were probably right, I used the only arguments that meant anything to them or to me. I said that Jewish culture was worth studying, *as* a culture. I said darkly that their hostility seemed to me suspicious, and that I doubted whether they would attack me for spending three days a week studying Chinese demonology. (I was wrong: they considered me foolish when I enrolled in a new course in Oriental literature—such studies were outside the proper concern of a true fledgling in Western civilization, they were irrelevant and therefore wasteful and therefore sinful.) I tried to recommend Judaism for its special qualities, and my most powerful weapons were two major attitudes which I ascribed to it. The first was that Judaism entertained no dualism of body and soul—an effective argument, because for us dualism was the ubiquitous villain of Western civilization—and the second was that Judaism remained the only culture beside the Greek which believed in learning for its own sake and which honored the sage more than it did the plutocrat. This too was effective, for "bourgeois" standards constituted another of our violent hatreds. My friends were impressed, but they still could not see spending all that time and effort over attitudes which, after all, we had already absorbed from Blake and Lawrence and Flaubert and a dozen other great figures of our pantheon. They would challenge me to produce great writers out of Jewish literature, and my feeble efforts to describe Judah Halevi as a metaphysical poet of the stature of Donne, and Mendele Mocher Seforim as a positively Swiftian satirist, were met with a shrug of the shoulders and a skeptical smile.

I think that the feeling of my friends was a good reflection, given the typical undergraduate intensity, aggressiveness, and exaggeration with which it was held, of the prevalent feeling among American Jewish intellectuals immediately after the Second World War. They were not yet hospitable to the idea that Jewish culture was respectable in their terms, worthy of interest as a thing in itself, apart from whatever relevance it might have to them as Jews. And in any case, they doubted that it was very relevant at all.

But there is another side to this picture. The Seminary is located six short blocks from Columbia College, and for me the walk up Broadway from 116th Street to 122nd Street was like the journey from Paris to the provinces. Undaunted, however, I came rampaging into the Seminary as an apostle, with all the evangelical fervor of a Paul bringing the truth that had been revealed to me at Hamilton Hall back to the Jews. The truth I burned to teach was that a fresh stream of thought, disinterested and free of ideology, must be turned on Jewish culture: I was not only Paul, I was Matthew Arnold too. It should be pointed out here that the level on which literature was taught and thought about at the Seminary was much lower than the level of Biblical, Talmudic, and historical studies. Some of the courses in Bible and Jewish history were easily a match for analogous courses at Columbia, and some were superior in their kind to anything offered at Columbia. Unfortunately, this was not true of literary studies, a fact which may have reflected the uneasiness Jews have traditionally felt toward literature as a pursuit for its own sake (Mr. Howe and Mr. Greenberg have an excellent section on that tradition in their introduction). It always seemed to me that there was something impurely partisan or insufferably crude in the way both Hebrew and Yiddish literature (which we read in Hebrew translations) were approached. Bialik was apparently honored not as a poet but as a kind of latter-day prophet; Sholom Aleichem was held in higher esteem than Mendele Mocher Seforim (my own favorite) because his picture of Jewish life was more "positive" than Mendele's; and our professors were forever rhapsodizing on how "beautifully" somebody or other wrote Hebrew—so much so that I was unpleasantly reminded of those bellelettristic Victorian critics against whom the wrath of my beloved quarterly reviews had long been directed. In short, Jewish literature was either a text, an exhortation, a party platform, or it was a milestone in the development of Hebrew as a modern language. My teachers and fellow students seemed to be either Jewish versions of Ralph Fox or of Sir Arthur Quiller-Couch. We had no Eliots, no Leavises, no Trillings, no Ransoms, no Tates, no Brookses. Not, that is, until I arrived on the scene.

My personal crusade to bring the wisdom of Columbia to the Seminary met with no more success than my half-hearted effort to bring the Seminary to Columbia. Of course, I was not very tactful about it, but I doubt if tact really had much to do with the matter. Once, in reporting to a class on a volume of contemporary Hebrew poetry, I nearly caused a riot when I attacked the prosody of a minor Israeli lyric poet by invoking e. e. cummings as standard. I was howled down with talk of the blood shed by the six million, I was accused of abysmal ignorance of the Hebrew language, I was told that my comparisons were inept, irrelevant, and even morally reprehensible. (I still think I was right about the poet.) In another class, I was foolish enough to admit that I considered Bialik a second-rate provincial, far inferior to the "cosmopolitan" Tchernichovsky—and the effect somewhat resembled what might happen if, at a Communist rally, a new party member were to declare Rosa Luxemburg a more profound philosopher than Lenin. My attempts to promote Judah Halevi and Ibn Gabirol as the Hebrew Donne and Marvell were greeted not with skeptical smiles, but with outraged stammerings, coughs, and gnashing of teeth. The only time I provoked no disproportionate opposition was when I said, in one of those everlasting discussions of What Makes a Work of Art Jewish, that Isaac Rosenfeld and Leslie Fiedler were the true American Jewish writers, not Fannie Hurst or Ludwig Lewisohn. But my most notable success came at a Hebrew-speaking summer study camp operated by the Seminary. In teaching a course in Jeremiah, I delighted my fifteen-year-old students by proclaiming that they need not believe God actually spoke to Jeremiah in order to appreciate the greatness of the book. I solemnly expounded Coleridge's theory of the "willing suspension of disbelief" to them, and I hinted that Jeremiah (unlike Isaiah) wanted to be a poet, not a prophet, which is why he was always complaining to God over the slights he had suffered. I presented this agonized religious genius as a sort of Hebraic prototype of the Artist persecuted by a Hebraic prototype of bourgeois society—a Flaubert among the Jewish philistines. (The prophet Amos, incidentally, I was fond of describing as "the first young man from the provinces.") The novelty of this approach was not lost even on fifteen-year-olds.

Meanwhile, something was happening in the world of Columbia that seemed too good to be true. Hasidism, ushered in by Martin Buber and Gershom Scholem, like a surprise witness in a sensational murder trial, exploded on the intellectual consciousness of New York. One suddenly found a rash of articles not only on Hasidism, but also on Maimonides, written by people who only yesterday were deep in Eliot, Original Sin, and Kierkegaard. One noticed respectful reviews of Sholom Aleichem, and it began to appear that some of our heroes among the younger critics actually read Yiddish. I remember too with what a sense of personal triumph I first heard that Lionel Trilling was writing an essay on Wordsworth and the Rabbis. About this time also, my friends and I discovered COMMENTARY, which was as unsettling to them as it was a delight to me. I was not, after all, alone in the world, there were *others*, and these others were *intelligent*, by which I suppose I meant that they knew all about the New Criticism. I began for the first time to believe my own arguments about the distinction of Judaism as a culture. It did not seem strange to me that the grandsons of Hasidim should travel through Wordsworth in order to get to the *shtetl*. What did astonish me was that the taste for Wordsworth should not have made them despise the *shtetl* and all its works for eternity.

My astonishment was, of course, naive, for the new interest in Jewishness was not quite of the same nature as the interest in Wordsworth. There were many impulses behind it, but the only one that concerns me here was the discovery by many American Jewish intellectuals that they were as much products of Jewish culture as of Western civilization. They became interested in Maimonides and the Baal Shem Tov at least partly because they felt that these men had something to teach them about themselves. However, my impression is that this was a veiled impulse, for publicly and officially, they praised Maimonides and Sholom Aleichem just as I had praised them to my friends—in terms of St. Thomas, Wordsworth, Blake, and Chekhov. In other words, before they would permit themselves the luxury of investigating their own origins, they had to be persuaded that these origins were objects of general interest. They had, as it were, to get the smell of garlic out of the breath of Jewish culture.

I said before that I thought the new interest in Jewishness was part of the same process as the new interest in Americanism, and more specifically, that the way Whitman has been taken up compares with the way Sholom Aleichem has been taken up. But this is not entirely true. For the quality of interest shown in Whitman has reverberations lacking in the quality of attention paid to Jewish writers. For one thing, there is a candid admission on the part of some recent critics of Whitman that they do not, *should* not, read him with the same detachment and by the same standards and for the same reasons that they read Donne or Shakespeare. One feels that the return to Whitman is a family affair, that he is celebrated nowadays not for his great poems on death, but for his teaching on what it means to be an American. And it is quite appropriate that this should be so. Not every literature has produced writers who enjoy a special role as embodiments of the na-

tional psyche, because not every culture has found the fact of nationality a problem to be thought about and discussed. Certainly neither
the British nor the French, for all their fervent sense of nationality,
worry about the significance of being French or English. The Russians,
on the other hand, the Germans, and we Americans are obsessed with
a conscious idea of our own nationality. And in this, of course, the
Jews occupy a preeminent position. Jewish literature—during the past
one hundred fifty years especially—has produced Fichtes, Whitmans,
and Gogols, but it has produced nothing else. Which is to say that it
differs as radically from other literatures as Jewish history differs from
any other history.

And here we have the clue to why my crude attempts to make
Jewish culture accessible to myself met with such hostility at the Seminary. I think my teachers rightly resented the arrogant assumption that
Jewish culture had to be justified in the eyes of the *Kenyon Review* or
be set at nought. And yet—raised in what is known as "a good Jewish
home," fairly fluent both in Yiddish and Hebrew, highly educated (by
American standards) in Jewish culture, and eager to know "the best
that has been thought and known in the world"—I felt that I could
approach it by no other road. From their side, my teachers were right
in feeling that the terms I wanted to use in interpreting this culture to
myself were ultimately an evasion, that they would in the end obfus-
cate far more than they could clarify. The very characteristic I despised
in all of them—their total involvement with their subject, their failure
to achieve distance and perspective, their unwillingness even to admit
the possibility of detachment—was the only key to a real understanding
of Jewishness. For them, there could be no distinction between understanding and a commitment to the destiny of the Jewish people: the
very object of understanding was a deepened commitment. All of
Jewish culture was a biography of their own souls, and more precious
to them even than their own souls. They must have felt that relegating
Judah Halevi to the category of a Donne was a way of disposing of
him, a way of refusing to meet the challenge he presented—would a
man give his life for Donne? For in their view, every Jewish writer
presented the same challenge over and over again: what are you going
to do about being a Jew? How could I have possibly responded to
Bialik when I was not urgently interested in that question? I was right
about literature in general: it is both more and less than an invitation
to action, and I would have been right in my quarrel with my teachers

if any other literature but this one were the issue. For the truth is that neither Hebrew nor Yiddish literature are like any other, to be studied and judged like any other. They refuse to yield their treasures except on their own eccentric terms. They share for good and ill the uniqueness of the people by whom and for whom they were produced.

In their introduction, Mr. Howe and Mr. Greenberg write brilliantly about Yiddish literature. They tell us it has special qualities that we need to become acquainted with—particularly the qualities of love and sweetness. They recommend Yiddish literature as a sort of antithesis to the literature of crisis we all dote on, and they feel it needs no more recommendation than to be seen as an opposing term in the dialectic of modern taste. They even imply—for they are nothing if not honest—that this literature is inevitably, intentionally, and sometimes aggressively parochial, and that it was addressed to readers who were as involved with its lone theme—the meaning of Jewishness—as the writers were. They point out that its emphasis on national destiny is so tyrannical and ruthless that no room is left for an interest in individual character, and they acknowledge that most of us read fiction primarily because we want to see individual character in its eternal struggle with society. This, of course, is tantamount to admitting that these stories cannot claim our attention as readers of fiction, but Mr. Howe and Mr. Greenberg cajole us into believing momentarily that a mature taste, when once it understands the reasons for such a development, will not deny itself the new experience offered. Perhaps.

To be perfectly honest, I cannot say whether I agree with them or not. In reading through this volume—which contains some things I had read before and many that I had not—I was oppressed more powerfully than ever by the feeling that very little of this has anything to do with that part of me which reads English, French, and Russian fiction, and everything to do with that part of me which still broods on the mystery of my own Jewishness. It is not as difficult as it would seem for a Jew to divorce the two parts of himself, and I tried reading the book as Mr. Howe and Mr. Greenberg advise. But I found that the pleasure I derived was quite unlike the pleasure I get from good fiction. It was the pleasure of Old World charm and quaintness, titillating but not challenging, and therefore not to be taken too seriously. What an irony, that this should be the effect of a literature which more than any other demands to be taken with the most apocalyptic seriousness! On the other hand, there were exceptions—a story by Mendele, two by

Sholom Aleichem, a few lovely pieces by Abraham Reisen and Lamed Shapiro, the wonderful tale of Gimpel the Fool by Isaac Bashevis Singer. Yet the volume as a whole did not, I feel, quite bear out the modest claims of the introduction: I do not think that the book would have convinced my friends in those days at Columbia. I am not saying that most of the writers presented in the volume are not talented enough to deserve a hearing. It is just that a sad, perhaps a tragic, limitation has been imposed upon them, and it is not their fault. But as they themselves would be the first to admit, 'S *iz shver tsu zein a Yid.*

LIONEL TRILLING

ISAAC BABEL:
TORN BETWEEN VIOLENCE AND PEACE

A GOOD MANY YEARS AGO, IN 1929, I CHANCED TO read a book which disturbed me in a way I can still remember. The book was called *Red Cavalry;* it was a collection of stories about the Soviet regiments of horse operating in Poland. I had never heard of the author, Isaac Babel—or I. Babel as he signed himself—and nobody had anything to tell me about him, and part of my disturbance was the natural shock we feel when, suddenly and without warning, we confront a new talent of great energy and boldness. But the book was disturbing for other reasons as well.

In those days one still spoke of the "Russian experiment" and one might still believe that the light of dawn glowed on the test tubes and crucibles of human destiny. And it was still possible to have very strange expectations of the new culture that would arise from the Revolution. I do not remember what my own particular expectations were, except that they involved a desire for an art that would have as little ambiguity as a proposition in logic. Why I wanted this I don't wholly understand. It was as if I had hoped that the literature of the Revolution would realize some simple, inadequate notion of the "classical" which I had picked up at college; and perhaps I was drawn to this notion of the classical because I was afraid of the literature of modern Europe, because I was scared of its terrible intensities, ironies, and ambiguities. If this is what I really felt, I can't say that I am now wholly ashamed of my cowardice. If we stop to think of the museum knowingness about art which we are likely to acquire with maturity, of our consumer's pride in buying only the very best spiritual com-
312

modities, the ones which are sure to give satisfaction, there may possibly be a grace in those moments when we lack the courage to confront, or the strength to endure, some particular work of art or kind of art. At any rate, here was Babel's book and I found it disturbing. It was obviously the most remarkable work of fiction that had yet come out of revolutionary Russia, the only work, indeed, that I knew of as having upon it the mark of exceptional talent, even of genius. Yet for me it was all too heavily charged with the intensity, irony, and ambiguousness from which I wished to escape.

There was anomaly at the very heart of the book, for the red cavalry of the title were Cossack regiments, and why were Cossacks fighting for the Revolution, they who were the instrument and symbol of Czarist repression? The author, who represented himself in the stories, was a Jew; and a Jew in a Cossack regiment was more than an anomaly, it was a joke, for between Cossack and Jew there existed not merely hatred but a polar opposition. Yet here was a Jew riding as a Cossack and trying to come to terms with the Cossack ethos. At that first reading it seemed to me—although it does not now—that the stories were touched with cruelty. They were about violence of the most extreme kind, yet they were composed with a striking elegance and precision of objectivity, and also with a kind of lyric *joy,* so that one could not at once know just how the author was responding to the brutality he recorded, whether he thought it good or bad, justified or not justified. Nor was this the only thing to be in doubt about. It was not really clear how the author felt about, say, Jews; or about religion; or about the goodness of man. He had—or perhaps, for the sake of some artistic effect, he pretended to have—a secret. This alienated and disturbed me. It was impossible not to be overcome by admiration for *Red Cavalry,* but it was not at all the sort of book that I had wanted the culture of the Revolution to give me.

And, as it soon turned out, it was not at all the sort of book that the Revolution wanted to give anyone. No event in the history of Soviet culture is more significant than the career, or rather, the end of the career, of Isaac Babel. He had been a protégé of Gorki, and he had begun his career under the aegis of Trotsky's superb contempt for the pieties of the conventional "proletarian" aesthetics. In the last years of the decade of the 20's and in the early 30's he was regarded as one of the most notable talents of Soviet literature.

This judgment was, however, by no means an official one. From the beginning of his career Babel had been under the attack of the literary bureaucracy. But in 1932 the party abolished RAPP—the Russian Association of Proletarian Writers—and it seemed that a new period of freedom had been inaugurated. In point of fact, the reactionary elements of Soviet culture were established in full ascendancy, and the purge trials of 1937 were to demonstrate how absolute their power was. But in the five intervening years the party chose to exercise its authority in a lenient manner. It was in this atmosphere of seeming liberality that the first Writers' Congress was held in 1934. Babel was one of the speakers at the Congress. He spoke with considerable jauntiness, yet he spoke as a penitent—the stories he had written since *Red Cavalry* had been published in a volume at the end of 1932, yet since that time he had written nothing, he had disappointed expectation.

His speech was a strange performance. It undertook to be humorous; the published report is punctuated by the indication of laughter.* It made the avowals of loyalty that were by then routine, yet we cannot take it for granted that Babel was insincere when he spoke of his devotion to the Revolution, to the government, and to the state, or when he said that in a bourgeois country it would inevitably have been his fate to go without recognition and livelihood. He may have been sincere even when he praised Stalin's literary style, speaking of the sentences "forged" as if of steel, of the necessity of learning to work in language as Stalin did. Yet beneath the orthodoxy of this speech there lies some hidden intention. One feels this in the sad vestiges of the humanistic mode that wryly manifest themselves. It is as if the humor, which is often of a whimsical kind, as if the irony and the studied self-depreciation, were forlorn affirmations of freedom and selfhood; it is as if Babel were addressing his fellow writers in a dead language, or in some slang of their student days, which a few of them might perhaps remember.

Everything, he said at one point in his speech, is given to us by the party and the government; we are deprived of only one right, the right to write badly. "Comrades," he said, "let us not fool ourselves: this is a very important right, and to take it away from us is no small thing." And he said, "Let us give up this right, and may God help us. And if there is no God, let us help ourselves. . . ."

* I am indebted to Professor Rufus Mathewson for the oral translation of Babel's speech which he made for me. Professor Mathewson was kindness itself in helping me to information about Babel; he is, of course, not accountable for any inaccuracy or awkwardness that may appear in my use of the facts.

The right to write badly—how precious it seems when once there has been the need to conceive of it! Upon the right to write badly depends the right to write at all. There must have been many in the audience who understood how serious and how terrible Babel's joke was. And there must have been some who had felt a chill at their hearts at another joke that Babel had made earlier in his address, when he spoke of himself as practicing a new literary genre. This was the genre of silence—he was, he said, "the master of the genre of silence."

Thus he incriminated himself for his inability to work. He made reference to the doctrine that the writer must have respect for the reader, and he said that it was a correct doctrine. He himself, he said, had a very highly developed respect for the reader; so much so, indeed, that it might be said of him that he suffered from a hypertrophy of the faculty of respect—"I have so much respect for the reader that I am dumb." But now he takes a step beyond irony; he ventures to interpret, and by his interpretation to challenge, the official doctrines of "respect for the reader." The reader, he says, asks for bread, and he must indeed be given what he asks for—but not in the way he expects it; he ought to be surprised by what he gets; he ought not be given what he can easily recognize as "a certified true copy" of life—the essence of art is its unexpectedness.

The silence for which Babel apologized was not broken. In 1937 he was arrested. He died in a concentration camp in 1939 or 1940. It is not known for certain whether he was shot or died of typhus. Both accounts of the manner of his death have been given by people who were inmates of the camp at the time. Nor is it known for what specific reason he was arrested. Raymond Rosenthal, in an admirable essay on Babel published in *Commentary* in 1947, says, on good authority, that Babel did not undergo a purge but was arrested for having made a politically indiscreet remark. It has been said that he was arrested when Yagoda was purged, because he was having a love affair with Yagoda's sister. It has also been said that he was accused of Trotskyism, which does indeed seem possible, especially if we think of Trotsky as not only a political but a cultural figure.

But no reason for the last stage of the extinction of Isaac Babel is needed beyond that which is provided by his stories, by their method and style. If ever we want to remind ourselves of the nature and power of art, we have only to think of how accurate reactionary governments are in their awareness of that nature and that power. It is not merely the content of art that they fear, not merely explicit doctrine, but whatever of energy and autonomy is implied by the aesthetic qualities a work may have. Intensity, irony, and ambiguousness, for example, constitute a clear threat to the impassivity of the state. They constitute a *secret*.

Babel was not a political man except as every man of intelligence was political at the time of the Revolution. Except, too, as every man of talent or genius is political who makes his heart a battleground for conflicting tendencies of culture. In Babel's heart there was a kind of fighting—he was captivated by the vision of two ways of being, the way of violence and the way of peace, and he was torn between them. The conflict between the two ways of being was an essential element of his mode of thought. And when Soviet culture was brought under full discipline, the fighting in Babel's heart could not be permitted to endure. It was a subversion of discipline. It implied that there was more than one way of being. It hinted that one might live in doubt, that one might live by means of a question.

It is with some surprise that we become aware of the centrality of the cultural, the moral, the *personal* issue in Babel's work, for what strikes us first is the intensity of his specifically aesthetic preoccupation. In his schooldays Babel was passionate in his study of French literature; for several years he wrote his youthful stories in French, his chief masters being Flaubert and Maupassant. When, in an autobiographical sketch, he means to tell us that he began his mature work in 1923, he puts it that in that year he began to express his thoughts "clearly, and not at great length." This delight in brevity became his peculiar mark. When Eisenstein spoke of what it was that literature might teach the cinema, he said that "Isaac Babel will speak of the extreme laconicism of literature's expressive means—Babel, who, perhaps, knows in practice better than anyone else that great secret, 'that there is no iron that can enter the human heart with such stupefying effect as a period placed at just the right moment.' "* Babel's love of the laconic implies certain other elements of his aesthetic, his commitment (it is sometimes excessive) to *le mot juste,* to the search for the word or phrase that will do its work with a ruthless speed, and his remarkable powers of significant distortion, the rapid foreshortening, the

* Eisenstein quotes from Babel's story "Guy de Maupassant." The reference to Babel occurs in the essay of 1932, "A Course in Treatment," in the volume *Film Form: Essays in Film Theory* (1949).

striking displacement of interest and shift of emphasis—in general his pulling all awry the arrangement of things as they appear in the "certified true copy."

Babel's preoccupation with form, with the aesthetic surface, is, we soon see, entirely at the service of his moral concern. James Joyce has taught us the word *epiphany,* a showing forth—Joyce had the "theory" that suddenly, almost miraculously, by a phrase or a gesture, a life would thrust itself through the veil of things and for an instant show itself forth, startling us by its existence. In itself the conception of the epiphany makes a large statement about the nature of human life; it suggests that the human fact does not dominate the scene of our existence—for something to "show forth" it must first be hidden, and the human fact is submerged in and subordinated to a world of circumstance, the world of things; it is known only in glimpses, emerging from the danger or the sordidness in which it is implicated. Those writers who by their practice subscribe to the theory of the epiphany are drawn to a particular aesthetic. In the stories of Maupassant, as in those of Stephen Crane, and Hemingway, and the Joyce of *Dubliners,* as in those of Babel himself, we perceive the writer's intention to create a form which shall in itself be shapely and autonomous and at the same time unusually responsible to the truth of *external reality,* the truth of things and events. To this end he concerns himself with the given moment, and, seeming almost hostile to the continuity of time, he presents the past only as it can be figured in the present. In his commitment to event he affects to be indifferent to "meanings" and "values"; he seems to be saying that although he can tell us with unusual accuracy what is going on, he does not presume to interpret it, scarcely to understand it, certainly not to judge it. He arranges that the story shall tell itself, as it were; or he tells it by means of a narrator who somehow makes it clear that he has no personal concern with the outcome of events—what I have called Babel's lyric joy in the midst of violence is in effect one of his devices for achieving the tone of detachment. We are not, of course, for very long deceived by the elaborate apparatus contrived to suggest the almost affectless detachment of the writer. We soon enough see what he is up to. His intense concern with the hard aesthetic surface of the story, his preoccupation with things and events, are, we begin to perceive, cognate with the universe, representative of its nature, of the unyielding circumstance in which the human fact exists; they make the condition for the epiphany, the showing forth; and the apparent denial of immediate pathos is a condition of the ultimate pathos the writer conceives.

All this, as I say, is soon enough apparent in Babel's stories. And yet, even when we have become aware of his pathos, we are, I think, surprised by the kind of moral issue that lies beneath the brilliant surface of the stories, beneath the lyric and ironic elegance—we are surprised by its elemental simplicity. We are surprised, too, by its passionate subjectivity, the intensity of the author's personal involvement, his defenseless commitment of himself to the issue.

The stories of *Red Cavalry* have as their principle of coherence what I have called the anomaly, or the joke of a Jew who is a member of a Cossack regiment—Babel was a supply officer under General Budienny in the campaign of 1920. Traditionally the Cossack was the feared and hated enemy of the Jew. But he was more than that. The principle of his existence stood in antithesis to the principle of the Jew's existence. The Jew conceived his own ideal character to consist in his being intellectual, pacific, humane. The Cossack was physical, violent, without mind or manners. When a Jew of Eastern Europe wanted to say what we mean by "a bull in a china shop," he said "a Cossack in a *succah*"—in, that is, one of the fragile decorated booths or tabernacles in which the meals of the harvest festival of Succoth are eaten: he intended an image of animal violence, of aimless destructiveness. And if the Jew was political, if he thought beyond his own ethnic and religious group, he knew that the Cossack was the enemy not only of the Jew—although that in special—but the enemy also of all men who thought of liberty; he was the natural and appropriate instrument of ruthless oppression.

There was, of course, another possible view of the Cossack, one that had its appeal for many Russian intellectuals, although it was not likely to win the assent of the Jew. Tolstoy had represented the Cossack as having a primitive energy, passion, and virtue. He was the man as yet untrammeled by civilization, direct, immediate, fierce. He was the man of enviable simplicity, the man of the body—and of the horse, the man who moved with speed and grace. We have devised an image of our lost freedom which we mock in the very phrase by which we name it: the noble savage. No doubt the mockery is justified, yet our fantasy of the noble savage represents a reality of our existence, it stands for our sense of something unhappily surrendered, the truth of the body, the truth of full sexuality, the truth of open aggressiveness. Something, we know, must inevitably be surrendered for the sake of civilization; but the "discontent" of civilization which Freud describes is our self-recrimination at having surrendered too much. Babel's view of the Cossack was more consonant with that of Tolstoy than with the traditional view of his own people. For him the Cossack was indeed the noble savage, all too savage, not often noble, yet having in his savagery some quality that might raise strange questions in a Jewish mind.

I have seen three pictures of Babel, and it is a puzzle to know how he was supposed to look. The most convincing of the pictures is a photograph, to which the two official portrait sketches bear but little resemblance. The sketch which serves as the frontispiece to Babel's volume of stories of 1932 makes the author look like a Chinese merchant—his face is round, impassive, and priggish; his nose is low and flat; he stares through rimless glasses with immovable gaze. The sketch in the *Literary Encyclopedia* lengthens his face and gives him horn-rimmed spectacles and an air of amused and knowing assurance: a well-educated and successful Hollywood writer who has made the intelligent decision not to apologize for his profession except by his smile. But in the photograph the face is very long and thin, charged with emotion and internality; bitter, intense, very sensitive, touched with humor, full of consciousness and contradiction. It is "typically" an intellectual's face, a scholar's face, and it has great charm. I should not want to speak of it as a Jewish face, but it is a kind of face which many Jews used to aspire to have, or hoped their sons would have. It was, surely, this face, or one much like it, that Babel took with him when he went among the Cossacks.

We can only marvel over the vagary of the military mind by which Isaac Babel came to be assigned as a supply officer to a Cossack regiment. He was a Jew of the ghetto. As a boy—so he tells us in his autobiographical stories—he had been of stunted growth, physically inept, subject to nervous disorders. He was an intellectual, a writer—a man, as he puts it in striking phrase, with spectacles on his nose and autumn in his heart. The orders that sent him to General Budienny's command were drawn either by a conscious and ironical Destiny with a literary bent—or at his own personal request. For the reasons that made it bizarre that he should have been attached to a Cossack regiment are the reasons why he was there. He was there to be submitted to a test, he was there to be initiated. He was there because of the dreams of his boyhood. Babel's talent, like that of many modern writers, is rooted in the memory of boyhood, and Babel's boyhood was more than usually dominated by the idea of the test and the initiation. We might put it that Babel rode with a Cossack regiment because, when he was nine years old, he had seen his father kneeling before a Cossack captain who wore lemon-colored chamois gloves and looked ahead with the gaze of one who rides through a mountain pass.

Isaac Babel was born in Odessa, in 1894. The years following the accession of Nicholas II were dark years indeed for the Jews of Russia. It was the time of the bitterest official anti-Semitism, of the Pale, of the Beilis trial, of the Black Hundreds and the planned pogroms. And yet in Odessa the Jewish community may be said to have flourished. Odessa was the great port of the Black Sea, an eastern Marseilles or Naples, and in such cities the transient, heterogeneous population dilutes the force of law and tradition, for good as well as for bad. The Jews of Odessa were in some degree free to take part in the general life of the city. They were, to be sure, debarred from the schools, with but few exceptions. And they were sufficiently isolated when the passions of a pogrom swept the city. Yet all classes of the Jewish community seem to have been marked by a singular robustness and vitality, by a sense of the world, and of themselves in the world. The upper classes lived in affluence, sometimes in luxury, and it was possible for them to make their way into a Gentile society in which prejudice had been attenuated by cosmopolitanism. The intellectual life was of a particular energy, producing writers, scholars, and journalists of very notable gifts; it is in Odessa that modern Hebrew poetry takes its rise with Bialik and Tchernikovsky. As for the lower classes, Babel himself represents them as living freely and heartily. In their ghetto, the Molda-vanka, they were far more conditioned by their economic circumstances than by their religious ties; they were not at all like the poor Jews of the *shtetlach,* the little towns of Poland, whom Babel was later to see. He represents them as characters of a Breughel-like bulk and brawn; they have large, coarse, elaborate nicknames; they are draymen and dairy farmers; they are gangsters—the Jewish gangs of the Moldavanka were famous; they made upon the young Babel an ineradicable impression and to them he devoted a remarkable group of stories.

It was not Odessa, then, it was not even Odessa's ghetto, that forced upon Babel the image of the Jew as a man not in the actual world, a man of no body, a man of intellect, or wits, passive before his secular fate. Not even his image of the Jewish intellectual was substantiated by the Odessa actuality—Bialik and Tchernikovsky were anything but

men with spectacles on their noses and autumn in their hearts, and
no one who ever encountered in America the striking figure of Dr.
Chaim Tchernowitz, the great scholar of the Talmud and formerly
the Chief Rabbi of Odessa, a man of Jovian port and large, free mind,
would be inclined to conclude that there was but a single season of the
heart available to a Jew of Odessa.

But Babel had seen his father on his knees before a Cossack captain
on a horse, who said, "At your service" and touched his fur cap with
his yellow-gloved hand and politely paid no heed to the mob looting
the Babel store. Such an experience, or even a far milder analogue
of it, is determinative in the life of a boy. Freud speaks of the effect
upon him when, at twelve, his father told of having accepted in a
pacific way the insult of having his new fur cap knocked into the
mud by a Gentile who shouted at him, "Jew, get off the pavement."
It is clear that Babel's relation with his father defined his relation to
his Jewishness. Benya Krik, the greatest of gangsters, he who was
called King, was a Jew of Odessa, but he did not wear glasses and
he did not have autumn in his heart—it is in writing about Benya
that Babel uses the phrase that sets so far apart the intellectual and
the man of action. The explanation of Benya's preeminence among
gangsters does indeed take account of his personal endowment—Benya
was a "lion," a "tiger," a "cat"; he "could spend the night with a
Russian woman and satisfy her." But what really made his fate was
his having had Mendel Krik, the drayman, for his father. "What does
such a father think about? He thinks about drinking a good glass
of vodka, of smashing somebody in the face, of his horses—and nothing
more. You want to live and he makes you die twenty times a day.
What would you have done in Benya Krik's place? You would have
done nothing. But *he* did something. . . ." But Babel's father did not
think about vodka, and smashing somebody in the face, and horses;
he thought about large and serious things, among them respectability
and fame. He was a shopkeeper, not well-to-do, a serious man, a
failure. The sons of such men have much to prove, much to test
themselves for, and if they are Jewish, their Jewishness is ineluctably
involved in the test.

Babel, in the brief autobiographical sketch to which I have referred,
speaks with bitterness of the terrible discipline of his Jewish education.
He thought of the Talmud Torah as a prison shutting him off from
all desirable life, from reality itself. One of the stories he tells—con-

ceivably the incident was invented to stand for his feelings about his
Jewish schooling—is about his father's having fallen prey to the
Messianic delusion which beset the Jewish families of Odessa, the
belief that any one of them might produce a prodigy of the violin, a
little genius who could be sent to be processed by Professor Auer in
Petersburg, who would play before crowned heads in a velvet suit,
and support his family in honor and comfort. Such miracles had
occurred in Odessa, whence had come Elman, Zimbalist, Gabril-
owitsch, and Heifetz. Babel's father hoped for wealth, but he would
have foregone wealth if he could have been sure, at a minimum, of
fame. Being small, the young Babel at fourteen might pass for eight
and a prodigy. In point of fact, Babel had not even talent, and
certainly no vocation. He was repelled by the idea of becoming a
musical "dwarf," one of the "big-headed freckled children with necks
as thin as flower-stalks and an epileptic flush on their cheeks." This
was a Jewish fate and he fled from it, escaping to the port and the
beaches of Odessa. Here he tried to learn to swim and could not:
"the hydrophobia of my ancestors—Spanish rabbis and Frankfurt
moneychangers—dragged me to the bottom." But a kindly proofreader,
an elderly man who loved nature and children, took pity on him.
"How d'you mean, the water won't hold you? Why shouldn't it hold
you?"—his specific gravity was no different from anybody else's and
the good Yefim Nikitich Smolich taught him to swim. "I came to love
that man," Babel says in one of the very few of his sentences over
which no slightest irony plays, "with the love that only a boy suffering
from hysteria and headaches can feel for a real man."

The story is called "Awakening" and it commemorates the boy's
first effort of creation. It is to Nikitich that he shows the tragedy he
has composed and it is the old man who observes that the boy has
talent but no knowledge of nature and undertakes to teach him how
to tell one tree or one plant from another. This ignorance of the
natural world—Babel refers to it again in his autobiographical sketch
—was a Jewish handicap to be overcome. It was not an extravagance
of Jewish self-consciousness that led him to make the generalization
—Maurice Samuel remarks in The World of Sholom Aleichem that
in the Yiddish vocabulary of the Jews of Eastern Europe there are but
two flower names (rose, violet) and no names for wild birds.

When it was possible to do so, Babel left his family and Odessa
to live the precarious life, especially precarious for a Jew, of a Russian

artist and intellectual. He went to Kiev and then, in 1915, he ventured to St. Petersburg without a residence certificate. He was twenty-one. He lived in a cellar on Pushkin Street, and wrote stories which were everywhere refused until Gorki took him up and in 1916 published in his magazine two of Babel's stories. To Gorki, Babel said, he was indebted for everything. But Gorki became of the opinion that Babel's first stories were successful only by accident; he advised the young man to abandon the career of literature and to go "among the people." Babel served in the Czar's army on the Rumanian front; after the Revolution he was for a time a member of the Cheka; he went on the grain-collecting expeditions of 1918; he fought with the northern army against Yudenitch. In 1920 he was with Budienny in Poland, twenty-six years old, having seen much, having endured much, yet demanding initiation, submitting himself to the test.

The test, it is important to note, is not that of courage. Babel's affinity with Stephen Crane and Hemingway is close in many respects, of which not the least important is his feeling for his boyhood and for the drama of the boy's initiation into manhood. But the question that Babel puts to himself is not that which means so much to the two American writers; he does not ask whether he will be able to meet danger with honor. This he seems to know he can do. Rather, the test is of his power of direct and immediate, and violent, action—not whether he can endure being killed but whether he can endure killing. In the story "After the Battle" a Cossack comrade is enraged against him not because, in the recent engagement, he had hung back, but because he had ridden with an unloaded revolver. The story ends with the narrator imploring fate to "grant me the simplest of proficiencies—the ability to kill my fellow men."

The necessity for submitting to the test is very deeply rooted in Babel's psychic life. This becomes readily apparent when we read the whole of Babel's work and perceive the manifest connection between certain of the incidents of *Red Cavalry* and those of the stories of the Odessa boyhood. In the story "My First Goose" the newcomer to the brigade is snubbed by the brilliant Cossack commander because he is a man with spectacles on his nose, an intellectual. "Not a life for the brainy sort here," says the quartermaster who carries his trunk to his billet. "But you go and mess up a lady, and a good lady too, and you'll have the boys patting you on the back. . . ." The five new comrades in the billet make it clear that he is an outsider and unwanted, they begin at once to bully and haze him. Yet by one action he overcomes their hostility to him and his spectacles. He asks the old landlady for food and she puts him off; whereupon he kills the woman's goose in a particularly brutal manner, and, picking it up on the point of a sword, thrusts it at the woman and orders her to cook it. Now the crisis is passed; the price of community has been paid. The group of five reforms itself to become a group of six. All is decent and composed in the conduct of the men. There is a general political discussion, then sleep. "We slept, all six of us, beneath a wooden roof that let in the stars, warming one another, our legs intermingled. I dreamed: and in my dreams I saw women. But my heart, stained with bloodshed, grated and brimmed over." We inevitably read this story in the light of Babel's two connected stories of the 1905 pogrom, "The Story of My Pigeon House" and "First Love," recalling the scene in which the crippled cigarette vendor, whom all the children loved, crushes the boy's newly bought and long-desired pigeon and flings it in his face. Later the pigeon's blood and entrails are washed from the boy's cheek by the young Russian woman who is sheltering the Babel family and whom the boy adores. It is after her caress that the boy sees his father on his knees before the Cossack captain; the story ends with his capitulation to nervous illness. And now again a bird has been brutally killed, now again the killing is linked with sexuality, but now it is not his bird but another's, now he is not passive but active.

Yet no amount of understanding of the psychological genesis of the act of killing the goose makes it easy for us to judge it as anything more than a very ugly brutality. It is not easy for us—and it is not easy for Babel. Not easy, but we must make the effort to comprehend that for Babel it is not violence in itself that is at issue in his relation to the Cossacks, but something else, some quality with which violence does indeed go along, but which is not in itself merely violent. This quality, whatever it is to be called, is of the greatest importance in Babel's conception of himself as an intellectual and an artist, in his conception of himself as a Jew.

It is, after all, not violence and brutality that make the Cossacks what they are. This is not the first violence and brutality that Babel has known—when it comes to violence and brutality a Western reader can scarcely have, unless he sets himself to acquire it, an adequate idea of their place in the life of Eastern Europe. The impulse to violence, as we have learned, seems indigenous in all mankind. Among certain groups the impulse is far more freely licensed than among others. Americans are aware and ashamed of the actuality or potentiality of violence in their own culture, but it is nothing to that of the East of Europe; the people for whom the mass impalings and the knout are part of their memory of the exercise of authority over them have their own appropriate ways of expressing their rage. As compared with what the knife, or the homemade pike, or the boot, can do, the revolver is an instrument of delicate amenity and tender mercy—this, indeed, is the point of one of Babel's stories. Godfrey Blunden's description of the method of execution used by the Ukrainian peasant bands is scarcely to be read. Nor is it only in combat that the tradition of ferocious violence appears, as is suggested by the long Russian concern with wife-beating as a national problem.

The point I would make is that the Cossacks were not exceptional for their violence. It was not their violence in itself that evoked Tolstoy's admiration. Nor is it what fascinated Babel. Rather he is drawn by what the violence goes along with, the boldness, the passionateness, the simplicity and directness—and the grace. Thus the story "My First Goose" opens with a description of the masculine charm of the brigade commander Savitsky. His male grace is celebrated in a shower of epithet—we hear of the "beauty of his giant's body," of the decorated chest "cleaving the hut as a standard cleaves the sky," of "the iron and flower of that youthfulness," of his long legs, which were "like girls sheathed to the neck in shining riding-boots." Only the openness of the admiration and envy—which constitutes, also, a qualifying irony—keeps the description from seeming sexually perverse. It is remarkably *not* perverse; it is as "healthy" as a boy's love of his hero of the moment. And Savitsky's grace is a real thing. Babel is not ready to destroy it by any of the means that are so ready to the hand of the intellectual confronted by this kind of power and charm; he does not diminish the glory he perceives by confronting it with the pathos of human creatures less physically glorious, having more, or a higher, moral appeal because they are weaker and because they suffer. The possibility of this grace is part of what Babel saw in the Cossacks.

It is much the same thing that D. H. Lawrence was drawn by in his imagination of archaic cultures and personalities and of the ruthlessness, even the cruelty, that attended their grace. It is what Yeats had in mind in his love of "the old disturbed exalted life, the old splendor." It is what even the gentle Forster represents in the brilliant scene in *Where Angels Fear to Tread* in which Gino, the embodiment of male grace, tortures Stephen by twisting his broken arm. This fantasy of personal, animal grace, this glory of conscienceless self-assertion, of sensual freedom, haunts our culture. It speaks to something in us that we fear, and rightly fear, yet it speaks to us.

Babel never for a moment forgets what the actualities of this savage glory are. In the story "The Brigade Commander" he speaks of the triumph of a young man in his first command. Kolesnikov in his moment of victory had the "masterful indifference of a Tartar Khan," and Babel, observing him with genuine pleasure, goes on to say that he was conscious of the training of other famous leaders of horse, and mentions "the captivating Savitsky" and "the headstrong Pavlichenko." The captivating Savitsky we have met. The headstrong Pavlichenko appears in a story of his own; this story is his own account of his peasant origin, of the insults received from his aristocratic landlord, of how when the Revolution came, he had wiped out the insult. "Then I stamped on my master Nikitinsky; trampled on him for an hour or maybe more. And in that time I got to know life through and through. With shooting . . . you only get rid of a chap. Shooting's letting him off, and too damn easy for yourself. With shooting you'll never get at the soul, to where it is in a fellow and how it shows itself. But I don't spare myself, and I've more than once trampled an enemy for over an hour. You see, I want to get to know what life really is. . . ." This is all too *raffiné*—we are inclined, I think, to forget Pavlichenko and to be a little revolted by Babel. Let us suppose, however, that he is setting down the truth as he heard it; let us suppose too that he has it in mind not to spare himself—this is part, and a terrible part, of the actuality of the Cossack directness and immediacy, this is what goes along with the grace and charm.*

In our effort to understand Babel's complex involvement with the Cossack ethos we must be aware of the powerful and obsessive significance that violence has for the intellectual. Violence is, of course, the negation of the intellectual's characteristic enterprise of rationality. Yet at the same time it is the very image of that enterprise. This may seem a strange thing to say. Since Plato we have set violence and reason over against each other as polar opposites. Yet it is Plato who

* The celebration of the Cossack ethos gave no satisfaction to General Budienny who, when some of Babel's *Red Cavalry* stories appeared in a magazine before their publication in a volume, attacked Babel furiously, and with a large display of literary pretentiousness, for the cultural corruption and political ignorance which, he claimed, the stories displayed. Budienny conceived the stories to constitute a slander on the Cossacks.

can tell us why there is affinity between violence and the intellectual life. In the most famous of the Platonic myths, the men of the cave are seated facing the interior wall of the cave, and they are chained by their necks so that it is impossible for them to turn their heads. They can face in but one direction, they can see nothing but the shadows that are cast on the wall by the fire behind them. A man comes to them who has somehow freed himself and gone into the world outside the cave. He brings them news of the light of the sun; he tells them that there are things to be seen which are real, that what they see on the wall is but shadows. Plato says that the men chained in the cave will not believe this news. They will insist that it is not possible, that the shadows are the only reality. But suppose they do believe the news! Then how violent they will become against their chains as they struggle to free themselves so that they may perceive what they believe is there to be perceived. They will think of violence as part of their bitter effort to know what is real. To grasp, to seize—to *apprehend*, as we say—reality from out of the deep dark cave of the mind—this is indeed a very violent action.

The artist in our time is perhaps more overtly concerned with the apprehension of reality than the philosopher is, and the image of violence seems often an appropriate way of representing the nature of his creation. "The language of poetry naturally falls in with the language of power," says Hazlitt in his lecture on *Coriolanus* and goes on to speak in several brilliant passages of "the logic of the imagination and the passions" which makes them partisan with representations of proud strength. Hazlitt carries his generalization beyond the warrant of literary fact, yet all that he says is pertinent to Babel, who almost always speaks of art in the language of force. The unexpectedness which he takes to be the essence of art is that of a surprise attack. He speaks of the maneuvers of prose of "the army of words . . . the army in which all kinds of weapons may be brought into play." In one of his most remarkable stories, "DiGrasso," he describes the performance of a banal play given by an Italian troupe in Odessa; all is dreariness until in the third act the hero sees his betrothed in converse with the villainous seducer, and, leaping miraculously, with the power of levitation of a Nijinsky or a panther, he soars across the stage, falls upon the villain and tears out his enemy's throat with his teeth. This leap makes the fortune of the Italian company with the exigent Odessa audience; this leap, we are given to understand, is art. And as the story continues, Babel is explicit—if also ironic—in what he demonstrates of the moral effect that may be produced by this virtuosity and power, of what it implies of human pride and freedom.

The spectacles on his nose were for Babel of the first importance in his conception of himself. He was a man to whom the perception of the world outside the cave came late and had to be apprehended, by strength and speed, against the parental or cultural interdiction, the Jewish interdiction; it was as if every beautiful violent phrase that was to spring upon reality was a protest against his childhood. The violence of the Revolution, its sudden leap, was cognate with this feral passion for perception—to an artist the Revolution might well have seemed the rending not only of the social but of the perceptual chains, those that held men's gaze upon the shadows on the wall; it may have seemed the rush of men from the darkness of the cave into the light of reality. Something of this is suggested in a finely wrought story, "Line and Color"—like other stories of the time of Babel's sojourn in France in the early 30's, it was written in French —in which Kerensky is represented as defending his myopia, refusing to wear glasses, because, as he argues very charmingly, there is so much that myopia protects him from seeing, and imagination and benign illusion are thus given a larger license. But at a great meeting in the first days of the Revolution he cannot perceive the disposition of the crowd and the story ends with Trotsky coming to the rostrum and saying in his implacable voice, "Comrades!"

But when we have followed Babel into the depths of his experience of violence, when we have imagined something of what it meant in his psychic life and in the developing conception of his art, we must be no less aware of his experience of the principle that stands opposed to the Cossack principle.

We can scarcely fail to see that when in the stories of *Red Cavalry* Babel submits the ethos of the intellectual to the criticism of the Cossack ethos, he intends a criticism of his own ethos not merely as an intellectual but as a Jew. It is always as an intellectual, never as a Jew, that he is denounced by his Cossack comrades, but we know that he has either suppressed, for political reasons, the denunciations of him as a Jew that were actually made, or, if none were actually made, that he has in his heart supposed that they were made. These criticisms of the Jewish ethos, as he embodies it, Babel believes to have no small weight. When he implores fate to grant him the simplest of proficiencies, the ability to kill his fellow man, we are likely to take this as nothing but an irony, and as an ironic assertion of the superiority of his moral instincts. But it is only in part an irony. There comes a moment when he should kill a fellow man. In "The Death of Dolgushov," a comrade lies propped against a tree; he cannot be moved, inevitably he must die, for his entrails are hanging out; he must be left behind and he asks for a bullet in his head so that the Poles will not "play their dirty tricks" on him. It is the narrator whom he asks for the *coup de grâce,* but the narrator flees and sends a friend, who, when he has done what had to be done, turns on the "sensitive" man in a fury of rage and disgust: "You bastards in spectacles have about as much pity for us as a cat has for a mouse." Or again, the narrator has incurred the enmity of a comrade through no actual fault—no moral fault—of his own, merely through having been assigned a mount that the other man passionately loved, and riding it badly so that it developed saddle galls. Now the horse has been returned, but the man does not forgive him, and the narrator asks a superior officer to compound the quarrel. He is rebuffed. "You're trying to live without enemies," he is told. "That's all you think about, not having enemies." It comes at us with momentous force. This time we are not misled into supposing that Babel intends irony and a covert praise of his pacific soul; we know that in this epiphany of his refusal to accept enmity he means to speak adversely of himself in his Jewish character.

But his Jewish character is not the same as the Jewish character of the Jews of Poland. To these Jews he comes with all the presuppositions of an acculturated Jew of Russia, which were not much different from the suppositions of an acculturated Jew of Germany. He is repelled by the conditions of their life; he sees them as physically uncouth and warped; many of them seem to him to move "monkeyfashion." Sometimes he affects a wondering alienation from them, as when he speaks of "the occult crockery that the Jews use only once a year at Eastertime." His complexity and irony being what they are, the Jews of Poland are made to justify the rejection of the Jews among whom he was reared and the wealthy assimilated Jews of Petersburg. "The image of the stout and jovial Jews of the South, bubbling like cheap wine, takes shapes in my memory, in sharp contrast to the bitter scorn inherent in these long bony backs, these tragic yellow beards." Yet the Jews of Poland are more than a stick with which

Babel beats his own Jewish past. They come to exist for him as a spiritual fact of consummate value.

Almost in the degree that Babel is concerned with violence in the stories of *Red Cavalry*, he is concerned with spirituality. It is not only Jewish spirituality that draws him. A considerable number of the stories have to do with churches, and although they do indeed often express the anti-clerical feeling expectable in the revolutionary circumstances, the play of Babel's irony permits him to respond in a positive way to the aura of religion. "The breath of an invisible order of things," he says in one story, "glimmers beneath the crumbling ruin of the priest's house, and its soothing seduction unmanned me." He is captivated by the ecclesiastical painter Pan Apolek, he who created ecclesiastical scandals by using the publicans and sinners of the little towns as the models for his saints and virgins. Yet it is chiefly the Jews who speak to him of the life beyond violence, and even Pan Apolek's "heretical and intoxicating brush" had achieved its masterpiece in his Jesus of the Berestechko church, "the most extraordinary image of God I had ever seen in my life," a curly-headed Jew, a bearded figure in a Polish greatcoat of orange, barefooted with torn and bleeding mouth, running from an angry mob with a hand raised to ward off a blow.

Hazlitt, in the passage to which I have referred, speaking of the "logic of the imagination and the passions," says that we are naturally drawn to the representation of what is strong and proud and feral. Actually that is not so: we are, rather, drawn to the representation of what is real. It was reality that Babel found in the Jews of the Polish provinces. "In these passionate, anguish-chiseled features there is no fat, no warm pulsing of blood. The Jews of Volhynia and Galicia move jerkily, in an uncontrolled and uncouth way; but their capacity for suffering is full of a somber greatness, and their unvoiced contempt for the Polish gentry unbounded."

Here was the counter-image to the captivating Savitsky, the image of the denial of the pride of the glory of the flesh to which, early or late, every artist comes, to which he cannot come in full sincerity unless he can also make full affirmation of the glory. Here too is the image of art that is counter to DiGrasso's leap, to the language in arms—the image of the artist's suffering, patience, uncouthness, and scorn.

If Babel's experience with the Cossacks may be understood as having reference to the boy's relation to his father, his experience of the Jews of Poland has, we cannot but feel, a maternal reference. To the one

Babel responds as a boy, to the other as a child. In the story "Gedali" he speaks with open sentimentality of his melancholy on the eve of Sabbaths—"On those evenings my child's heart was rocked like a little ship upon enchanted waves. O the rotted Talmuds of my childhood! O the dense melancholy of memories." And when he has found a Jew, it is one who speaks to him in this fashion: ". . . All is mortal. Only the mother is destined to immortality. And when the mother is no longer living, she leaves a memory which none yet has dared to sully. The memory of the mother nourishes in us a compassion that is like the ocean, and the measureless ocean feeds the rivers that dissect the Universe. . . ."

He has sought Gedali in his gutted curiosity shop ("Where was your kindly shade that evening, Dickens?") to ask for "a Jewish glass of tea, and a little of that pensioned-off God in a glass of tea." He does not, that evening, get what he asks for; what he does get is a discourse on revolution, on the impossibility of a revolution made in blood, on the International that is never to be realized, the International of the good and the gentle.

It was no doubt the easier for Babel to respond to the spiritual life of the Jews of Poland because it was a life coming to its end and having about it the terrible strong pathos of its death. He makes no pretense that it could ever claim him for its own. But it established itself in his heart as an image, beside the image of the other life that also could not claim him, the Cossack life. The opposition of these two images made his art—but it was not a dialectic that his Russia could permit.

HAROLD ROSENBERG

THE COMEDY OF THE DIVINE

As THOMAS MANN'S *Joseph* NEARS ITS END, ITS HERO has become increasingly aware that he is an actor in a sublime charade, "the God-invention of Joseph and His Brothers," as Mann calls it. Everything has been working to make the favorite son of the last of the Fathers a provider for many and to bestow upon him an exalted place in the hereditary descent. The figures of this design have become unmistakable to Joseph himself—it is almost as if he had read his own story in the Bible. Thus he feels himself to be less the author of his history, in the sense that we today make our lives, than its stage manager. He is not permitted to choose his acts, it rests with him to behave in such a way as not to let the great Plot down. "What a history, Mai, is this we are in!" he exclaims to his steward. "One of the very best. And now it depends on us, it is our affair to give it a fine form and make something perfectly beautiful of it, putting all our wits at the service of God."

Once again Mann is re-telling the story of the Artist but with a difference. Joseph's world is complete; he may collaborate in perfecting it but, unlike Aschenbach in *A Death In Venice* or the artist-heroes of other contemporary novels, it is not up to him to create it. He lives in a story already written; moreover, one "written by God" and not to be tampered with by men. To be enclosed in such a known history, that is to say, in a fate, is to derive of a psychic substance notably different from that of persons reared in uncertainty and the unknown. By the fact alone that one's future has been predicted, one enters the clarified landscape of the epic hero. Mental duality has been overcome—

332

Joseph is not split like Aschenbach or Castorp—and with it the ir-
reconcilable ego that may well be the symptom of a disorder.

Conscious at every turn of what he may expect, Joseph's acts hardly
go deeper than the esthetic; by our standards he lacks emotional
seriousness. His second descent into the pit, punishment for arousing
the passions of Potiphar's wife, may be a symbolic passage through
the netherworld but is in no sense a plunge into a night of the soul.
Nor are his lifting up by Pharaoh and his subsequent reunion with his
brothers and his father occasions for strong dramatic feelings. They
occur rather as tableaux in a pageant of correct gestures moving toward
the familiar sad-happy ending. . . . This quality of ordered response
different from detachment, to which we apply the name "Classical,"
comes from living within a history that has revealed itself, whether
through myth or through philosophy. It is the mark of a life that has
the character of a celebration and wherein action is inseparable from
the pleasure of the mind in contemplating with mingled awe, credulousness and skepticism a legend that has become part of itself.

Like a jesting rabbi, Mann elaborates the Biblical text for the sake
of this ritual pleasure. Of all his themes, the *Joseph* tale provided the
one best suited to his genius, which is less that of a dramatist than of a
dialectical comedian. In the idea of the God-story he discovered the
high-comedy conception of an historically self-conscious age.

For a history to be known in advance it must be conceived as
omnipotently managed. With half-lyrical, half-mocking acceptance of
man's dependence on the absolute, Mann continues the investigation
of the data of the divine which is the profoundest undertaking of our
scientific culture.

It is part of Mann's later method to define individuals in terms of
their objects of belief; for men "only imitate the gods, and whatever
picture they make of them, that they copy." During her infatuation
with Joseph, Potiphar's wife was a devotee of "omni-friendly Atum-Re
of On, Lord of the Wide Horizon," and gossiping with this soft
voluptuous deity, drunken with good will, her personality was
dimmed and her mind took on the other's graceful imprecision. But
after the collapse of her romance she switched to "him rich in bulls
of Ipet-Isowet, and to his conservative sun-sense" and thereupon grew
hard and haughty.

The individual derives the shape of his being from the god-type. In
becoming himself, he thus becomes more the other and like those who
resemble that other. As he rises he loses himself in the common; as

Mann had put it in the early *Royal Highness,* representing is something naturally higher than mere being. This doubling of self and not-self is a joke, though one depressing to human pride.

Absorption in the image that rules society is the rule. But *Joseph* shows an additional possibility: the possibility of the stranger. Bound to a foreign god, Joseph has a different sense of fact from the Egyptians; feels differently; most important, has a different story to tell. When we speak of the alien, we mean that a new god-story is there to be heard, by which whoever so wishes may change himself.

Like the shaping of the individual, the telling of the new story also involves a doubling of god and man and demands a double language, in order that the odd, accidental doings of human beings shall reveal their steadfast core of divine plot-direction. To mediate between the gross fact and the compelling dream of meaning that makes it worth repeating the double tongue of wit is needed. This is especially true of the Biblical god-narrative or history, which was all planned beforehand and managed in the happening yet came about through the passions and mistakes not of demigods but of ordinary men and women. "Just because it is so solemn it must be treated with a light touch. For lightness, my friend, flippancy, the artful jest, that is God's very best gift to man, the profoundest knowledge we have of that complex, questionable thing we call life."*

Modern positivism has popularized the observation that everything divine is ambiguous. Mann seems to maintain an interesting reverse principle: that everything ambiguous is divine (compare Empson's contention that the ambiguous is the essence of the poetic). The many-in-the-one is the order of the dream and the vision; it has, we are told, the same source in the preconscious; and it induces a comparable state of dreaminess and profusion coupled with a sense of discovery. Joseph demonstrated his simultaneous grasp of the human and the divine by habitually dealing in ambiguities. With these he fascinated the "mystical" Amenhotep, one-sided in his decadence, as he had earlier seduced the "formal" Potiphar, god's eunuch. "All your speaking," exclaims the delighted Pharoah, "turns on the Yes and at the same time on the No . . . The wrong right one, you say, and the wrong one

---

* That no one who is without wit can give a true account of what is happening in a history seen as planned justified Trotzky in making "stupidity" his major accusation against Stalin, although this seemed to many a mere personal insult, moreover one inconsistent with the shrewdness of Stalin in defeating his rivals.

that was the right one? That is not bad; it is so crazy that it is witty."

Wit through consciousness of their god-story is for Mann the typical genius of the lead-personages of Joseph's tribe. The Jews are a people of wit because they were constantly faced with the need to reconcile a primary opposition. From the start they conceived that God had a plan for them, yet their very sense of history induced them to cling tightly to the human character; they refused to spoil their story by converting it into a ritual masque. The Fathers, dreamers of the sheepfold, had learned how to come to terms with their destiny through a masterly shuffling of antitheses. To Mann skill in preserving the tension between the order of eternity and the life-scale of the individual is also moulded into whatever there is in the Greek and Christian traditions that is witty and double-minded in relation to spirit and earth. The humanistic hero appears in *Joseph* as the ironist who unites in himself the remotest unknown with the most pressing here-and-now.

The confrontation between this "Western" type and the godly Amenhotep is the climax of the *Joseph* narrative and even, as Mann says, the occasion for which the entire tale is a preparation. Egypt had no ironists, and its imagination remained divided. Wise in science and religion, in the ways of things and of the dead, its magic excluded both the disorder of existence and the arbitrariness of individuality. This weakness of the Egyptian "monkey-land" was exposed by the scion of Jacob-Ulysses in balancing his contradictions of the most-distant-and-nearest god before the feeble, trance-driven Pharaoh, life-denying in his excessive divinity; inducing the other to yield to him the staff of authority so that he might organize the feeding of the people.

In affirming historical prediction while questioning it, Mann's own wit raises fascinating problems for contemporary historical thinking. Seven years of fatness and drought were dreamed by Pharaoh and foreseen by him through the Socratic prodding of Joseph. Could those symmetrical numerals stand up under investigation? Was the change from wealth to starvation as dramatic as in the dreamer's vision and the interpreter's explanation? "In these fourteen years, things were neither quite so definitely good nor so definitely bad as the prophecy would have them. It was fulfilled, no doubt about that. But fulfilled as life fulfils, imprecisely. For life and reality always assert a certain independence, sometimes on such a scale as to blur the prophecy out of all recognition. Of course, life is bound to the prophecy; but within those limits it moves so freely that one almost has one's choice as to whether the prophecy has been fulfilled or not. . . . In fact and in reality the prophesied seven looked rather more like five. . . . The fat and the lean years did not come out of the womb of time to balance each other so unequivocally as in the dream. [They] were like life in not being entirely fat or entirely lean. . . . Indeed, if the prophecy had not existed [a couple of the lean years] might not have been recognized as years of famine at all. . . ." I recommend this passage to those who see history as following a plan, as well as to those who see it as following no plan.

Man cannot help fitting himself into god-stories. To have a part in one, especially a "speaking part," is to have a part in the permanent, to be assured of personal continuity. What if a grand god-story, asks Mann, were unfolding under one's eyes and yet one had no part assigned in it? A good question for a generation defining itself by action in wars and revolutions. It is possible, Mann replies, that one might get in anyway—through luck or determination. For instance, Mai-Sachme, Joseph's jailer, wasn't cast for a serious part in the *Joseph* epic, but he was a good fellow and Joseph liked him for his philosophic calm, so he took him into the later events as his steward and confidant. As for Tamar, she wasn't intended to be in the *Joseph* narrative at all—being just the luckless wife of two obscure nephews who died early. But somehow she could sense that big doings were afoot stretching far into the future. Desiring to be immortal, she forced herself into the line of Jacob, indeed the top line, that of Judah, so that by a single calculated act of whoring at the gate she became a grandmother of the House of Kings and of the god to come. . . . With this chapter that doesn't belong and yet does belong—because Tamar "wanted to be of the family, to shove herself and her womb into the course of history, which led, through time, to salvation"—Mann not only had the time of his life but reached a peak of the insight of our time into man's fate.

LESLIE FIEDLER

NEGRO AND JEW: ENCOUNTER IN AMERICA

I HAVE NEVER READ ANYTHING BY JAMES BALDWIN which has not moved me. Both his novel, *Go Tell It on the Mountain*, and his recent collection of essays possess a passion and a lyricism quite unlooked for in another book about "the Negro." There is no securer or more soporific refuge from the realities of Negro-white conflict than most of the writing on the subject; and the greatest tribute one can pay to Baldwin is to state unequivocally that he does not contribute to that pious bedtime literature. Since I am impelled to take off from, and in certain respects to amend what he has to say about the relations of Negro and Jew to each other and to America, I feel his honesty as a challenge. To write with less involvement or risk of pain would be an offense.

I am moved to begin with Baldwin's title. Unlike the Negro, the Jew is apt to feel himself not a "native son" but a sojourner in America. I do not mean that he cannot by assimilation and adaptation become as American as anyone else, merely that he knows he can only achieve that end by accepting a role which he has played no part in creating. The Jew is, by and large, a late-comer in the United States; and when he begins to arrive in significant numbers toward the end of the nineteenth century, he and America are already set in their respective ways; theirs is a marriage of the middle-aged. The guilts and repressions, the boasts and regrets of America are already formulated when he debarks, waiting for him. Their genesis goes back to an experience he does not share; and he himself is determined by quite other experiences—twice determined, in fact: by the dim pre-history of *Eretz Yisrael* and by the living memory of Exile.

Indeed, the Jew may already have been determined a third time, by the impact of the Enlightenment, perhaps even in the form of anarchism or socialism. Whatever the shape of his own life, the Jew comes to America with a history, the memory of a world he cannot afford to and does not want to deny. But the Negro arrives without a past, out of nowhere—that is to say, out of a world he is afraid to remember, perhaps could not even formulate to himself in the language he has been forced to learn. Before America, there is for him simply nothing; and America itself, white America, scarcely exists until he is present. Whatever the fate of the Jew in America, he knows he has not helped forge the conscience of the country. He may give a special flavor to New York or Hollywood, even to one or more of the arts in recent days; but he does not exist for the American imagination at those deep levels where awareness is determined. The encounter with the Jew is irrelevant to America's self-consciousness.

Nowhere in all of American literature is there a sentence bearing on the Jew with the terrible resonance of Benito Cereno's cry in Melville's story, "It is the Negro!" This is an exclamation of terror, to be sure; but it is also a statement of fact: the black man is the root of our guilt and fear and pain. Similarly, in Whitman's "Song of Myself," where the United States found in the mid-nineteenth century a lyric voice, the Negro is evoked in all his suffering: "I am the hounded slave, I wince at the bite of dogs, Hell and despair are upon me . . ." but there is no Jew. No more than he can forget he was a slave can the Negro forget that he was the occasion, whatever the cause, of a war which set white American against white American and created a bitterness we have not yet ceased to feel. It is the historical fact of the Civil War, not specifically alluded to in Baldwin's book, which gives special sanction to his grim vaunt: "The time has come to realize that the interracial drama acted out on the American Continent has not only created a new black man, it has created a new white man, too. . . . One of the things that distinguishes Americans from other people is that no other people has ever been so deeply involved in the lives of black men. . . ." Certainly, none has witnessed its white citizens killing each other over the question of their relation to the blacks. Yet at the time of the Civil War, the single Jewish member of my own family by marriage or blood who was in this country (and I suspect this is not untypical) was called on to mount guard on the roof of a Fifth Avenue shop during the draft riots in New York. Baldwin's boast is one no Jew could make; and "Thank God for that!" one is tempted to add, for the Negro, insofar as he considers himself responsible for that war and all it sums up that is dark and ambiguous in the American experience, must endure a sense of guilt of which we are free.

Indeed, superficially at least, the history of the Jew in America is singularly free of guilt on either hand. We represent, rather disconcertingly, the major instance in America of an ethnic minority redeemed rather than exploited or dispossessed. Other foreign groups, the Italians or Scandinavians, for instance, were also welcomed in the time of the great immigrations; but they did not arrive like the Jews, on a dead run, universally branded and harried. Only the Irish can be compared with us in the urgency of their flight. We fled to the Golden Door not merely from poverty and hunger, but impelled by an absolute rejection and the threat of extinction; and it is, therefore, no accident that the lines on the Statue of Liberty: "Give me your tired, your poor, your huddled masses yearning to breathe free . . ." were written by a Jew. They are sentimental enough, to be sure; but they could at least be inscribed by one of our people without the destructive irony that would have undercut them had they been written by a Negro.

The Jews have prospered in the United States, the single Western country never to have had a real ghetto, as they have nowhere else in the world. Even the niggling social snobbery, the occasional outbursts of violence against us can be understood, without extraordinary injustice to the facts, as hangovers from the European experience we have all fled, remnants of debased religion and ancient terror that we have not yet sloughed off. The American, who must wince when the Negro is mentioned, thinking of the slave ships; stutter when the Indian is brought up, remembering the theft of the land; and squirm when the Japanese are touched on, recalling the concentration camps of the last war—can cite the Jews with pride. We are (it is fashionable to forget this now, but salutory to recall) the boast of the United States, as the Negroes are its shame; and it is across the barrier of this discrepancy that our two peoples confront each other. The Negro boasts grimly that he has helped shape with terror the American spirit; we admit shamefacedly that we have profited by its generosity. It is no good showing our minor wounds, on the one hand; or insisting, on the other, upon the squalor and brutality of the Africa out of which the Negro was kidnapped; the guilt of Isaac toward Ishmael can not be so easily dispelled.

The problem, however, is more complicated than that; the relationship of Negro and Jew to America involves their relationship to Europe; for America, transmuted as it is, remains still somehow the Europe it thought to flee. But Europe is "the West"—that is to say,

Christendom in decay. What, then, is the relationship of the Jew to the Christian world he invented and rejected; and how does it compare with the relation to that world of the Negroes—that is, of the last heathen to be converted by force? We are strangers both, outsiders in some senses forever, but we are outsiders with a difference.

America is for the Negro a way into the West, a gateway to Europe —and not only for the young colored writers and students and artists, like Baldwin himself, whom one sees sitting in the cafés of Paris and Rome, sustained by awards from our large Foundations. They are merely the vanguard, the symbolic representatives of their whole people. The Jew, conversely, is the gateway into Europe for America; for he has carried with him, almost against his will, his own history, two thousand years of which is European. The anti-American Frenchman or Italian condemning our culture and its representatives will brush aside the names of certain writers and thinkers offered in our defense, protesting, "But he's a *Jew,*" meaning, of course, a European, not really an American. And there is a kind of miserable half-truth in the rejoinder.

Certainly, no young Jewish-American writer (*returning* to Europe, after all) can feel what Baldwin does confronting a group of ignorant Europeans in a remote Swiss village, "the most illiterate among them is related in a way I am not to Dante, Shakespeare, Michelangelo . . . the Cathedral of Chartres says to them which it cannot say to me. . . ." Alien as the Jew may feel himself, he is an alien with a culture ambiguously related to that which informs all the monuments of European art. It is not merely that people of our blood, whether converts to Christianity or skeptics or orthodox believers, have been inextricably involved in the making of the European mind: Leone Ebreo, Maimonides, Montaigne and Spinoza and Marx—perhaps even St. John of the Cross and Christopher Columbus; but that we have haunted the mind of Europe for two thousand years as the black man has haunted that of America for two hundred. Standing before the cathedrals that make Baldwin feel a stranger, we remember that here a spokesman of our people was dragooned into debating the incarnation; there, every Sunday, the elders of the ghetto were forced to listen to a sermon on the destruction of the Temple. Walk down into the Forum, and there is the arch of Titus; enter the palace of the Dukes of Urbino, and there is Uccello's painting of the Jew burning the bleeding host; open Shakespeare, and there is Shylock.

But even this, of course, is by no means all. The Jew is bound to

Europe not only by ties of guilt and mutual hatred, and he lives in its imagination not only as the sinister usurer and defiler of altars. The images of all it most aspires to and reveres are also Jewish images: the David and Moses of Michelangelo, the Virgin of Dante—the very figure of the Christian God are collaborations of our mind and theirs. Before the Cathedral at Chartres, the Jew cannot help thinking, wryly, ironically or bitterly: this is our gift to the barbarians. And this the barbarians cannot deny. The boast of that Church most deeply rooted in the history of Europe is "Abraham is our father. Spiritually we are Semites." The West may, in occasional spasms, try to cast us out; but it cannot without spiritual self-castration deny its own Jewishness. The Jew is the father of Europe (irksome as that relationship may sometimes seem on both sides); the Negro only an adopted child. If Christendom denies us, it diminishes itself; but if we reject the West, we reject not our legend, only a historical interruption of it. We are what we always were—ourselves. The Negro, on the other hand, cannot endure alienation from the West; for once he steps outside of it, he steps outside of culture—not into Africa, to which he cannot return, but into nothing. The cases of Liberia and modern Israel make the point vividly: a homeland urged on the American Negro and (by and large) rejected, versus one denied the Jew, but fought for and, against ridiculous odds, achieved. Similarly, the Negro is the prisoner of his face in a way the Jew is not. The freedom of the Jew is no mere matter of plastic surgery and nose-shortening; this would be a vanity as pointless as the Negro's skin bleaches and hair-straighteners. A generation or two in America, however, and the Jew is born with a new face. A blond and snub-nosed little boy looks out of the Barton's Pesach ad in *The New York Times,* crying, "Happy Passover, Grandma!" and it is hard to tell him from the pink Protestant image of "Dick" in the school primers. But no Negro dares imagine his child with such a face. This, too, lies between the Jew and Negro in America: the realization that for one (whether he finally choose it or not) there is always a way out, by emigration or assimilation; for the other there is no exit.

Both Negro and Jew exist for the Western world, as I have already suggested, not only in history but also in the timeless limbo of the psyche—that is, as archetypes, symbolic figures presumably representing the characters and fates of alien peoples, but actually projecting aspects of the white Christian mind itself. It is the confusion between these legendary projections (necessary to the psychological well-being of Europe and America) and actual living men called by the same labels which makes the elimination of race prejudice a problem beyond the scope of mere economic and social measures.

The differences between the archetypes of Negro and Jew are especially illuminating. They begin with the fact, which we have noticed earlier, that the myth of the Jew is a European inheritance, or, perhaps better, a persistence; while the myth of the Negro is a product of the American experience and of a crisis in the American mind. The image of the usurer and bad father with a knife that lies behind Shylock existed long before even the dream of America; indeed, it represents a distortion of our own myths of Jacob and Abraham in alien and hostile minds. The evil Jews of American writers like Fitzgerald, Pound or Cummings are no more than refurbishings of the original symbolic figure out of the Middle Ages; for there is, in the world of the imagination, no American Jew. The key Archetypes of the Negro, however, are purely American: Aunt Jemima and Uncle Tom, those insipid and infuriating but (as Mr. Baldwin justly observes) inescapable images that, still in the best American tradition, belong really to childhood. From Uncle Tom, in particular, there descend such important characters of our literature as Mark Twain's Nigger Jim and Faulkner's Lucas Beauchamp, who symbolically grant the white man forgiveness in the name of their whole race, redeem him by enduring the worst he can inflict.

It is intriguing that the chief literary archetypes of the Jew are frankly villains and figures of terror, while the myth of the Negro as it takes flesh in our classic novels is more often than not the symbol of a reconciliation more hoped-for than real, a love that transcends guilt. It is the noblest American sentimentality. By the same token, the counterimages of Jew and Negro in the "enlightened" fiction of the most recent past differ equally from each other but in reverse: the conciliator has been transformed into the murderer, the murderer into the conciliator; that is, Uncle Tom has become Bigger Thomas, while the Jew's daughter who lured Hugh of Lincoln to his death has been transformed into Majorie Morningstar.

The Negro, however, whether thought of as killer or pious slave, has always represented for the American imagination the primitive and the instinctive, the life of impulse whether directed toward good or ill. The Jew, on the other hand, stands symbolically for the uses and abuses of intelligence, for icy legalism or equally cold vengefulness.

They represent the polar opposition of law and lawlessness, the eternal father and the eternal child, who is also, according to the Romantic poets, "father of the man." In Freudian terminology, the one can be said to stand for the superego, the other the id, though both are felt, like the peoples with whom they are identified, as *other* by the white, Gentile ego.

Toward id and superego alike, the American, with his double inheritance of Romanticism and Puritanism, has a divided attitude; and this ambivalence is transferred to the symbolic Negro and Jew. The black man is associated with the primitive and the forest, with the "natural," which Americans like to think of as their element. But the Devil was called in Massachusetts the "Black Man," too; and what we label nowadays the unconscious had earlier no other name than the "satanic." The heart is another symbol for the same "natural" for which the Negro comes to stand, but so are the genitals; and if the Negro comes into classic fiction as a source of pity and love, he lurks in the back of the popular mind always as the rapist—the projection of the white man's own "dark" sensuality which he can neither suppress nor justify.

No Christian, however, can without calling Jehova the Devil (and even this was tried long ago and condemned as a heresy) think of the Jews as wholly satanic; recalcitrant or rejected, they are still God's people. The final Puritan equivalent of the id is Satan, but that of the superego is God: and this is why no good Protestant American can, whatever the presumable Gospel justification, hate the Jew (who stands forever on Sinai, the Tables in his hand), without a sneaking suspicion that he is also hating God.

Perhaps this explains, too, why a certain kind of Romantic anti-Puritanism, which aims at setting traditional morality on its head and prefers whim to law, ends with a violent and sentimental espousal of the dark-skinned peoples and a complementary hatred of the Jews. D. H. Lawrence is one example of this tendency; but its clearest exponent is, as one would expect, an American. For Sherwood Anderson, the Negro in his *Dark Laughter*, his visceral, impulsive joy in life, represents a positive pole, while the Jew, cerebral, talkative, melancholy, the enemy of his own sexuality, stands for all that is negative and reprehensible in modern life.

Yet despite the many spectacular differences between the history and status of Negroes and Jews, between the ways in which they have come to America and the ways in which the American imagination uses them—they are somehow bound together and condemned to a common fate, not less real for being so hard to define. "Prejudice against Negroes and Jews"—it is a phrase that comes naturally and inevitably; and for all its banality, it contains a truth. As far as economic and professional opportunities are concerned there is no comparison between the status of Negroes and Jews; but in a certain kind of social exclusion, in the *quality* of that exclusion rather than its degree (for it is much more severe in the case of the Negro), they are one. Similarly though not equally, both peoples are bound by restrictions that determine where they can live, what clubs and fraternities they can join, what hotels they can enter and finally (and this is the crux, though we are often driven to deny its importance for what seem good strategic reasons) *whom they can marry.*

There are no other white ethnic groups against whom such thoroughgoing exclusions are practiced; for there is no other group which is felt, viscerally not rationally, as so completely alien, so totally other. Though none of our state laws against miscegenation apply, as far as I am aware, to Jews, every Jew knows that the spoken and occasionally printed injunction "For White Only" may exclude him. There is at work everywhere in the United States, the Protestant-North European tendency to think of all Mediterranean peoples as more black than white, Dagos and Gypsies, swarthy fiddlers and actors, not to be trusted with women; but only in respect to the Jews among those peoples is there the true primitive fear of the *contamination of blood.* Historically, the Jew has been rejected on two grounds, for his religion and for his "race"; but in America in recent years the decay of piety into interfaith good will has rendered the former more and more negligible. The last irrational grounds of our exclusion are not very diffeent from those which surround the Negro with horror: we are taboo peoples, both of us. The secret of our fraternity lies in the barbarous depths of the white, Gentile heart; and it is that shared secret which makes us aware of how we resemble each other and are mutually different from the Irish, the Poles or the Yugoslavs, discriminated against only for comparatively *rational* reasons: because they have arrived here later than other groups and now displace them in jobs, etc.

To be so alike and so different; different in ourselves and alike only in the complicated fear we stir in the hearts of our neighbors, this is what exacerbates our relations with each other. Surely the Negro cannot relish (for all his sentimental desire to think of himself metaphorically as Israel, "Let my people go . . .") this improbable and unwanted yoking any more than the Jew; and yet even physically our people have been thrust together. It is in the big cities of the industrial North, in New York or Philadelphia or Chicago or Detroit, that the Negro and the Jew confront each other and that their inner relationship is translated into a spatial one. The "emancipated" Negro fleeing poverty and the South, and the "emancipated" Jew fleeing exclusion and Europe, become neighbors; and their proximity serves to remind both that neither is quite "emancipated" after all. In America, to be sure, the ultimate ghetto (there is no way of avoiding the word, which gives its name to Baldwin's chief essay on the subject I am treating, "The Harlem Ghetto") is reserved for Negroes. Jews inhabit at one remove or another the region between it and the neighborhoods which mean real belonging, except for the marginal Jewish merchant who finds himself inside the Negro quarter, forced to squeeze his colored customers for his precarious livelihood and to bear the immediate brunt of their hatred for all white men.

It doesn't matter how much newer and richer are the homes which the Jews attain in their flight toward the tonier suburbs and how shabby the dwellings they leave to the Negroes always behind them, five years away or twenty or thirty; and they can never lose the sense of being merely a buffer between the blacks and the "real" whites. Insofar as they are aware of their undeniable economic superiority to the Negroes, middle-class Jews are likely to despise them for lagging behind at the same time that they resent them for pressing so close. It is not an easy relationship.

Most Jews have, I think, little sense of how the Negroes regard them specifically as Jews. They are likely to assume to begin with that Negroes are incapable of making subtle distinctions between whites and whites; and they are, moreover, accustomed to look for anti-Semitism chiefly from people who are, or whom the Jews believe to be, socially more secure than themselves. And so they are easily taken in by the affable play-acting of the Negroes, from whom they believe they have no cause to expect hatred. Jews, more often than not, take it for granted that the Negroes are grateful to them for the historical accident of their never having been the masters of black slaves; and they are shocked at the sort of black anti-Semitism which Baldwin describes: "But just as society must have a scapegoat, so hatred must have a symbol. Georgia has the Negro. Harlem has the Jew."

But why should the Negro hate the Jew? As far as he is aware, the Jew does not hate the Negro—at least not as much as the Gentiles do! To be sure, most Jews are conscious that the Negro is their lightning rod, that he occupies a ghetto which might otherwise be theirs and bears the pogroms which might otherwise be directed at them. But no Jew has ordained these ghettos, and if the owner of a Negro tenement happens to be a Jew, after all, he must live! In any court of law, the Jew would be declared innocent of major complicity in the oppression of the Negro in America. What if he sometimes bamboozles or overcharges a colored customer, or refuses to sell his house to the first Negro to try to enter a neighborhood? He and his ancestors have never owned a slave or participated in a lynching or impregnated Negro women while worrying publicly about miscegenation. Almost alone among Americans, the Jew seems to have no reason to feel guilt toward the Negro; and this is, though Baldwin makes no point of it, a matter of great importance.

Yet it is not true that the Jew feels no guilt toward the Negro; he merely believes that he *should* feel none, and is baffled when he does. There is no reason, the Jew tells himself, why he should be expected to be more liberal than any other Americans in regard to such problems as fair employment codes and desegregation; and yet I am sure that most Jews are. On the record and at the polls, they are the Negroes' friends; and if the overwhelming majority of them would object to their daughters' marrying Negroes, they would object with hardly less violence to their marrying *goyim*. If we discriminate against Ham in this regard, we discriminate also against Japheth. Some Jews, to be sure, adopt the anti-Negro attitudes of their neighbors in an excess of as-similationist zeal, as a way of demonstrating by the all-American quality of their hatred that they, too, are "white." There is, however, also a particularly Jewish distrust of the black man, buried deep in our own tradition. Are we not told in the Torah itself that the offspring of Ham will be cursed: "A servant of servants shall he be unto his brethren."

There is no use quibbling about it; though he does not oppress the Negro, the Jew does hate him with a double though muted hatred: for being at once too like himself and too like the *goyim*—for resembling what the Jew most resents in his own situation and also what he most despises in the whole non-Jewish world. The Jew sees in the Negro a carefree and improvident life-style, that he has also observed and envied a little, all around him, but which he feels he could not afford (even if, improbably, he could approve) in his rejection and devotion to God. Yet though the Negro is also poor and rejected and pious, he is able to laugh overloud and drink overmuch, to take marriage lightly and money without seriousness, to buy spangles at the expense of food, to despise thrift and sobriety and to be so utterly a fool that one is *forced* into taking financial advantage of him. Real or legendary, this Negro the Jew finds or thinks he finds in his run-down, slovenly house; and he considers him no more admirable at worship than at play, jerking and howling and writhing on the floor in a final degradation of the alien Evangelical tradition.

Perhaps the Jew cannot be taken to task for despising improvidence and superstition. And yet he knows that somehow he has failed an obligation that he does not quite understand, failed his own history of persecution and oppression by not managing to—to do *what?* What he might have performed he can never really say, some bold revolutionary blow for emancipation, some superhuman act of love. So he cries out, if he is disturbed enough, against segregation to a group of his friends who are also against segregation, or he writes a letter to the papers, or makes a contribution to the NAACP. And, after all, what else can he do? What else can *I* do?

At least it is necessary to say "I" and pass on from safe generalizations about what the abstract "Jew" thinks about the abstract "Negro," generalizations from which it is possible to be secretly exempting oneself all the time. Even at the cost of some pain, it is necessary to say what "this Jew," what *I* feel on these matters in my own quite unstatistical flesh.

I can begin by saying, in the teeth of the usual defensive cliché, that none of my best friends is black. I have known many Negroes in my life and have talked to some, chiefly comrades in one radical party or another, far enough into the night to have some notion of the distrust we would have had to overcome, the masks we would have had to penetrate, to discover our real selves, much less become real friends. I cannot see how that gap could be closed without genuine passion; and my only passionate relation to a Negro I do not even remember, but take on trust from stories of my mother. When I was little more than a year old, I was taken care of by a black girl, whom I loved so deeply, caressing and kissing her black skin in a way which horrified my family, that she was fired. I assume that I was desolate for a little while; I do not really recall, and my mother never carried her account that far.

My only other connection with a Negro that involves any tenderness comes at a much later date. I was thirteen or fourteen, working at my

first job in a shoe store, and more than a little scared at the cynicism
and worldliness of the other "boys" (some of whom were as old as sixteen!), much less the salesmen and the hose girls. My only friend in
the store, the only one who never mocked me, intentionally or unwittingly, was the colored porter. We would eat our lunches together
in the basement out of paper bags, while all the others were off at
cafeterias or lunch counters. He would speak to me gravely and without
condescension about life—mostly sex, of course, which he thought the
salesmen made too much of in their boastful anecdotes and I was over-
impressed with in my callow innocence. After we finished eating, I
would retouch the crude sketch of a gigantic, naked woman that someone had roughed out on one of the cellar walls, while he leaned back
and criticized my efforts. Before we went upstairs to work again, he
would help me push a pile of empty hose boxes in front of our private
mural.

In retrospect, it seems to me that I found in this Negro porter, quite
in accord with the best American traditions, my own Nigger Jim or
Sam Fathers—but with what a difference! Urban Jew that I was, I had
no nighttime Mississippi for the encounter, no disappearing virgin
forest—only the half-lit cellar with the noise of the city traffic rumbling
dimly above and the rustling of rats in the trashbin. It was not, however, a relationship with a person, but with a type.

Aside from these, my early encounters with Negroes were casual and
public. There was, of course, the colored tenor who could sing "Eli,
Eli" in Yiddish and was therefore in great demand at all Jewish events
as a curiosity, a freak. What his fellow Negroes thought of him God
only knows! I can remember the old women shaking their heads incred-
ulously as he sang, and the kids afterwards arguing about whether
one could really be both black and a Jew. Beyond this, there were the
Negro customers in the shoe store and in my father's pharmacy. The
shoe-store customers fell into two classes: ignorant working girls and
old servants with broad, horny heels and monstrous bunions, who
could be sold practically anything (even extra arch-supports for their
rubbers!); and middle-class Negro women from the suburbs whom we
hated for assuming, quite correctly, that we were trying to put something over on them. My father's customers I would see less frequently;
his drugstore was in a distant and disreputable part of the city, with a
Mission for repentant drunks on one side and a factory across the
street. I would visit him occasionally, taking along a "hot meal" that
had grown rather cold on the long streetcar ride, and watch him wait

on the Negroes who made up a large part of his trade and whom he supplied with asafoetida to charm off the "misery," hair-straightener and large boxes of candy tied with even larger pink ribbons.

Last of all, there were the maids—which is to say, the kind of part-time help that would appear at my grandmother's house or ours when we were prosperous enough to afford it. I think it was a long time before it entered my head that a maid might not be a Negro, or a healthy young Negro woman not a maid. In conversations between my grandmother and my mother, the girl who helped us was always referred to simply as "the *schwarze*," which did not really mean "Negro," nor, God forbid, "nigger," but only "servant." After a while, we settled down to one *schwarze*, Hattie, who was an ardent disciple of Father Divine, and would dance abandonedly in one corner of the kitchen when the spirit moved her or preach at us in the name of peace. It pleased my mother, I know, to be called "Miz Lillie" in an unfamiliar style handed down from plantation days and reminiscent of movies about the South; and she would certainly roar with laughter when Hattie clowned and grimaced and played the darkie for all she was worth. When I was adolescent and very earnest on the Negro question, I would rush out of the house sometimes, equally furious with Hattie for her play-acting and my own family for lapping it up and laughing at the display with winks and condescension.

Things have changed a good deal since I was a kid; and when I return now to the city where I was born, there are not only colored cops on the corners, but in the stores, even the biggest ones, colored salesgirls as well as customers, black salesgirls who do not hesitate to be as insolent as the white ones. Indeed, when my grandmother was dying and I came back to see her for the last time, I found not only Hattie, quite old but spry enough to caper on seeing me as absurdly as she knew was expected, but also a Negro nurse. The nurse was a follower of Father Divine, too, but this was her only bond with Hattie; for she was not only a "professional woman," but a West Indian, very light-skinned, and spoke a painfully refined brand of British English. She insisted on having a papaya every day for lunch, presumably to keep her origins clear in the minds of everyone; but she was kind and patient all the same, though she slipped away, quietly but firmly, a few hours before my grandmother's death. "It's coming," she whispered to my mother in the kitchen. "I'm sorry, but it's against my principles to stay in a house of death."

Despite my lack of intimacy with Negroes, I have possessed from my earliest childhood very strong theoretical opinions on the question of their rights. The first book I ever bought for myself with my own money (I was eight) was *Uncle Tom's Cabin*, which I read over and over, weeping in secret, and making vows to myself that I would work always (imagining, of course, a heroic stand against the ignorant multitude) until the last vestiges of racial inequality were wiped out. Needless to say, no heroic exploits followed, though I have a vivid memory of myself at twelve, shouting and pounding the table until I grew red-faced in an argument with the rabbi of the chief Reform temple of our city. I can still remember his face, unspeakably moderate (either he looked like the late Senator Taft or I have remade his remembered face into that image), nodding at me disapprovingly, while my family, acutely embarrassed, tried to signal silence from behind his back. His apology for discrimination was certainly one of the spiritual scandals that drove me in despair from the bourgeois Jewish community. The poor Orthodox Jews did not, it seemed to me, even know there was a Negro problem: while the richer, Reformed ones had, for all their "liberalism," surrendered to Gentile conformism.

If the first impulse that took me as a young man into the radical movement was a desire to be delivered of the disabilities of being a Jew, the second was the counterdesire to be delivered of the guilt of the discriminations practiced by Jews in their efforts to free themselves from those disabilities. Only in the Marxist scheme for remaking society could I then see the possibility of winning my freedom rather than buying it at the expense of somebody else—particularly of the Negro. Besides, I thought that one could discover in the Movement a society in which already Negro and white were living together on the basis of true equality. Did not white girls and Negro boys dance together at their social evenings? Were they not even lovers without special recrimination or horror? I soon became uncomfortably aware, however, that the radical movement was plagued by the same inability as bourgeois society to treat the Negroes as more than instances of their color. Turning this inability upside down helped very little.

That the girls chose Negroes as boy friends *because* they were Negroes, or that the top leadership (who were, it happened, Jews once more) appointed Negro organizers not in spite of their color but because of it—and that they would, when their directives changed, hurry them out of sight—all this became distressingly clear. That one could not call a sonofabitch a sonofabitch if he happened to be black, that a comrade who was sullen, uncooperative and undependable was immune to blame because he was colored—this became unendurable. The fear of being labeled a "white chauvinist" is as disabling as that of being called a "nigger-lover"; and to be barred a priori from hating someone is as debasing as being forbidden a priori to love him.

It is not, finally, a question of the Marxian movement failing its own dream, the dream of an assimilated Jew not above calling a political opponent a "Jew-nigger." Such a failure could be an accident of history, reparable under changed circumstances. The fatal flaw of all such approaches is that they begin with self-congratulation: permitting us to set ourselves apart from the guilty others and to think of ourselves as immune to the indignity and hatred which are the very condition of the coexistence of white and black in America. Only with the recognition of our own implication can we start to be delivered: not to fight for Negro rights as if we were detached liberators from another planet, but to know that those rights must be granted to ease us of the burden of our own guilt.

Of all my own experiences, the one which seems to me now central to an understanding of my problem, a real clue to the nature of Negro-Jewish relations, is that of merely *walking to school*. For some six months, when I was in the ninth grade, I went to what was called "The Annex," an aging, standardly dismal primary-school building used to catch the overflow from one of our high schools. It stood in a neighborhood largely inhabited by Negroes, though there were still Jewish delicatessens and kosher poultry slaughterers among the "race record" shops; and one of the streets was lined throughout the day with pushcarts, among which Yiddish was the commonest language spoken. The sons of butchers and the few trapped Jewish property owners left in the area seemed to become almost as often as not gangsters (one especially successful one, I recall, ran a free soup kitchen all through the Depression); and a standard way of proving one's toughness was "nigger-smashing." This sport involved cruising a side street at a high rate of speed, catching a lonely Negro, beating the hell out of him and getting back into the car and away before his friends could gather to retaliate. I remember that one of the local figures associated, in kids' legend at least, with "nigger-smashing" was himself called "Niggy" because of his kinky hair and thick lips, features not so uncommon among Jews, after all.

I had to walk to school through those streets, and it was not long before I was repeating to my friends what was quickly whispered to me: that it was not safe for either a white boy or for a colored one to walk there alone. It was a strange enough feeling to pass even in packs through so black a neighborhood to one's totally white class; for though the grade school was predominantly Negro, there was not a single colored student in my ninth-grade room. Especially on the warm days in late spring, when everyone was out on his stoop or sidewalk, in shirt sleeves or undershirt, one had a sense of an immense, brooding hostility. The fattest and most placid-looking woman leaning out of her window or the knot of yelling kids who parted to let one pass could suddenly seem a threat. It was like entering the territory of a recently subdued enemy, still too weary and disorganized for resistance but not for hatred. And saying to oneself, "I am a friend of the Negro people. I am on your side," didn't help a bit. It would have been absurd to cry it aloud, though sometimes the temptation was great; for in such a context, it would seem as false to the mouth that spoke it as to the ear that heard.

The sense of entering an alien country was exaggerated during my first month in school by the barricades which blocked off the streets just past the last plush Jewish apartment house and on the verge of that real ghetto. A smallpox epidemic had spread through the crowded, filthy living quarters of the Negroes, and only those with business in the neighborhood were permitted to enter, though even they were snatched up and rudely vaccinated on the spot. After a while, the sense of poverty and dirt, the dark faces looking out of the windows and the fear of the most dreadful of diseases blended into one; and even a kid going to school had the sense that he was entering not a place but a condition, that he was confronting the sickness and terror of his own soul made manifest.

Once toward the end of my endless term there, I was walking with my mother down the same street I followed daily to school. We were after something special, who knows, hot pastrami, maybe, or onion rolls or a fresh-killed chicken; when suddenly and quite casually she pointed to one of those drab, alien houses from which I had shrunk day after day, saying, "I was born there." It is the familiar pattern of the decay of urban neighborhoods; when the Jews are ready to go and it no longer pays to patch and paint, the Negroes are permitted to move in. The street where I myself was born is now almost all Negro, as is my high school; and the neighborhood where I lived until I was married is now surrounded. But at that moment beside my mother, I heard behind her familiar voice another which prompted it: the voice of a mild, horrified, old Gentile lady over her tea: "First the Jews, then the Negroes . . ."

But this is also the voice of T. S. Eliot, "And the jew squats on the window sill, the owner . . ."

Emancipated and liberal, I could scarcely shake off my resentment and rage; for I saw the comedy and pathos of our plight, how *we* looked to the *goyish* eye at the very moment we were looking at the Negro: the first symptom of a disease, as inexorable as age itself, which eventually reduces newly seeded lawns and newly painted houses to baked gray mud and scabby boards. I could feel the Jew's special rancor at the Negro for permitting himself visibly to become (there is no question of the justice of such a notion, only of its force) the image, the proof of the alien squalor that the white, Gentile imagination finds also in the Jew. "As he to me," the Jew thinks helplessly, "so *I* to *them!*" And the "them" refers to the Gentiles already in the new, restricted addition to which the Jew will eventually come, by hard work and with much heartburning, only to find the Gentiles gone and the Negro still at his heels.

For the Jew, the Negro is his shadow, his improbable caricature, whom he hates only at the price of hating himself; and he learns quickly (unless he allows rage to blind him) that for this reason his own human dignity depends not only theoretically but in terrible actuality upon that of the Negro. No Jew can selflessly dedicate himself to the fight for the equality of the Negro; when he pretends that he is not also fighting for himself, he is pretending that he is indistinguishable from a *goy*.

THEODORE SOLOTAROFF

PHILIP ROTH
AND THE JEWISH MORALISTS

"GOODBYE, COLUMBUS," A NOVELLA AND FIVE STO-
ries by Philip Roth, has been widely reviewed and has already stirred
up considerable enthusiasm and some acrimony. Neither is surprising.
Roth, who is only twenty-six, writes mainly of contemporary Jewish
life and does so with special color, freshness and honesty. The first
two qualities are what have pleased most of the reviewers, and the
third is what has gotten him into trouble, in a depressingly predictable
way, with a number of Jews and liberals. However, the really surprising and elating achievement of Roth's work, at least for this reader, is
the way he has triumphed over the major disabilities of his subject.

For one thing, Jewish life seems so self-contained and peculiar, so
drenched with nearly invariable shades of local color, that it can become almost inaccessible to the imagination. The writer simply begins
to remember and details of character and milieu come by the bucket,
along with their own directives for the story's tone and contours; and
usually the material is long since played out, overly nostalgic or bitter,
and only half true. Also, the Jewish writer's judgment as well as his
imagination is likely to find itself being dictated to by his world, which
makes so much of morality as well as the main chance that the writer
begins to worry about the Jewish heritage, the need for good public
relations, the fate of the six million; or if he has shaken that, he can
fall into lambasting the goats and ignoring the sheep. In either case,
Jewish material can be as intractable morally as it is imaginatively: one
result is that until fairly recently American-Jewish fiction has been
mainly a vehicle for either reverence or outrage but seldom for both;
354

the other is that it has been usually very literal, claustral, repetitive, and rather dull.

All of which makes *Goodbye, Columbus* seem so remarkable. The consistent vitality of Roth's stories and their full emotional range give one the sense of a writer who has somehow broken through, who is really in touch with both the American-Jewish scene and with himself. Like Wallace Markfield, Roth appears to have managed it by making the energy and color of his stories flow in from direct connections to his own wit and feelings and observations, and by an almost aggressive frankness about Jewish experience. In any case, he deals with his situations and characters in the rare, right way—without piety or apology or vindictiveness, and by combining a first-rate eye for surfaces with a sense of depth. All of which sharply distinguishes his Jews from the bland, sentimentalized robots that Herman Wouk assembles in *Marjorie Morningstar*. Roth really sees—sees through the Jewish types, which takes some doing—and his reports are wonderfully candid. Beneath a more or less "typical" character such as the aging Epstein—harassed by the lack of a son to inherit his business as well as by the springtime and the sexuality of the young people around him—you find a man. And along with the man, you find again in his strife and griefs something fundamentally Jewish—for example when he is defending himself for having had an affair:

"But what! But *this?*" He was pointing at his crotch. "You're a boy, you don't understand. When they start taking things away from you, you reach out, you *grab*—maybe like a pig even, but you grab. And right, wrong, who knows! With tears in your eyes, who can even see the difference!" His voice dropped now, but in a minor key the scolding grew more fierce. "Don't call *me* names. I didn't see you with Ida's girl, there's not a man for that? For *you* it's right?"

Roth does it equally as well and as truly with his unsavoury characters. Here is one of his contemporary rabbis—an Army Chaplain—illustrating a contemporary and a probably timeless characteristic:

"It is about the food that I want to speak to you for a moment. I know, I know, I know," he intoned, wearily, "how in the mouths of most of you the *trafe* food tastes like ashes. I know how you gag, some of you, and how your parents suffer to think of their children eating foods unclean and offensive to the palate. What can I tell you? I can only say close your eyes and swallow as best you can. Eat what you must to live and throw away the rest. I wish I could help more. For those of you who find this impossible, may I ask you that you try and try, but then come to see me in private where, if your revulsion is such, we will have to seek aid from those higher up."

Throughout *Goodbye, Columbus* Roth works into his stories what he has seen and felt, fortifying it with his sense of traditional Jewish values and conduct that shows up, for example, in the contrast between the chaplain and the impressive figure of Leo Tzuref in "Eli, the Fanatic." And whether angered or touched or amused by his Grossbarts and Tzurefs and Patimkins, Roth is so obviously attached to Jewish life that the charge of his being anti-semitic or a "self-hater" is the more absurd. The directness of his attack against arrogance, smugness, finagling and acquisitiveness should not obscure the perfectly obvious fact that he does so flying a traditional Jewish banner of sentiment and humaneness and personal responsibility—all of which makes the accusation have some further melancholy implications.

Most of the reviewers of *Goodbye, Columbus,* however, have been content with reading it as a penetrating social commentary on present-day Jewish life, particularly on the rearrangements of its middle class—whose more prosperous members are drifting out of their urban neighborhoods and parochial culture and into the suburban mainstream of modern American life. Roth's short novel, which tells the story of a sharp-eyed boy caught between these two classes in a love affair, is a particularly well-illuminated picture of the new suburban family, whose home, bursting with food and sporting goods, rather resembles a ZBT house at one of the Big-Ten schools. "Eli," provides some equally telling observations of a Jewish group who are nervously assimilating with a formerly Christian community in Westchester. However, the focus of "Eli" is not on social questions but moral ones and generally this is true of Roth's work as a whole, including the other published stories that are not in this collection. In fact, what gives real depth to Roth's notation of the social and ethnic changes that assimilation has produced is that he fixes them not only by their external signs (country club membership, horse-shows, the schools the children go to, the "right" synagogue and so forth), but also by their subtle effects upon the individual's sense of his personal, moral identity as a Jew. The boy in "The Conversion of the Jews" struggles to get out from under the shadow of the old, unreasonable dogmas, but the characteristic problem is rather that of Sergeant Marx in "Defender of the Faith" or of Eli Peck, both of whose Jewishness has become merely a vague feeling and requires both a direct challenge from the outside and an act of moral imagination to come alive and identify them and their basic values. Even "Goodbye, Columbus," for all its thick social and cultural reference, turns out to be really a story about the fatal moral demands that Neil Klugman has made on Brenda Patimkin and (as

Neil's aunt puts it) on her "fancy-schmancy" world, and involves, though in different terms and with more ambiguous results, the same problem of identity, the same moral question of "What am I?" that lies at the center of Roth's other stories.

For, at bottom, what directs and defines his stories are a few brave values that connect human feeling with human conscience. In stories such as "Eli" and "Defender of the Faith" he associates these values with Jewish tradition; and even the criticism of the Orthodox dogma in "The Conversion" is one that the early Hassidim would have had no trouble understanding. However, as these stories make clear Roth tries to put his values through the fire—working from the impulses, strains and solutions of a modern Jew outward to the traditional morality of sentiment, suffering and rectitude that a writer such as Sholom Aleichem more or less takes for granted. At the same time, Roth's hard, clear comedies of Jews who discover in their hearts that they are neither more nor less than human, suggest by the comic mode of his moral analysis, as well as by its terms and its firmness, Roth's affiliations with other contemporary Jewish writers, led by Malamud and Bellow, and in its own way, *Goodbye, Columbus* helps to make their particular imprint on American fiction more visible and significant.

Despite sharp differences, Roth seems closest in his general moral intentions to Malamud. His characters and situations are usually quite different: Roth's emerge from the Jewish here and now in America while the life of most of Malamud's Eastern-European Jews runs in lonely, isolated channels in New York that make it seem folk-like and almost timeless. While Roth is clearly writing about the modern Jew in America, Malamud appears to be writing mainly about Jewishness itself as it survives from age to age and from place to place. Also Roth's style, which is open, voluble and contemporary, is in striking contrast to Malamud's prose, which is as terse and sternly restrained as Babel's, for all of the same magic and feeling he gets into the stories themselves. However, both Roth and Malamud seem involved in a similar effort to feel and think with their Jewishness and to use the thick concreteness of Jewish moral experience to get at the dilemmas and decisions of the heart generally. Writing from the struggle to illuminate and assess and extend the fading meaning of being a Jew, they write from their hearts —sophisticated, witty, tough-minded as they may be—and usually it is back to the heart that their work leads us: to its suffering and its trials and, particularly, to its deep moral potency.

This underlying affinity between Roth and Malamud can be seen by comparing *The Assistant* and "Eli, the Fanatic." In Malamud's novel, a young Italian drifter, Frank Alpine, takes part in robbing and beating up a poor Jew, who keeps a rundown grocery store in the Bronx. But still destitute, and bothered by his conscience, Alpine continues to hang around the neighborhood and, in little ways, to help out his victim, Morris Bober. In time he becomes Bober's assistant, chases after his lonely daughter, Helen—who earnestly tries to make him like Dostoevsky, Tolstoy and Flaubert—and works hard to build up Bober's pitiful trade. But at the same time that Alpine is lusting after Helen, he is stealing from Bober. Eventually Bober catches him and sternly casts him out, and on the same evening, Alpine loses the girl when, after saving her from a rape, he rapes her himself. Deeply suffering now from this double rejection, Alpine is also horrified, as Malamud tells us, by a recognition that underneath he is himself a man of stern morality. He continues to stay in the vicinity, hiding in the basement of the store where at one point he prevents Bober—the honest man— from setting fire to the property to collect the insurance. Twice after Bober falls ill, the haunted assistant comes back to run the failing business again and even takes a night job in a diner to keep it going. He wastes away himself from these labors to prove to the Bobers, mainly to the girl, that his heart his changed; but they ignore him as much as possible. Meanwhile his antics as well as his serious striving become more grotesque and meaningful; for example, he takes to wearing his version of a *yarmulke* in the store and after Bober dies, he stumbles into his open grave at the funeral. At the funeral the rabbi defines Bober, who had been indifferent in his religion, as a Jew by his suffering and by his hopeful sacrifices for the higher ambition he had for his daughter, and here the point behind Alpine's behavior begins to emerge. He continues the ordeal of holding both his jobs, doing so finally to send Helen to college. And as the cycle of his days begins to run in the grooves of the dead grocer's former routine, the conversion of the young Italian into the elderly Jew comes clear, even before Alpine gets himself circumcized and becomes a Jew.

In "Eli, the Fanatic" much of the same inner pattern and much of the same fusion of the comic form and the suffering hero are compressed and pointed to much the same moral. Alpine's role of the aggressor who through suffering and sacrifice becomes his victim, is played here by an assimilated Jew, an unstable lawyer named Eli Peck, who has been commissioned by his fellow Jewish townsmen to get an Orthodox school for refugees evicted from their pink and chrome, Scarsdale-like community. Starting out as their agent against the orphans and the elders—Leo Tzureff, the Patriarch-like director and his assistant, who is particularly obnoxious to the "Jewish community" of Woodenton because he wears the long gabardine and beard of the fanatical Chassidim—Peck soon comes to the point of helping the refugees by trying to work out a compromise. He first sacrifices his best suit (a good deal is made of this in the story) to the offensive assistant so that the latter will be less so to the aroused and nervous Jews of Woodenton. The "greenie" does put on the suit and shaves his beard and sidelocks, and everyone is delighted and satisfied—except Peck, for by now he has become involved in deeper issues with himself. Moved, despite his reason, by Tzureff's appeal to the heart instead of to the law ("the heart is law! God!"), by the suffering that the Yeshiva people represent (the assistant, for example, has had a "medical experiment" performed on him by the Nazis), and by Tzureff's question of which of the two communities Peck really belongs to, the lawyer has become vaguely aware that his best suit is not enough. When the assistant leaves his Chassidic outfit on Peck's doorstep, he slowly tries on the black clothes and then walks outside. He wanders up to the Yeshiva but the assistant, still wearing Peck's suit, casts him out by pointing in the direction of the town. Their appearances and roles reversed, pondering on who is who, Peck walks down into the town. He stops traffic along its main street by his appearance and then goes to the hospital where his first child has just been born. And as he goes, Eli silently recognizes and endures what Tzureff has had the black clothes sent to him for. His friends think that he is having another of his nervous breakdowns but as Roth tells us—"he knew who he was down to his marrow," and standing before his new son, Peck swears aloud that the child will always know, too.

Thus, in both works, there is the similar conversion into the essential Jew, achieved by acts of striving, sacrificing, and suffering for the sake of some fundamental goodness and truth in one's self that has been lost and buried. Further, both Roth and Malamud emphasize the vague, semi-conscious character of the decision, proceeding not from any clear idea but rather from awakening feelings of sympathy, love, identification, and guilt which, becoming more and more powerful, finally indicate their purpose—to produce the suffering and sacrifice that lead to purification and to a discovery of one's true identity. And in both Alpine's and Peck's case, this "consummation of his heart's ultimate need" is represented by becoming thoroughly a Jew, which is apparently Malamud's and Roth's composite symbol, into which the separate terms are knitted—striving, sacrifice and suffering; purification and true identity. But, more importantly, becoming and being a Jew refers beyond this definition of its morality to the moral role and power of the human heart and will discover and recreate the self, and this what Malamud seems so mean by his frequently quoted statement that "all men are Jews."

Roth probably wrote "Eli" with *The Assistant* in mind; however, the theme of conversion is a familiar one in Jewish literature and "Eli" is much more than a reworking of Malamud's novel with a new twist. It is more just to say that Roth is drawing upon the same idea, embedded in the same traditional morality, and like Malamud he has provided a different, contemporary context in which to display its power. Also a comic action of suffering that leads to the truths of the heart is a familiar one to readers of Saul Bellow or Herbert Gold or the late Isaac Rosenfeld. "Seize the Day," "The Heart of the Artichoke," "The Hand That Fed Me," are stories that come to mind as clear examples of it and as having some sort of Jewish background upon which it focuses.

The phrase I quoted above—"the consummation of his heart's ultimate need"—is from Bellow's comic and shattering "Seize the Day," and a consideration of it may help to make these connections clearer. The "day" that Tommy Wilhelm (originally named William Adler) seizes is the day of his Gethsemane. In the course of it Wilhelm, a forty-year-old failure, has his last eight hundred dollars swept away in a crazy speculation in lard; his partner in the investment, a quack psychologist named Tamkin, swindles and deserts him; his father, a retired doctor whose help and blessing Wilhelm desperately needs, curses him; and his wife continues to torture him by refusing Wilhelm the divorce he needs to hold onto a girl he loves, and by refusing to let him reduce his extravagant payments to her and their two children. Without a job and—though he has been a successful sales- man until recently—without prospects, his health shattered, Wilhelm takes these blows one after another. However, as Bellow writes:

since there were depths in Wilhelm not unsuspected by himself, he re- ceived a suggestion from some remote element in his thoughts that the business of life, the real business—to carry his peculiar burden, to feel shame and impotence, to taste these quelled tears—the only important business, the highest business was being done. Maybe the making of mistakes expressed the very purpose of his life and the essence of his being here. Maybe he was supposed to make them and suffer from them on this earth . . .

The point of Wilhelm's suffering begins to emerge when Tamkin —another of Bellow's fascinating mixtures of hokum and insight—tells Wilhelm of the two souls inside each man. There is the "pretender soul" and the "true soul"—the former the instrument of "egotism" and "social control," and the latter the searcher for love and truth that "pays the price" for the pretender's ways, that "suffers and gets sick." Wilhelm is moved by this description, for there are two distinct sides to him that he believes correspond to his two names. Or at least he knows that Tommy is the pretender soul but is unsure who is the true soul, thinking it might be named "Velvel," his grandfather's name for him. But whatever its name, Wilhelm's "true soul" rises powerfully at the end of all his antics and suffering to define itself and him. By now "stripped and kicked out," Wilhelm finds his way into a funeral parlor and, for no apparent reason, falls in with the mourners passing before the bier of an important Jew. He begins to weep for the man, "a fellow human creature . . . so fallen in the eyes," then for himself, and then beyond any reason and control. As Bellow puts it, "the great knot of ill and grief swelled upward," and the story ends:

The flowers and lights fused ecstatically in Wilhelm's blind, wet eyes; the heavy sea-like music came up to his ears. It poured into him where he had hidden himself in the center of a crowd by the great happy oblivion of tears. He heard it and sank deeper than sorrow, through torn sobs and cries toward the consummation of his heart's ultimate need.

"Seize the Day," then, moves, though more obliquely and negatively, in the same general direction as do the two works I have been considering. There is the same drama of the heart under its burden of baffled love, aspiration, and guilt, the same stern payment for confusions and mistakes, the same brutal suffering that leads to the indication of the hero's true identity—for the suffering of Wilhelm's "true soul" and his "heart's ultimate need" are one and the same. Of course, unlike Alpine's or Eli Peck's, the fullfillment of Tommy Wilhelm is the doom of a man whose fate, as well as his need, is to suffer; he is Henderson without Henderson's strength or his millions. However, there is a different moral grain to these two works by Bellow and partly it has something to do, I think, with the Jewish background of "Seize the Day." Bellow does not identify its implications explicitly with Jewish-

ness, though the points about "Velvel," about Wilhelm's recognition
that it is the Tommy Wilhelm in him who is the pretender, and
about the final "consummation" taking place at a Jewish funeral—all
suggest this connection.

At any rate, what is definite is the preoccupation with the griefs
and potencies of the heart that Bellow shares with Roth and Malamud
(it is also worth noting that they use the term "heart" repeatedly),
and with a tough, realistic morality that develops out of it. Thus, the
Yiddish proverb that Roth uses as the epigraph to *Goodbye, Columbus*
—"The heart is half a prophet"—illuminates much of Malamud's
work and much of Bellow's (even showing the links between such
very different novels as *The Victim* and *Augie March*) as well as
Roth's own stories. Moreover, it illuminates the work of such otherwise
ill-assorted writers as Rosenfeld and Gold and the underrated novelist
Leonard Bishop. For at least two things are suggested by Roth's
epigraph that one keeps finding among their stories and novels. First,
there is the intense concern with situations in which the blood feelings
become powerfully engaged—pity, love, guilt, hate. What almost
always generates them is the hero's involvement in some basic, human
relationship—sometimes sought by him but, as often as not, inflicted
upon him, with the distinction tending to become lost as a relationship
develops: the seeker becoming the victim or vice versa. Often, too, a
complicated moral problem is involved, some radical question of right
and wrong. However, what lies at the center of the tale are the feelings
that direct the hero finally to a truer recognition of himself, or at least
direct the reader to a truer recognition of him, and often produce a solu-
tion to his personal moral problem. Sometimes the recognition comes
from strong, new feelings of love or pity but often these are mixed with
a recognition of personal guilt as in Bellow's *The Victim,* or Malamud's
"The Last Mohican" and "The Mourners," or Rosenfeld's "The
Colony" or "Coney Island Revisited" or Bishop's *Days of My Love.* And
sometimes, too, the recognition is produced by an act of hatred as in
Malamud's "Take Pity," or Roth's "Defender of the Faith" or Gold's
"The Heart of the Artichoke." Nonetheless, whatever the feelings or
combination of them, it is the trust in the strong, instinctive impulses
of the heart that is one of the things that characterizes this fiction.
It is also characterized, as Roth's epigraph suggests, by its moral rectitude that is flexible and searching but firmly centered too. Definite
concepts of right and wrong reinforce these writers' moral analyses as
well as a tough-minded realism. Nothing of real value is easily won

in their fiction; moral development tends to be a very painful process and mistakes and failures, as well as sins, are paid for, often at an appalling price. Thus, though these writers often deal with life's losers and victims with deep compassion, they do so with a firmness and intelligence that guards their pity from the sentimentality that keeps leaking into the fiction of a writer like Nelson Algren.

In Roth's story "Defender of the Faith," a sergeant named Nathan Marx, who fought through the German campaigns and is now training a company of recruits, has the orders of a wheedling Jewish private changed so that he is sent to fight in the Pacific theatre along with the rest of the company. Marx does so, as he says himself, out of a feeling of vindiciveness, for Grossbart, the private, has been cynically using him for weeks by trading on the fact that both are Jews. Out of vindictiveness, then, comes Marx's righteous act to "defend the faith," but his final act is that of accepting the consequences of what he has had to do to defend it. At the same time, these are the culminating happenings in a story which has also been explicitly about Marx's regaining his identity as a Jew and about the "softening" of his "infantryman's heart," which like his feet, had grown "horny enough for him to travel the weirdest paths without feeling a thing." The terms of the moral analysis here, as well as its subtlety, complexity and rigor, sum up the general moral position I have been trying to suggest. Moreover, Roth's story suggests a final generalization: that the values placed on free-flowing feeling on the one hand, and on moral firmness, even toughness, on the other—fortifying, testing, correcting each other—is what comes from the peculiar heritage of the modern Jew (who has kept himself aware of it) into the fiction I have been mentioning. It is what he carries and preserves within the larger, more immediate experience of being an American today, and it is what helps to direct these writers in their search for values that men can still live by and remain human. Exploring and affirming the potency of the heart to make men better and truer and to help them survive as men, they indicate a course through our shifting sands of determinism and nihilism. And given the moral evasiveness, rootlessness, and blankness that characterizes so much modern literature, this is a considerable contribution.

At the same time, it would be mistaken to view these writers only as moralists and their stories and books as preachments. On the contrary, Roth—like Malamud, Bellow and Isaac Rosenfeld—is a shrewd craftsman, and like them, he appears to be involved in a deliberate attempt to restore and broaden the base of the novelist's and story writer's special interest—the tale or action itself—and to move serious fiction out of the *longeurs* of technique and literary decorum that often mark it today in America. Along with the intelligence, concreteness and roughened texture of their writing, one of its noticeable features is the presence usually of a clear, explicit action. As a rule, their tales are strongly and carefully plotted; they write of happenings rather than of cooly objectified states of mind. Thus one follows their stories and novels through visible conflicts, complications, crises, climaxes, instead of from sets of veiled coordinates which require that the reader detect them and draw the lines in order to find the story. The Chekhov-Joyce-Mansfield story—the story of low dramatic pressures, of impersonality, indirection and implication—is still the influential one today: it is canonized in the anthologies, taught determinedly in the colleges to illustrate "the art of the short story," and becomes more and more bloodless and vague by its development, as Harry Levin remarks, into "an industry."

Similarly in the novel: Flaubert remains "our Penelope" as much as he was Pound's. "Do you have feelings? There are correct and incorrect ways of indicating them. Do you have an inner life? It is nobody's business but your own. Do you have emotions? Strangle them." So, early in his career, Saul Bellow phrased the position that he was rebelling against in *Dangling Man*—the position of detachment and impersonality that goes back to Flaubert. In his best work Bellow has continued to do so, though after *Dangling Man* he began to experiment with actions that would translate his inner life into viable fiction. Moreover, his rebellion against Flaubert has continued and he has publicly asked for a re-evaluation of Flaubert's tremendously influential literary method, which he believes cuts the writer off from the real conditions of life and makes his content thin and pessimistic. In a recent lecture at The University of Chicago, Bellow made clear the grounds of his opposition to the Flaubertian image of the alienated writer and, more importantly, to the lack of moral circumspection and artistic vitality that his method has produced.

Bellow, Malamud, and Roth are anything but alienated men and their attempt to confront the human situation as they see and live it, and to make moral sense out of it, is bound up, it seems to me, with their concern for constructing definite actions and characterizations. The esthetic that they share at these points (the kind of double life Bellow leads in his fiction makes generalizations here rather shaky) is close to that of Gogol and Dostoevsky, both committed moralists and first-rate story tellers, who, as Malamud has defined his own "moral-esthetic," "keep the moral invisible, locked in the tale, the fabric one might say, of the human action, being, feeling." It is the primacy of the "tale" that seems to be important here—the return to a reliance upon a visible, strongly developed story in which the other elements—all given considerable force—cohere and are illuminated. All of which is what gives such dramatic power and clarity of meaning to *The Victim* and "Seize the Day," to *The Assistant* and such stories as "The Magic Barrel," "Take Pity," and "Angel Levine," as well as to their more introspective stories as "Looking for Mr. Green" and "The Last Mohican." And it is where their hold upon the "story" is weak and where sheer invention and "ideas" take over—as in *The Natural* and *Augie March*—that their fiction loses both dramatic strength and moral clarity. And this is equally true of Roth's work.

Roth seems at his best where the current of his imagination is guided by a strong, clear action—where, in other words, the story comes closest to telling itself, to defining its characters and feeling, and to making its point. This is true of "Epstein" and "Defender of the Faith," and the last forty pages or so of *Goodbye, Columbus*. For all the impact of its concluding pages, "Eli" doesn't quite come off, I think; nor does "You Can't Tell a Man by the Song He Sings," though this, too, has some of Roth's best writing in it. In both stories, as in "The Conversion of the Jews," the moral or idea is heavier than the story itself. Eli Peck's conversion seems to me the material for a much longer story; it is prepared for by clever details as much as by happenings and it comes too quickly; the result is that the character and the conversion itself become less real beside the concrete actuality of Woodenton and beside the massive and beautifully executed figure of Tzuref. In "You Can't Tell a Man" and in "The Conversion" one finds a compact and sensitive story suddenly being inflated to get in the message: in the former, the action trails off into a discussion of its implications; in "The Conversion," it becomes flabby with its bravura, jokes and symbolism. Also where Roth's plot lapses, his tendency to overwrite emerges to get between the reader and the story, and his general weakness for tags (most of his minor characters are tagged rather than rendered) and for gags seems particularly marked.

Similarly "Goodbye, Columbus," though it flows resonantly between its feeling and its satire, seems to lack the fusion of its materials, the sense of being really "done," that one finds in "Epstein" and

"Defender of the Faith". Again, I think the trouble is with the action and one sign of it is the kind of abstractness that Neil Klugman takes on. He is seen too much as an observer and he is too far along the path he is supposed to be traveling in the story. One could wish, for example, that he were more his aunt's nephew, more troubled and attracted by the life of the Patimkins and more willing to test it and himself. As is, already classless, fixed vaguely by his job in a library and by his degree in philosophy, he seems less genuinely involved with the Patimkins, including the girl (who, too, isn't dramatized enough), than he is with the Negro boy that he takes risks and tells lies for. For two-thirds of the story, then, Neil's social ambitions and moral problems connected with Short Hills are too often stated rather than made visible to the reader by the action and it is only when he forces the situation by demanding that Brenda get a diaphragm that the story takes on complexity and force. But until this point, the faint overtones of Scott Fitzgerald in "Goodbye, Columbus" make it seem a little like *The Great Gatsby* with a single hero being both Carroway and Gatsby.

All of which is not to take away from Roth's remarkable eye and ear, his strong narrative sense, and the verve and sparkle of his prose. These are what keep his stories going and also what keep even the weakest of them, "The Conversion of the Jews," from being clearly second-rate. Also, too, the faults I have been mentioning are those of a story-teller learning his art, not weaknesses in his basic equipment, with which Roth is as well-endowed as any young writer that has appeared in recent years. On the whole, then, *Goodbye, Columbus* is a more than promising beginning. At an age when most writers are still looking for their own voice, Roth already has one that rings out with a live, personal and commanding tone. And at this stage of his career, that is probably as important as his other virtues and more important than his present limitations.

ARTHUR A. COHEN

WHY I CHOOSE TO BE A JEW

UNTIL THE PRESENT DAY, THE JEW COULD NOT *choose* TO be a Jew—history forced him to accept what his birth had already defined.

During the Middle Ages he was expected to live as a Jew. He could escape by surrendering to Islam or Christianity, but he could *not* choose to remain anonymous. In the nineteenth century, with the growth of nationalism, Christianity became the ally of patriotism. The Jews of Europe were compelled to prove that their religion did not compromise their loyalty to King, Emperor, Kaiser, or Tsar. But no matter how desperately they tried to allay suspicion by assimilation or conversion, the fact of their birth returned to plague them. Finally, in the Europe of Nazism and Communism, the Jew could not choose—on any terms—to exist at all.

In the United States today, it is at last possible to choose *not* to remain a Jew. The mass migrations of Jews from Europe have ended and the immigrant generation which was tied to the European pattern of poverty and voluntary segregation is dying off. Their children, the second generation, were as suspicious of the gentile American society in which they grew up as they were condescending toward the ghetto world of their parents. The second generation, however, made the Jewish community economically secure and fought anti-Semitism so effectively that, though still present, it is no longer severe. *Their* children— the third generation of Jews now in its twenties and thirties—are able to choose.

For this generation the old arguments no longer hold. It was once

367

possible to appeal to history to prove that Jewish birth was inescapable, but history is no proof to those who are—as many Jews are—indifferent to its evidence. Loyalty to the Jewish people and pride in the State of Israel are no longer enough to justify the choice to be a Jew. The post-war American Jew no longer needs the securities which European Jewry found in Jewish Socialism, Jewish Nationalism, the revival of Hebrew, and the Zionist Movement. *Fear*—the fear of anti-Semitism—and *hope*—the hope for the restoration of Israel—are no longer effective reasons for holding onto Jewish identity. The fear has waned and the hope has been fulfilled.

The irresistable forces of history no longer *compel* the Jew to choose Judaism. In many cases, moreover, he is choosing to repudiate Judaism or to embrace Christianity. I do not say the numbers are alarming. That they exist at all is, however, symptomatic. It is only the exceptional—those who are searching deeply or are moved profoundly, who ever reject or embrace. The majority tend more often to undramatic indifference—to slide into the routine of maturity without asking questions for which no meaningful answers have been offered.

Given the freedom to choose I have decided to embrace Judaism. I have not done so out of loyalty to the Jewish people or the Jewish state. My choice was religious. I chose to believe in the God of Abraham, Isaac, and Jacob; to acknowledge the law of Moses as the Word of God; to accept the people of Israel as the holy instrument of divine fulfillment; to await the coming of the Messiah and the redemption of history.

Many Jews will find my beliefs unfamiliar or unacceptable—perhaps outrageous. The manner in which I arrived at them is not very interesting in itself, but I think two aspects of my experience are worth noting because they are fairly common: I come from a fundamentally unobservant Jewish home and my first religious inclination was to become a Christian.

My parents are both second-generation American Jews whose own parents were moderately religious, but, newly come to America, lacked either the education or the opportunity, patience, and time to transmit to their children their own understanding of Judaism. My parents went to synagogue to observe the great Jewish holidays—Passover, the New Year, and the Day of Atonement—but worship at home, knowledge of the liturgy, familiarity with Hebrew, concern with religious thought and problems, did not occupy them. Their real concern—and they were not unique—was adjusting to American life, achieving security, and passing to their children and those less fortunate the rewards of their struggle.

It would be ungrateful to deny the accomplishments of my parents' generation. They managed to provide their children with secular education and security. But although the flesh was nourished, the spirit was left unattended. When I had finished high school and was ready to leave for college I took with me little sense of what my religion, or any religion, involved. I knew only that in these matters I would have to fend for myself.

When an American Jew studies at an American university it is difficult for him not to be overwhelmed—as I was at the University of Chicago—by the recognition that Western culture is a Christian culture, that Western values are rooted in the Greek and Christian tradition. He may hear such phrases as "Judaeo-Christian tradition" or "the Hebraic element in Western culture," but he cannot be deluded into thinking that this is more than a casual compliment. The University of Chicago, moreover, insisted that its students study seriously the philosophic sources of Western culture, which, if not outspokenly Christian, were surely non-Jewish. I soon found myself reading the classics of Christian theology and devotion—from St. Augustine and St. Anselm through the sermons of Meister Eckhart.

It was not long before my unreligious background, a growing and intense concern with religious problems, and the ready access to compelling Christian literature all combined to produce a crisis—or at least my parents and I flattered ourselves that this normal intellectual experience was a religious crisis. The possibility of being a Christian was, however, altogether real. I was rushed, not to a psychoanalyst, but to a Rabbi— the late Milton Steinberg, one of the most gifted and profound Jewish thinkers of recent years. Leading me gently, he retraced the path backwards through Christianity to Judaism, revealing the groundwork of Jewish thought and experience which supported what I have come to regard as the scaffolding of Christian "unreason."

It was extremely important to me to return to Judaism through the medium of Christianity—to choose after having first received the impress of Western education and Christian thought. Since it would have been possible to become a Chistian—to accept Christian history as my history, to accept the Christian version of Judaism as the grounds of my own repudiation of Judaism, to believe that a Messiah had redeemed *me*—I could only conclude that Judaism was not an unavoidable fate, but a destiny to be chosen freely.

My own conversion and, I suspect, the conversion of many other Jews to Judaism, was effected, therefore, through study, reflection, and thought. What first seized my attention was not the day-to-day religious life of the Jewish community around me, but rather principles, concepts, and values. I had first to examine the pressing theological claims of a seemingly triumphant Christianity, before I could accept the ancient claims of a dispersed, tormented, and suffering Jewry.

This may sound reasonable enough to a gentile, but I must point out that it is an extremely unconventional attitude for a Jew. Historically, Judaism has often looked with disfavor upon theology. And today, despite the fact that traditional emotional ties can no longer be relied upon to bind the third generation to Jewish life, American Jewish leadership has not seen fit to encourage the examination of the theological bases of Jewish faith. In fact, the leading rabbinical seminaries teach little Jewish theology as such, give scant attention to Jewish philosophic literature, and have allowed the apologetic comparison of religious beliefs to become a moribund discipline. Even practical problems involving some theological insight—the nature of marriage, the Jewish attitude toward converts, the life of prayer—are dispatched with stratospheric platitudes, or not discussed at all.

Why this distrust of theology? I suspect that some Jewish leaders fear—perhaps not unjustifiably—that theological scrutiny of what they mean by God, Israel, and Law might reveal that they have no theology at all. Others no doubt fear—again not unjustifiably—that their unbending interpretations of Jewish Law and life might have to be revised and re-thought. Theology often produces a recognition of insufficiency, an awareness that valid doctrine is being held for the wrong reasons and that erroneous doctrine is being used to rationalize right action. But the major Jewish argument against Jewish theology is that it is a Christian pastime—that it may, by insinuation and subtle influence, Christianize Judaism. In this view, Christianity is a religion of faith, dogma, and theology and Judaism is a religion which emphasizes *observance* of God's Law, not speculation about it.

For me this argument is a vast oversimplification. Christianity is not without its own structure of discipline, requirements, and laws—the Roman sacraments and the Lutheran and Anglican liturgy, for example—and this structure does not move with the Holy Spirit as easily as St. Paul might have wished. Judaism, on the other hand, is not tied to the pure act. It has matured through the centuries a massive speculation and mystic tradition which attempts to explain the principles upon which right action are founded. Judaism need not, therefore, regret the renewal of theology. It already has one. It is merely a question of making what is now a minor chord in Jewish tradition sound a more commanding note.

As a "convert" who thinks that theology must come first, what do I believe?

The convert, I must point out, is unavoidably both a thinker and a believer—he thinks patiently and believes suddenly. Yet belief, by itself, cannot evict the demons of doubt and despair. As a believer I can communicate my beliefs, but as a thinker I cannot guarantee that they are certain or will never change. As all things that record the encounter of God and man, beliefs are subject to the conditions of time and history, and the pitiable limitation of our capacity to understand such enormous mysteries. As I shall try to show, however, the four beliefs which I have already set down lie at the center of my faith as a Jew. They depend upon one another; they form a whole; they differ profoundly from the substance of Christian belief.

First, I chose to believe in the God of Abraham, Isaac, and Jacob. This is to affirm the reality of a God who acts in history and addresses man. Although this God may well be the same as the abstract gods formulated by philosophers, he is still more than these—he is the God who commanded Abraham to quit the land of the Chaldeans and who wrestled with Jacob throughout the night.

The philosopher and the believer must differ in their method. The philosopher begins by examining that portion of reality to which reason allows him access. The believer, however, must at some point move beyond the limits which reason has defined. He may rightly contend that reason points beyond itself, that the rational is real, but that much in human life—evil, suffering, guilt, and love—is terrifyingly real without ever being rationally comprehensible.

Reason may thus push a man to belief, and it is inaccurate to speak of the believer as though he had deserted or betrayed reason. Informed belief demands philosophic criticism and refinement. The believer is bound to uphold his faith in things he cannot see or verify; but he is foolish if he does not try to define what that belief is and clarify the unique ways in which it makes reality meaningful for him.

For me then to believe in the Biblical God, the God of the Patriarchs, the smoking mountain, the burning bush, was not to surrender reason, but to go beyond it. More than accepting the literal word of the Bible, it meant believing in the Lord of History—the God who creates and unfolds history, and observes its tragic rifts and displacements—from the Tower of Babel to the Cold War; who, in his disgust, once destroyed the world with flood and later repented his anger; who, forgoing anger, gave the world counsels of revelation, commencing with the gift of Torah to Moses and continuing through the inspired writings of the ancient rabbis; and who finally—through his involvement with the work of creation—prepares it for redemption.

It may seem difficult—indeed for many years it was—to consider the Bible, which is the source of this belief, as more than the unreliable account of an obscure Semitic tribe. But gradually I came to discover in it an authentic statement of the grandeur and misery of man's daily existence—a statement which I could accept only if I believed in a God who could be addressed as "Lord, Lord."

My second belief is an acknowledgement that *the Law of Moses is the Word of God*. The Bible tells us that the Word of God broke out over the six hundred thousand Hebrews who assembled at the foot of Sinai. That Word was heard by Moses—he who had been appointed to approach and receive. The Word became human—in its humanity, it undoubtedly suffers from the limitation of our understanding—but it lost none of its divinity.

The Law is always a paradox: it is both the free Word of God and the frozen formality of human laws. But the Law of Moses was vastly different from what we usually understand law to be. It is true that in the days before the Temple was destroyed by Titus in 70 A.D. divine law was the enforceable law of the judge and the court; but later the great rabbis who interpreted it conceived of the revelation of God to Israel, not as law in its common usage, but as *Torah*—teaching.

Torah is a fundamental concept for the Jew. Narrowly conceived, it refers to the Pentateuch—the first five books of the Bible which are the pristine source of all Jewish tradition. In them are the laws of the Sabbath and the festivals; the foundations of family and communal morality; and the essentials of Jewish faith—the unity of God, the election of Israel, and the definition of its special mission. But, broadly conceived, Torah refers to *any* teaching which brings man closer to the true God, who is the God of Israel and the Lord of History.

Torah has two aspects—the actual way of law and observance (the *halachah* as it is called in Hebrew) and the theology of the rabbis which interprets that way (called the *aggadah*). By means of both, according to Jewish tradition, God proposes to lead *all* of his creation to fulfillment, to perfect its imperfections, to mend the brokenness of his creatures. The Jewish people—the guardian of the *halachah* and the *aggadah*—has been elected to be pedagogue to all the nations of the world, to become on its behalf "a kingdom of priests and a holy people."

Jews can achieve holiness—the primary objective, I believe, of their religion—neither by prayer nor meditation alone. Judaism values prayer only in conjunction with the act; it praises study only in relation to life.

God does not propose or suggest ways to achieve holiness; he commands them. According to Torah, he lays upon each Jew "the yoke of the commandments." To observe the Sabbath is as much a commandment as is the obligation to daily prayer; the grace which accompanies eating as essential as the study of sacred literature. Although tradition distinguishes between practical and intellectual commandments, it considers both to be equally the expressed will of God. The arbitrary and the reasonable—the dietary laws and the prohibition of homosexuality for example—both proceed from God.

Judaism begins with an explicit fact: the revelation of Torah. Many of its commandments may seem trivial. But it should not be expected that God will leave the trivial to man and concern himself only with the broad, general, and universal. The corruption of man takes place not only in the province of principle, but in the small and petty routine of life. The Torah is therefore exalted and picayune, universal and particular, occupied equally with principle and the details of practice. It tolerates no separation between the holy and the profane—all that is secular must become sacred, all that is profane must be kept open to the transforming power of God.

The exact degree to which Jews should fulfill all the commandments of the Law is one of the most difficult and perplexing dilemmas for modern Jews. Orthodox Jews are in principle obligated to observe all of Jewish Law, Reform Jews have cut observance to a minimum (though there is a movement to increase it), Conservative Jews stand somewhere in between. I will not attempt it in this space, but I believe it is possible to show that the fundamental question is not whether the Jew performs the required acts of observance, but whether he is truly aware of the sacred intention of these acts. One can, for example, recite the blessings over the food one eats and feel nothing of the sanctity of food; on the other hand one can silently acknowledge the holiness of eating, and fulfill the command of God. Both are needed—the blessing and the inner acknowledgment, but the former is surely incomplete without the latter.

The third of my beliefs is, as I have indicated, simply an element of

God's revelation in Torah—that *the Jewish people have been chosen as a special instrument of God.*

The Jews did not request the attentions of God. There is significant truth—truth moreover which the rabbis of the Talmud endorse—in the popular couplet: "How odd of God, to choose the Jews." Odd, and unsolicited. The ancient rabbis disclaim particular merit. If anyone possessed merit, they repeat, it was not the generation that fled Egypt and braved the wilderness for forty years, but the generations of the Biblical patriarchs—Abraham, Isaac, and Jacob. They had no organizer such as Moses, nor strength of numbers, nor the miracles of the well, manna, and quail. They made a covenant with God on sheer trust. The generation of Sinai was *compelled* to become the people of God or perish. A God of History grows impatient with delay. The God of Israel was profoundly impatient on Sinai.

This tradition of election should not be confused with racial pride or an attitude of arrogant exclusion toward others. The Jew believes neither that the truth flows in his blood nor that the gentile cannot come to possess it. Judaism is exclusive only in the sense that we affirm we possess important truth which is available to all—everyone can join but only on our terms.

The election of Israel is not a conclusion drawn from history—the survival and endurance of the Jews through twenty centuries of destructive persecution could be no more than blind accident. At best it could be construed as a compliment to the resiliency and stubbornness of the Jewish people. Judaism has insisted, however—not as a declaration after the fact, but as a principle of its very existence—that it is both a holy nation chosen by God to be his own and a suffering nation destined to endure martyrdom for his sake. God announces not only that "Ye shall be holy unto me; for I the Lord am Holy, and have separated you from the people, that ye should be mine" (Leviticus 20: 26) but that "You only have I known of all the families of the earth: therefore I will visit upon you all your iniquities" (Amos 3:2).

Israel is thus called not only to be the example to the nations, but, being the example, is tried all the more sorely for its transgressions. To be sure, this is not a doctrine for the uncourageous. No one even slightly familiar with the agonies of Jewish history could claim that the election of Israel has brought with it particular reward and security. It is, however, precisely the fact of Jewish suffering which makes its election and mission all the more pertinent to the modern world. To have believed and survived in spite of history is perhaps the only evidence which Judaism can offer to the accuracy of its conviction that it is called to be a holy community.

In the face of Christendom and the obvious success which its claims have enjoyed, it may seen foolish or presumptuous for Judaism—a small and insignificant community of believers—to assert my fourth belief: that *Jesus is not the Messiah of which the Bible speaks,* that Christianity has conceived but one more imperfect image of the end, and that *a Messiah is yet to come who will redeem history.*

But there are enduring reasons why Jews cannot accept Jesus as the Messiah. Both Christian and Jew begin with the conviction of the imperfection of man. The Christian argues, however, that creation has been so corrupted by man as to be saved only through the mediation of Jesus. The Jew considers creation imperfect but, rather than corrupt, he finds it rich with unfulfilled possibility. The role of man is to bring creation to that point at which the Messiah can come to glorify man by bringing him the praise of God—not to save him from self-destruction, as Christianity would have it. According to Jewish tradition, Moses died from the kiss of God. It would be fitting to conceive the advent of the Messiah and the Kingdom of God as the bestowal of a kiss.

This does not mean that God congratulates man for his good works but rather that he shares both in the agony of history and in its sanctification. Judaism does not imagine that every day we are getting better and better, and that finally we will reach a point where the Messiah will come. As likely as not, it seems to me, history is coming closer each day to suicide. The mission of Judaism is not to stave off disaster but to enlarge man's awareness of the Divine Presence.

Jews believe, if they are to remain Jews, that the Messiah has not come. They can accept Jesus of Nazareth as little more than a courageous witness to truths to which his own contemporaries in Pharisaic Judaism by and large subscribed. Jesus was, as Martin Buber has suggested, one in the line of "suffering servants" whom God sends forth to instruct the nations. It is to the dogmatizing work of St. Paul that one must ascribe the transformation of "prophet" into "Christ"—and it is therefore St. Paul who severs Jesus from the life of Israel. The rejection of Jesus must now stand to the end of time.

The role of Israel and Judaism, until the advent of the true Messiah, is to outlast the world and its solutions—to examine its complacencies, to deflate its securities, to put its principles to the test of prophetic judgment. This is an aristocratic and painful mission, for though Judaism may address the world and lay claim to it, it does not seek to convert it.

Judaism does not say "The world is not changed—therefore we do not believe in the Messiah." This is only partially true, for the coming of the Messiah will mean more than a reformed world in which the wolf and lamb shall share bread together and war shall cease. This social image of salvation is true as far as it goes, but it does not go far enough. The Messiah is not a handyman or a plumber—his task does not consist in "mending" a world that is temporarily faulty but is essentially perfect. The world is to be transformed—not reformed—by the Messiah.

This transformation will come to pass, Judaism believes, only when the world wishes it so deeply that it cannot abide itself more a single moment. At that moment the Messiah may come. This moment of expectancy has not yet arrived. The rabbis have taught us that I, and all of the House of Israel, prevent him from coming. Of this there is no question, but we cannot avoid concluding that he has not come.

For the Jew who comfortably repeats the rituals of his religion without confronting the principles of faith which they express, and for the Jew who was not aware that Judaism had any principles of faith at all, this personal statement may seem shocking. But I do not think my position or my background are by any means unique. If, as I have argued, the present generation of American Jews is indeed the first generation of Jews in centuries who are free to choose to believe as Jews, then, in my terms at least, my argument is important. Now as never before it will be possible for the Jewish people and the State of Israel to survive, but for Jewish *religion* to perish. For me, and for other believing Jews, it is crucial for mankind that Judaism survive. The mission of Judaism is not completed nor the task of the Jewish people fulfilled. If the Jewish people is an instrument sharpened by God for his own purposes, it must go on serving that purpose, sustaining its burden, and keeping that trust which alone can bring all men to redemption.